Advanced Algebra Through Data Exploration

A Graphing Calculator Approach

TEACHER'S RESOURCE BOOK

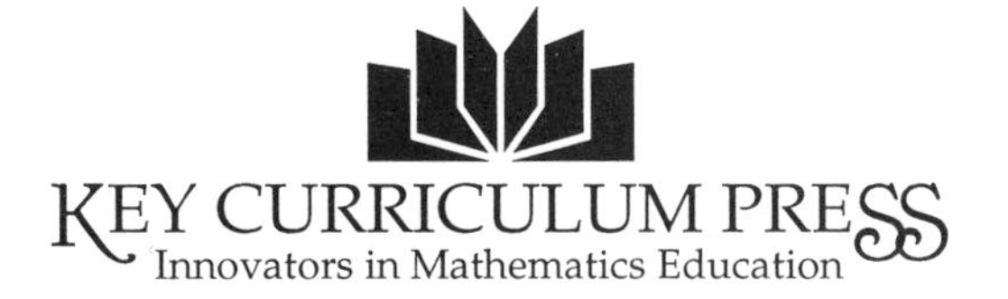

Project Editor Crystal Mills
Editorial Assistant Jeff Gammon
Production Editor Deborah Cogan
Copy Editor Margaret Moore
Mathematics Checkers Dudley Brooks, Judy Hicks, Jennifer North Morris
Production Coordinator Diana Krevsky
Art and Layout Kirk Mills
Cover Design Dennis Teutschel
Contributors Eric Kamischke, Jerry Murdock, Karen Wootten

Publisher
Steven Rasmussen

Editorial Director
John Bergez

This material is based upon work supported by the National Science Foundation under award number MDR9154410. Any opinions, findings, and conclusions or recommendations expressed in this publication are those of the authors and do not necessarily reflect the views of the National Science Foundation.

Key Curriculum Press
P.O. Box 2304
Berkeley, CA 94702
510-548-2304
editorial@keypress.com
http://www.keypress.com

Printed in the United States of America 10 9 8 7 6 5 4 3 2 01 00 99 98 ISBN 1-55953-284-X

Contents

Advanced Algebra Through Data Exploration
Teacher's Support Materials

Teacher's Guide and Answer Key

- Overview and philosophy
- Course outlines
- Cooperative learning suggestions
- Assessment suggestions
- Section guides
- Answers for Problem Sets

Teacher's Resource Book

- Transparency and worksheet masters
- Extra projects
- Extra Take Another Looks
- Extra assessment problems
- Data and programs disk for popular calculator models with linking capabilities

Quizzes, Tests, and Exams

- Two quizzes per chapter
- Form A and Form B chapter tests
- Form A and Form B exams (midyear and final) for three different course plans
- CD-ROM with quizzes, tests, and exams formatted for Microsoft Word® for Windows® and Macintosh® computers
- Answers to quizzes, tests, and exams

Solutions Manual

- Complete solutions for Problem Sets
- Project hints and answers
- Take Another Look answers

Blackline Masters for Calculator Notes

- Separate volumes for popular calculator models, keyed to the text

Constructive Assessment in Mathematics
Practical Steps for Classroom Teachers
by David Clarke

- Guide to implementing assessment strategies, including observational assessment, student-constructed tests, group assessment, student self-assessment, student journals, and portfolios
- Tips for recording, interpreting, and communicating assessment information
- Annotated bibliography of assessment resources

Suggested Supplemental Resources

The Geometer's Sketchpad

- Dynamic geometry software for Windows and Macintosh computers

Exploring Trigonometry with The Geometer's Sketchpad

- Add-on module for The Geometer's Sketchpad that teaches students to actively explore trigonometry
- Includes sample activity disks for Windows and Macintosh computers and a book of blackline activity masters

Exploring Conic Sections with The Geometer's Sketchpad

- Add-on module for The Geometer's Sketchpad that deepens students' understanding of the conic sections
- Includes sample activity disks for Windows and Macintosh computers and a book of blackline activity masters

Overview of Teacher's Resource Book

The *Advanced Algebra Through Data Exploration Teacher's Resource Book* is a versatile resource designed to supplement the sections, investigations, projects, activities, and problem sets in the student text. The four sections of the *Teacher's Resource Book* contain a guide to supplementary resources, transparency and worksheet masters, supplementary assessment problems, and additional Take Another Look activities. Each section begins with an introductory page that recommends how and when to use the materials. We hope this resource book will provide you with years of interesting and useful ideas to use in your *Advanced Algebra Through Data Exploration* classroom.

Supplementary Resource Guide

The guide lists resources available for the sections in the student text. The resources include those contained in this book and in *Advanced Algebra Through Data Exploration Quizzes, Tests, and Exams.*

Transparency and Worksheet Masters

Blackline masters are provided to assist you with presentations to the class. The masters contain illustrations, graphs, and selected problems and examples from the student text.

Supplementary Assessment Materials

Assessment items supplement those in the student text and in the *Quizzes, Tests, and Exams* book. The assessment items include journal prompts, open-ended problems, skill questions, projects, and group problems.

Additional Take Another Look Activities

More Take Another Look activities are provided in addition to those in the student text.

Calculator Programs and Data on Disk

You will find disks in pockets on the inside back cover of this book, both for computers running Microsoft® Windows® (version 3.1 or later) and for Macintosh® computers (System 7.0 or later). The disks contain programs and data from the student text for the most popular graphing calculator models with computer-linking capabilities.

Supplementary Resource Guide

The *Advanced Algebra Through Data Exploration* supplementary resources listed in the following tables were created to be appropriate for specific sections. The tables are set up so that you can easily identify the resources available for a particular section. Resources available for every lesson, such as the section guides in the *Teacher's Guide and Answer Key* and the solutions for problem sets, Take Another Looks, and projects in the *Solutions Manual,* are not identified in the tables.

The transparency and worksheet masters (T/W), supplementary assessment materials (with answers), and additional Take Another Look activities (with answers) can be found here. The quizzes can be found in the *Quizzes, Tests, and Exams* (QTE) book. For a complete listing of calculator programs and data on disk, see the tables in the section at the end of this book.

	TRB			QTE
Section	**T/W**	**Additional Take Another Look Activities**	**Calculator Programs and Data on Disk**	**Quizzes**
Chapter 0: Introducing the Calculator				
0.1	W			
0.2				
0.3				√
Chapter 1: Patterns and Recursion				
1.1				
1.2				
1.3				√
1.4		√		
1.5	T			
1.6				√
1.7				
Chapter 2: Sequences and Explicit Formulas				
2.1				
2.2				
2.3				√
2.4				

	TRB			QTE
Section	T/W	Additional Take Another Look Activities	Calculator Programs and Data on Disk	Quizzes
Chapter 2 (cont.)				
2.5				
2.6	W(3)			√
2.7				
Chapter 3: Introduction to Statistics				
3.1	T(2)			
3.2	T			√
3.3				√
3.4				
Chapter 4: Data Analyisis				
4.1	T(3), W(1)			
4.2		√		
4.3		√		
4.4	T(3)	√		√
4.5	T(3), W(4)			
4.6		√		
4.7				√
4.8		√		
4.9				
Chapter 5: Functions				
5.1	T(3)			
5.2		√		
5.3				√
5.4		√		
5.5				
5.6				
5.7				
5.8				√
5.9	T, W	√		
5.10				

		TRB		QTE
Section	T/W	Additional Take Another Look Activities	Calculator Programs and Data on Disk	Quizzes
Chapter 6: Parametric Equations and Trigonometry				
6.1	T			
6.2				
6.3	T, W			√
6.4	T(2)			
6.5	T	√		√
6.6				
6.7				
Chapter 7: Exponential and Logarithmic Functions				
7.1	T, W			√
7.2				
7.3		√		
7.4				√
7.5		√		
7.6				
7.7	W			√
7.8		√		
7.9	W			
7.10	W(5)*			

*Worksheets for Fractal Dimension Project in the TRB

		TRB		QTE
Section	T/W	Additional Take Another Look Activities	Calculator Programs and Data on Disk	Quizzes
Chapter 8: Topics in Discrete Mathematics				
8.1				
8.2		√		
8.3		√		√
8.4	T(2)			
8.5	T(2)/W(1)			
8.6				
8.7	T			√
8.8	T, W*			

*Random Number Table

		TRB		QTE
Section	T/W	Additional Take Another Look Activities	Calculator Programs and Data on Disk	Quizzes

Chapter 9: Systems of Equations

Section	T/W	Additional Take Another Look Activities	Calculator Programs and Data on Disk	Quizzes
9.1				
9.2				
9.3				√
9.4				
9.5	T(2)			
9.6				√
9.7				
9.8				
9.9				

Chapter 10: Polynomials

Section	T/W	Additional Take Another Look Activities	Calculator Programs and Data on Disk	Quizzes
10.1	T			
10.2				
10.3				√
10.4				
10.5				
10.6				√
10.7				
10.8		√√		
10.9				

Chapter 11: Probability and Statistics

Section	T/W	Additional Take Another Look Activities	Calculator Programs and Data on Disk	Quizzes
11.1		√		
11.2	T			
11.3				√
11.4				
11.5	T			√
11.6				
11.7				

		TRB		QTE
Section	T/W	Additional Take Another Look Activities	Calculator Programs and Data on Disk	Quizzes

Chapter 12: Functions and Relations

Section	T/W	Additional Take Another Look Activities	Calculator Programs and Data on Disk	Quizzes
12.1	W			
12.2				
12.3	T			√
12.4				
12.5				
12.6				
12.7				
12.8				
12.9				√
12.10				

Chapter 13: Trigonometric Functions

Section	T/W	Additional Take Another Look Activities	Calculator Programs and Data on Disk	Quizzes
13.1				
13.2				
13.3		√		√
13.4		√		
13.5				
13.6	T/W			
13.7				√
13.8	T/W(3)*			

*Miscellaneous grids

Introduction to the Transparency and Worksheet Masters

The transparency and worksheet masters are designed for you to use in your classroom presentations and discussions. The masters contain illustrations for selected examples, problems, and investigations. A list of all the masters is included in the Supplementary Resource Guide tables at the beginning of this book.

Each master is identified in its upper right-hand corner as a transparency master (T), a worksheet master (W), or a transparency/worksheet master (T/W). Transparency masters contain enlarged graphs and diagrams from the student text so that they can easily be seen when displayed on an overhead projector. Worksheet masters are designed as aids to be given to students when they need help performing investigations, working on special projects, or completing exercises. Transparency/worksheet masters can be used for both purposes.

At the end of this section are several masters for grids. There is a full page four-to the-inch grid, a full page five-to-the-inch grid, and a master containing many smaller grids. You will find these grid masters useful for activities, investigations, problem sets, quizzes, and tests that require graph paper.

Investigation 0.1.1: Cross-Number Puzzle

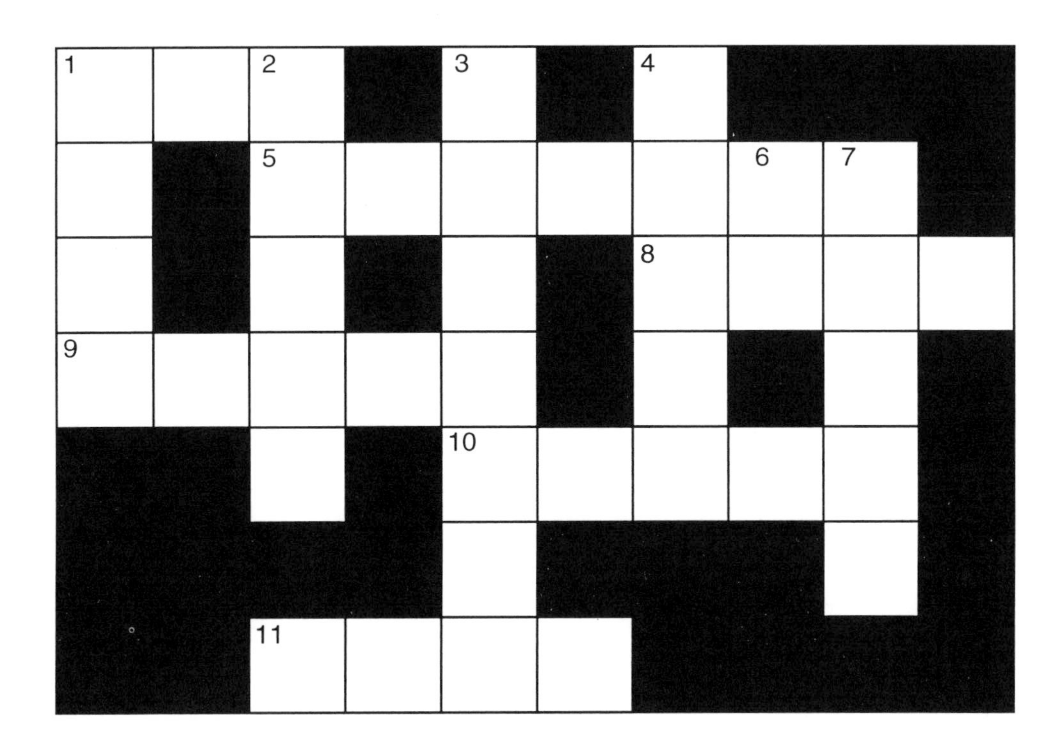

Across

1. $12 + 11 \cdot 10$

5. $6543(132 + 329)$

8. $\sqrt{765^2 + 1836^2}$

9. $\left(\frac{1}{2}\right)^4 + 3.7^3$

10. $\frac{(3.6 \cdot 10^6)(2.8 \cdot 10^{10})}{2.4 \cdot 10^{12}}$

11. $6\sqrt{11} + \sqrt[3]{4.4} - 1.83^5$

Down

1. $\frac{12+3}{7+5}$

2. $\frac{463}{94} \cdot 47$

3. -320^2

4. $-\sqrt{500(17852+1993)}$

6. $\sqrt{337+504}$

7. $\frac{9710}{15(17)}$

Calculator Note 1C: The RECUR Program

What you enter:	What you see:
[PRGM] [▸] [▸] 1 RECUR [ENTER]	PROGRAM:RECUR
3 [ENTER]	*** :3
[PGRM] [4] [ALPHA] N [,] 1 [,] 6 [)] [ENTER]	:FOR(N,1,6)
[PGRM] [▸] [1] [2nd] [ANS] [ENTER]	:DISP ANS
[ENTER]	:
2 [2nd] [Ans] [ENTER]	*** :2ANS
[PGRM] [5] [2nd] [QUIT]	*** :END

Problem 1: GeomeTree

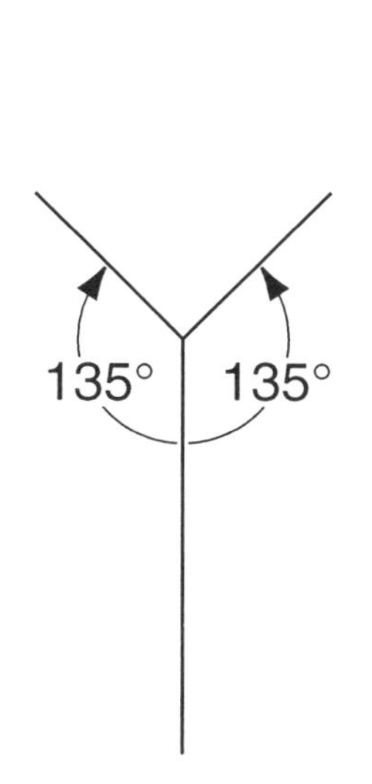

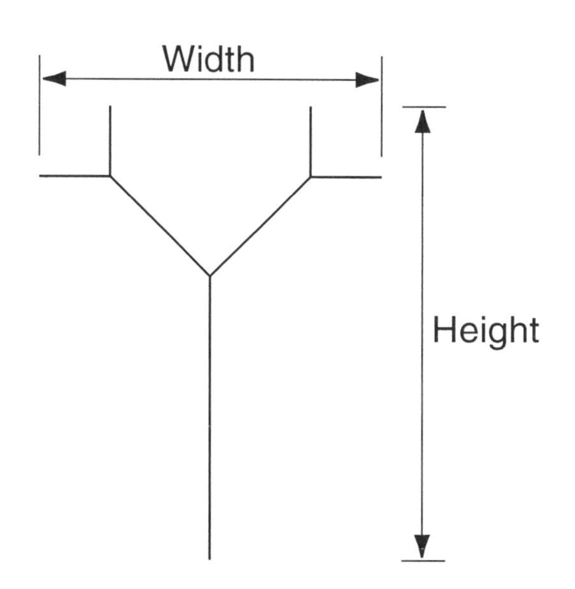

	1	2	3	4	...	n	...	∞
a. Length of the last segment	1				...		...	
b. Total length of a path	1				...		...	
c. Total number of segments	1				...		...	
d. Sum of the lengths of all segments	1				...		...	
e. Height of the tree	1				...		...	
f. Width of the tree	0				...		...	

Problem 2: Koch Snowflake

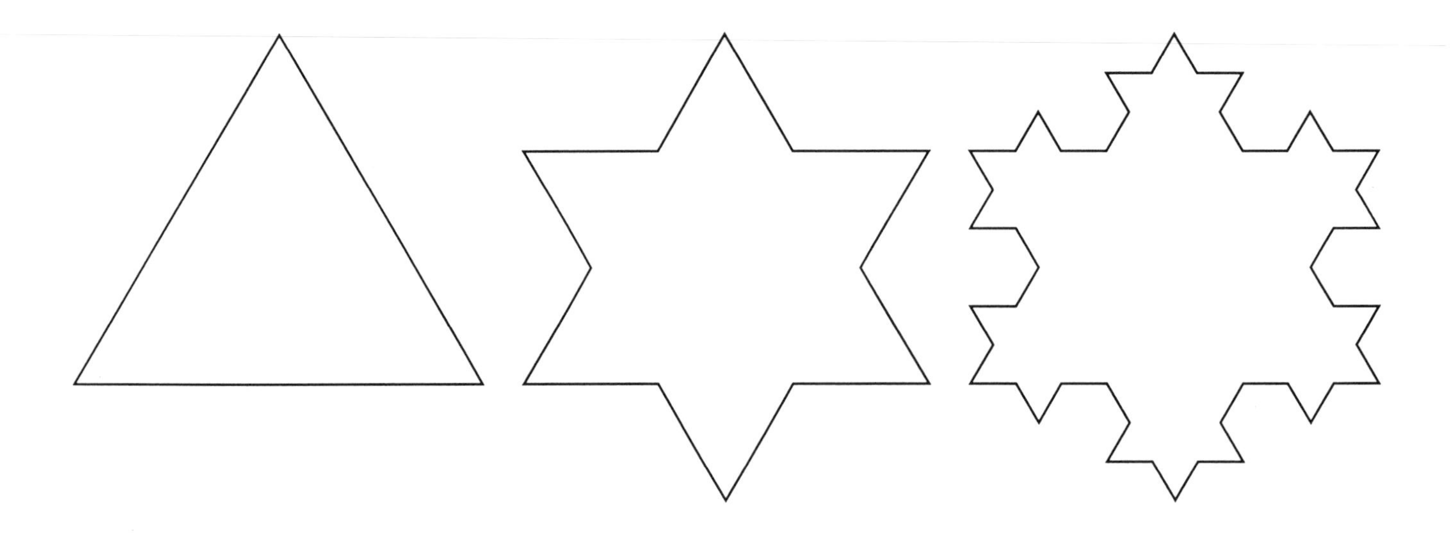

	1	2	3	4	...	n	...	∞
a. Length of each segment	1				. . .		. . .	
b. Total number of segments	3				. . .		. . .	
c. Perimeter	3				. . .		. . .	
d. Area	0.43301				. . .		. . .	

Problem 3: Sierpiński Triangle

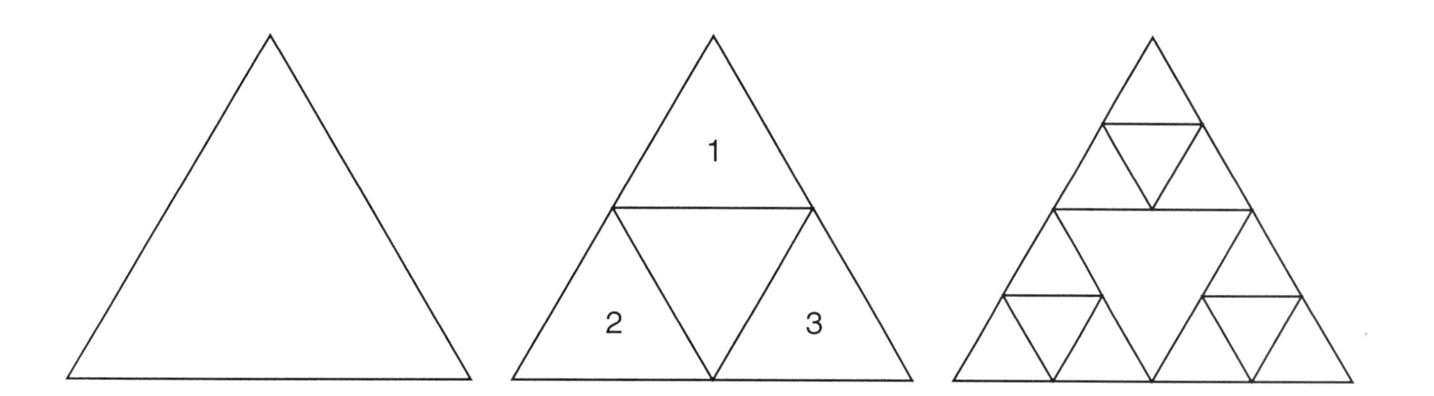

	1	2	3	4	...	n	...	∞
a. Length of each side	1				. . .		. . .	
b. Number of new triangles	1	3			. . .		. . .	
c. Perimeter of each triangle	3				. . .		. . .	
d. Area of each triangle	$\frac{\sqrt{3}}{4}$				. . .		. . .	
e. Sum of perimeters	3				. . .		. . .	
f. Sum of areas	$\frac{\sqrt{3}}{4}$				. . .		. . .	

Toothpaste Data

Product	Size (oz)	Price ($)	Cost per month ($)	Rank
Ultra brite Original	6.0	1.56	0.58	86
Gleem	7.0	2.23	0.66	79
Caffree Regular	5.9	2.96	1.02	77
Crest Tartar Control Mint Gel	6.4	1.99	0.53	75
Colgate Tartar Control Gel	6.4	2.04	0.57	74
Crest Tartar Control Original	6.4	2.00	0.53	72
Ultra brite Gel Cool Mint	6.0	1.53	0.52	72
Colgate Clear Blue Gel	6.4	2.06	0.71	71
Crest Cool Mint Gel	6.4	1.99	0.55	70
Crest Regular	6.4	2.01	0.59	69
Crest Sparkle	6.4	2.03	0.51	64
Close-up Tartar Control Gel	6.4	1.94	0.67	63
Close-up Anti-Plaque	6.4	1.97	0.62	62
Colgate Tartar Control Paste	6.4	2.04	0.66	62
Tom's of Maine Cinnamint	6.0	3.29	1.07	62
Aquafresh Tartar Control	6.0	1.97	0.80	60
Aim Anti-Tartar Gel	6.4	2.24	0.79	58
Aim Extra-Strength Gel	6.4	1.70	0.44	57
Slimer Gel	3.0	1.79	1.04	57
A & H Baking Soda Mint	6.3	3.26	1.12	55

Box Plot of Toothpaste Data

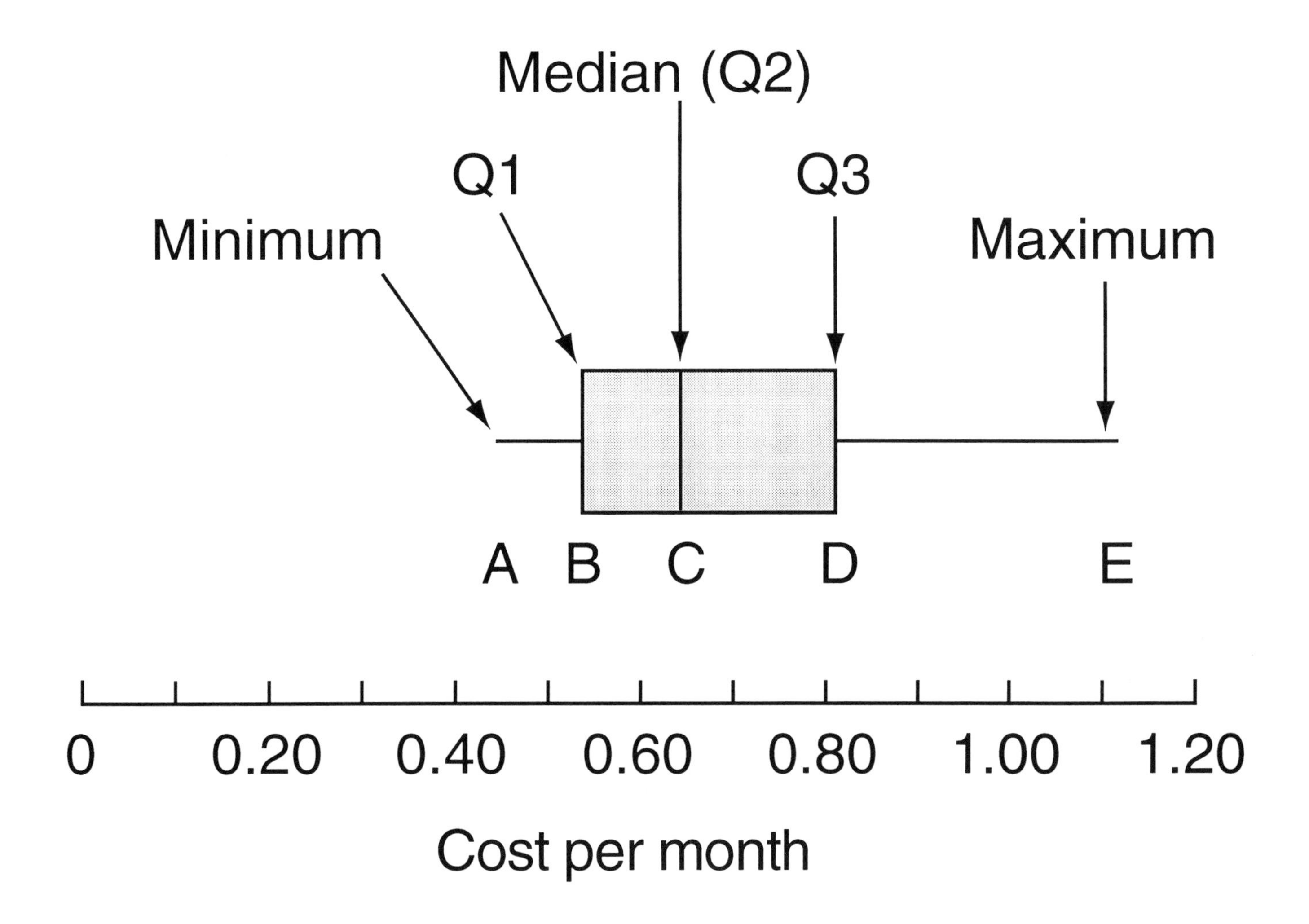

Deviations

Connie Sistant			Ozzie Laiting		
Level	Deviation	Absolute deviation	Level	Deviation	Absolute deviation
182	−2	**2**	152	−32	**32**
186	2	**2**	194	10	**10**
182	−2	**2**	166	−18	**18**
184	0	**0**	216	32	**32**
185	1	**1**	200	16	**16**
184	0	**0**	176	−8	**8**
185	1	**1**	184	0	**0**
Sum		**8**			**116**
Mean		**1.14**			**16.57**

Line of Best Fit

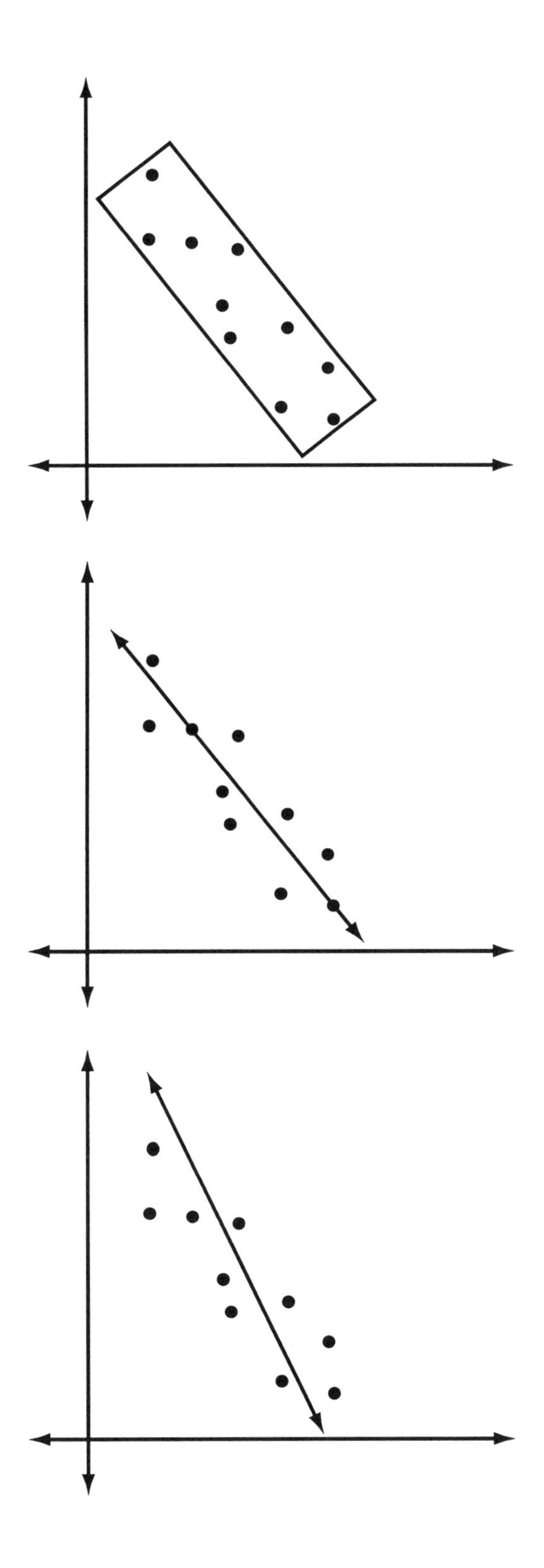

Line of Best Fit

- The line should show the direction of the points. The smallest rectangle that contains the points shows the general direction of the line.
- The line should divide the points equally. There should be nearly as many points above the line as below the line. Connect each point to the line and measure the lengths of these vertical "connectors." The sum of the lengths of the connectors above the line should be nearly equal to the sum of those below the line.
- As many points as possible should be *on* the line, but the previous two guidelines are more important.
- The points above the line should not be concentrated at one end, nor should the points below the line.

Problem 1

a.

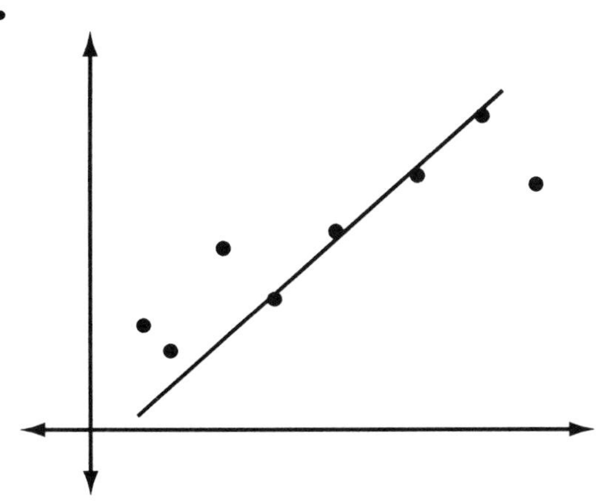

b.

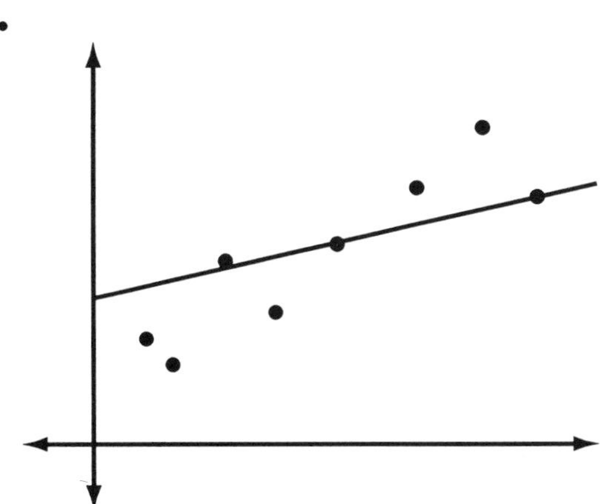

c.

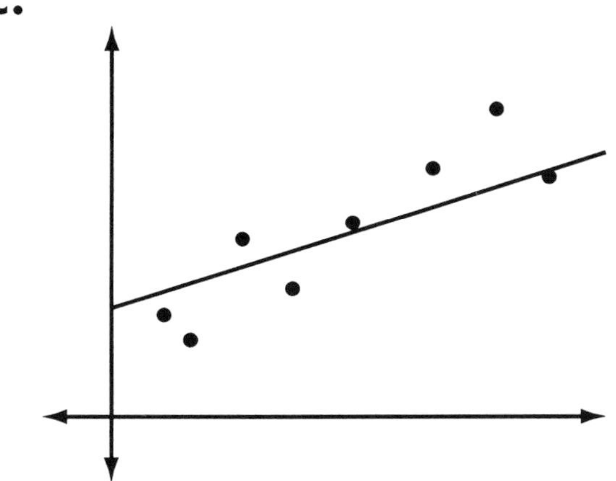

d.

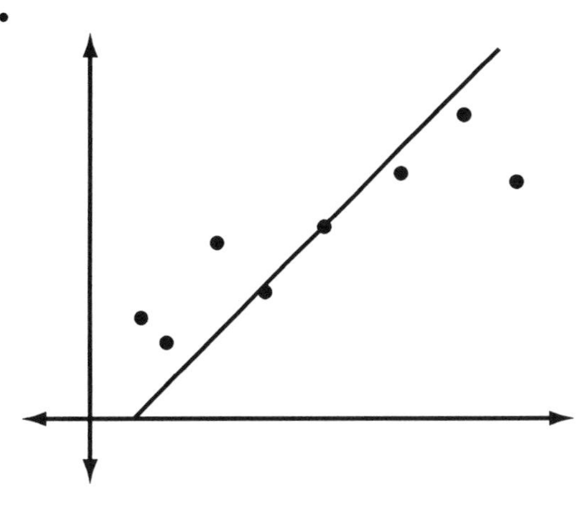

e.

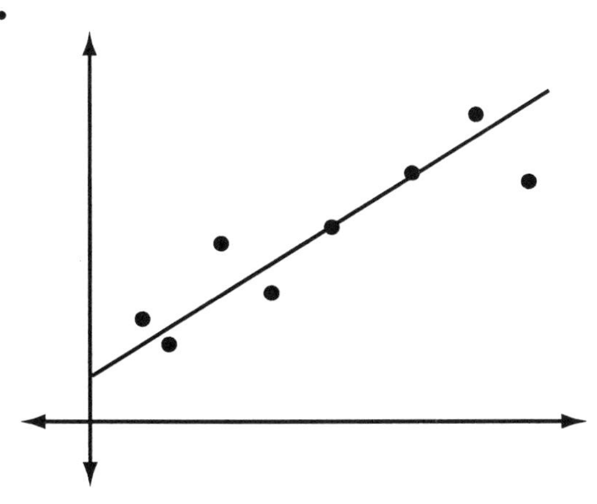

f.

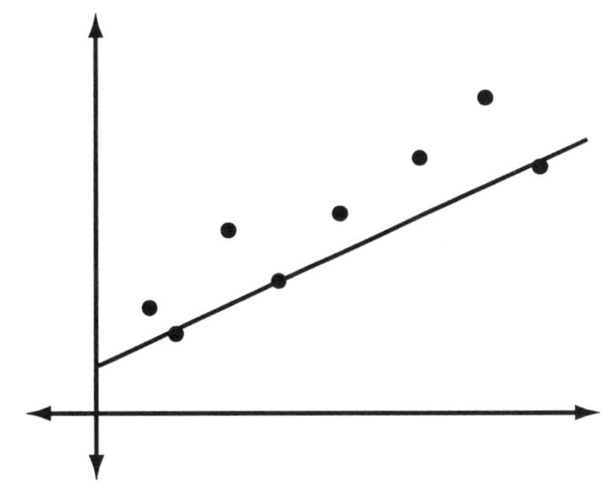

Problem 2

a.

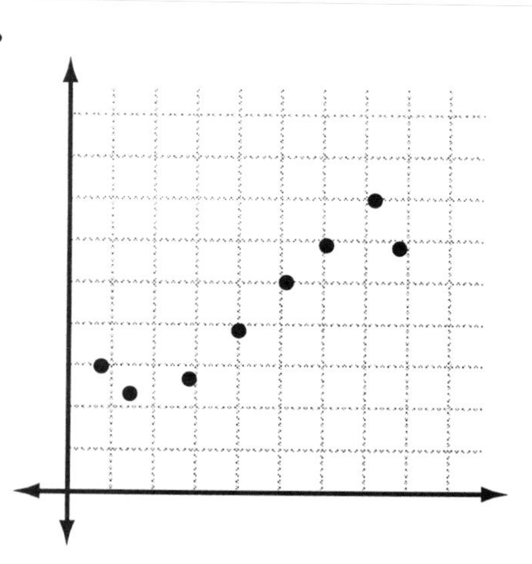

b.

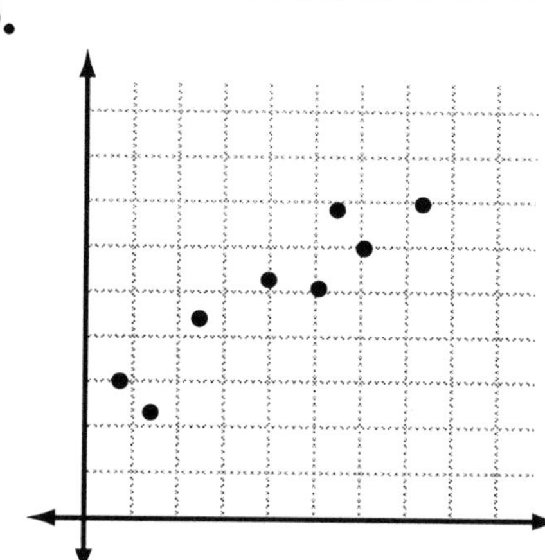

c.

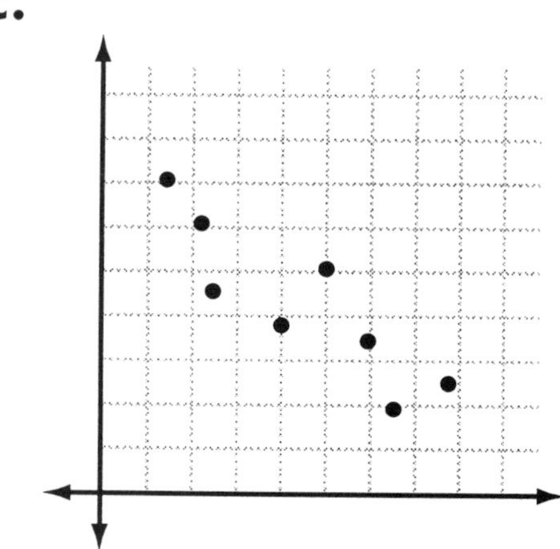

d.

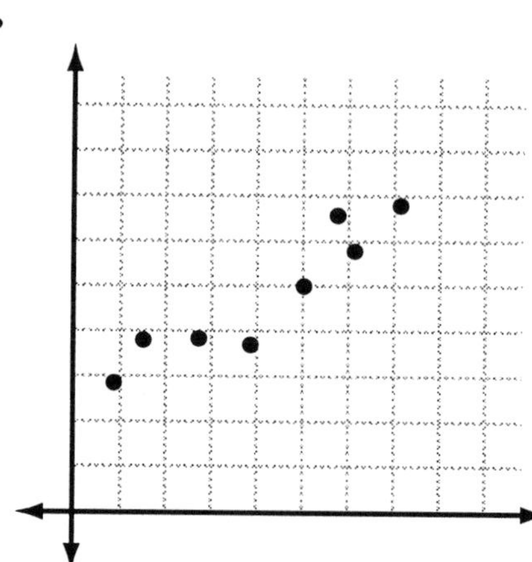

e.

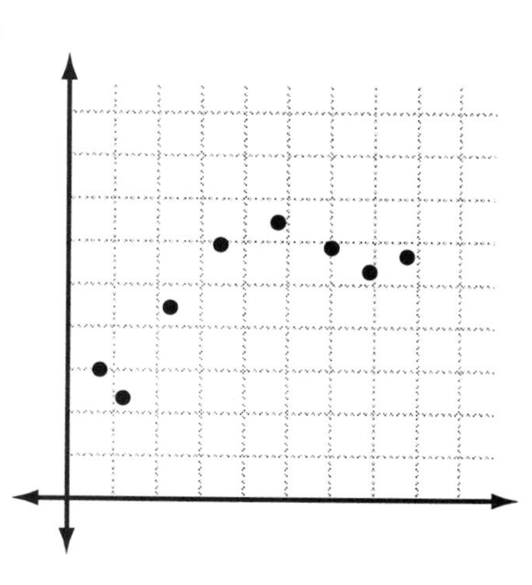

f.

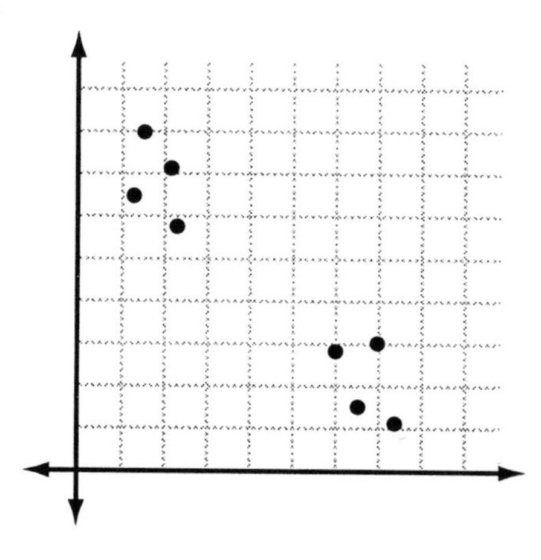

Median-Median Line

x	y	(median x, median y)
4.0	23	
5.2	28	
[5.8]	[29]	(5.8, 29)
6.5	35	
7.2	35	
7.8	40	
[8.3]	[42]	(8.6, 44.5)
[8.9]	50	
9.7	[47]	
10.1	52	
11.2	[60]	(11.9, 60)
[11.9]	58	
12.5	62	
13.1	64	

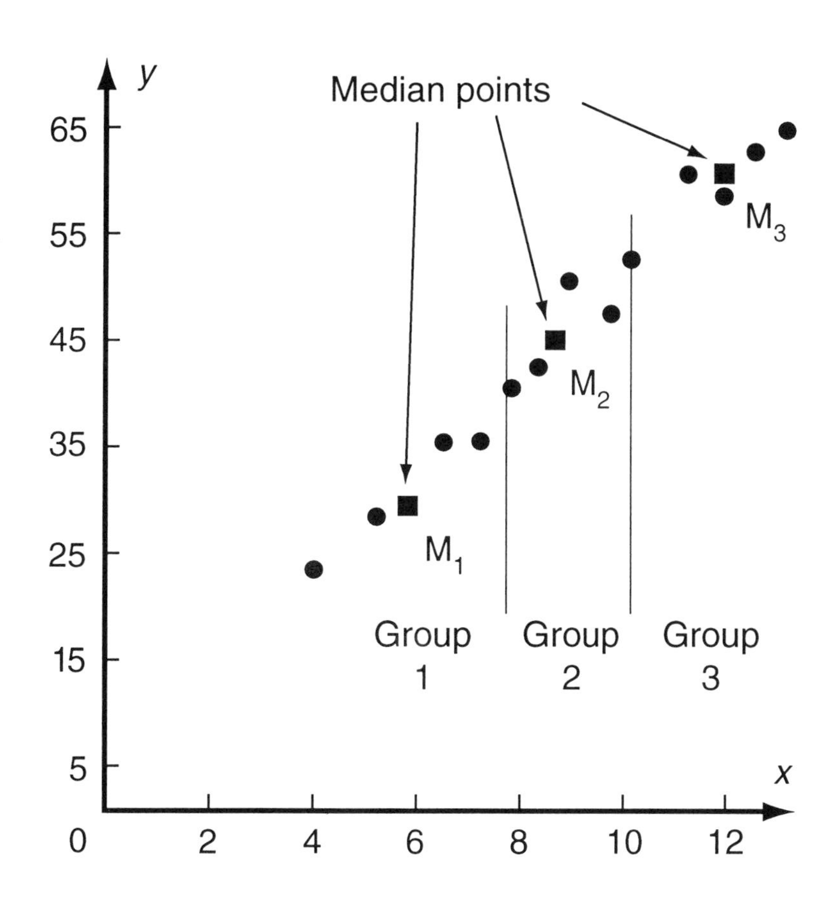

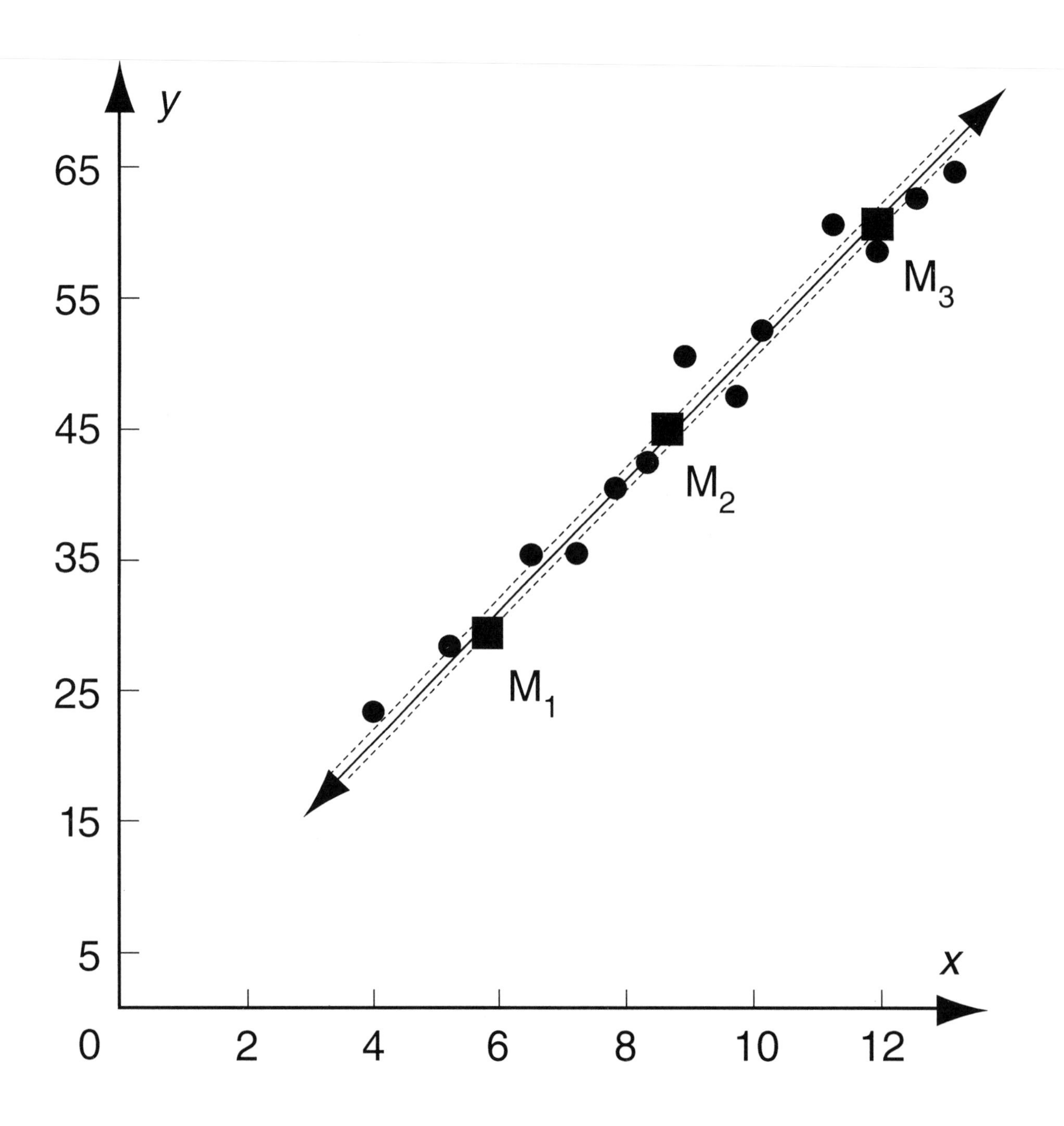
y
65
55
45
35
25
15
5
0
2
4
6
8
10
12
x
M1
M2
M3

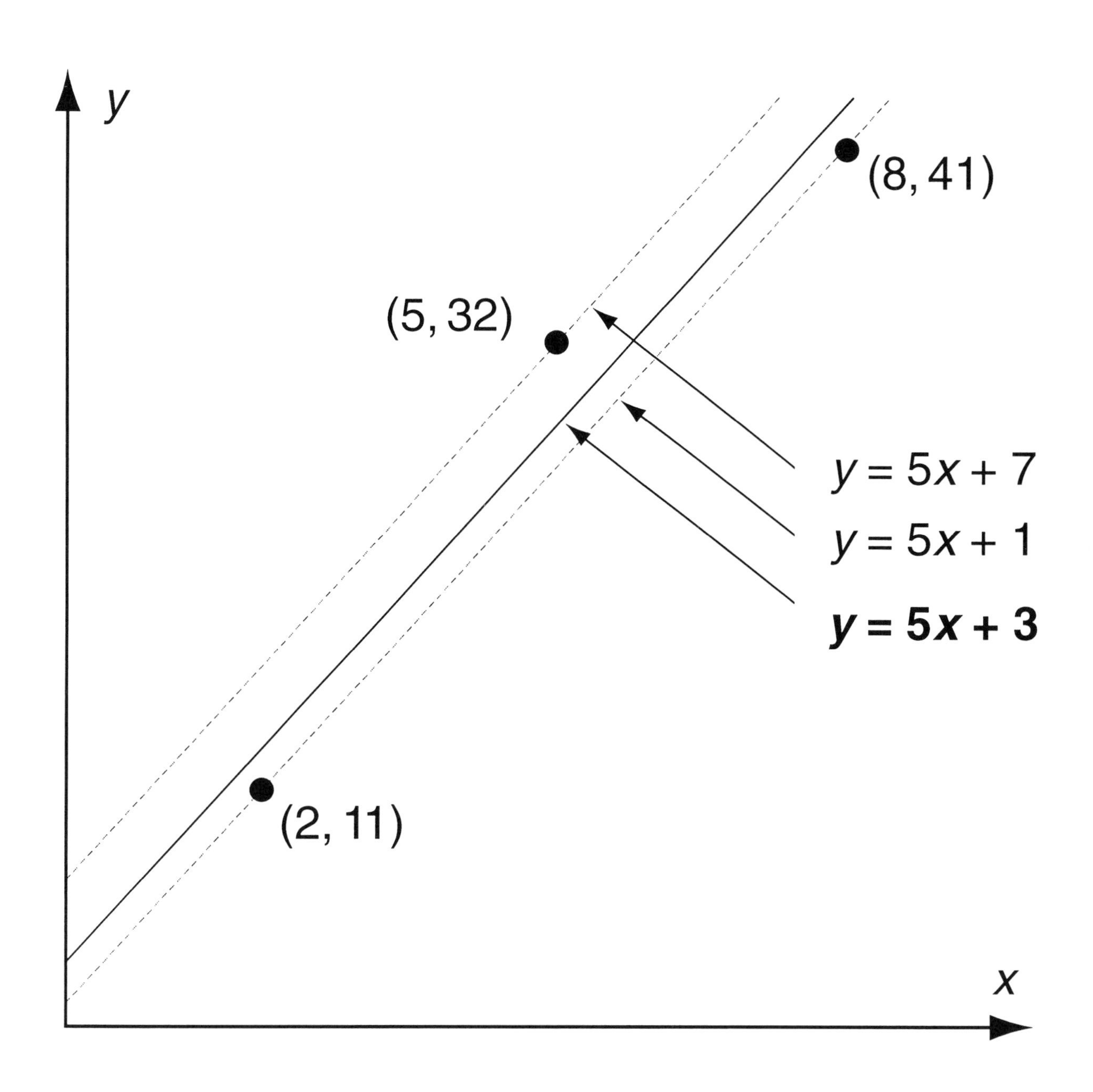
y
(8, 41)
(5, 32)
y = 5x + 7
y = 5x + 1
y = 5x + 3
(2, 11)
x

Residuals

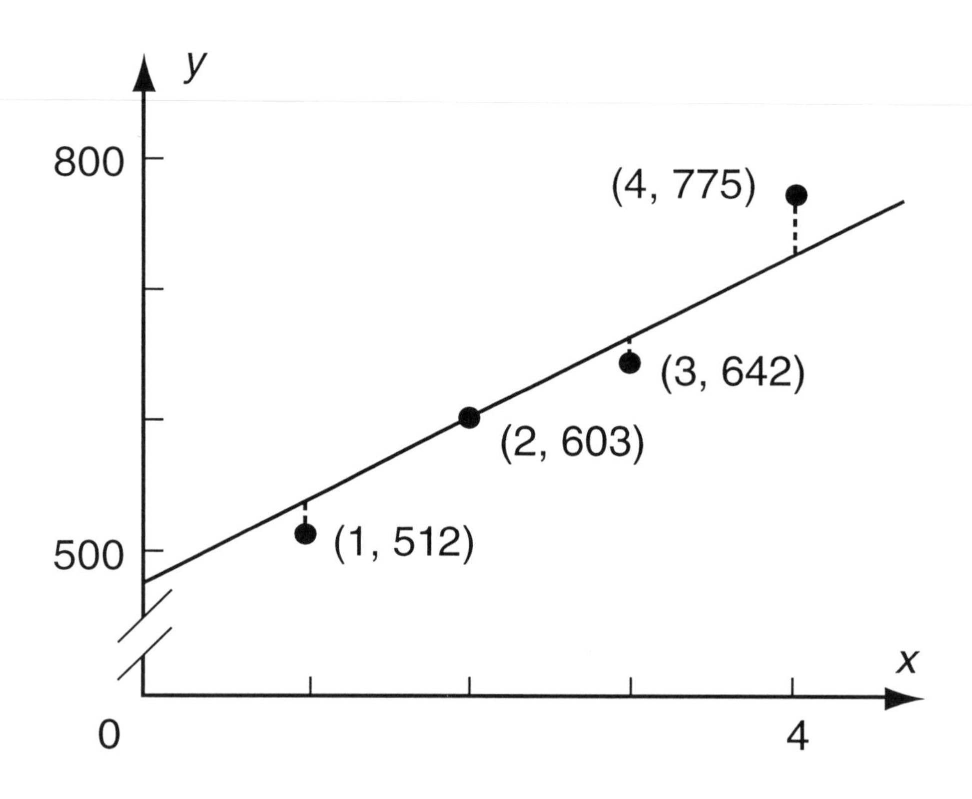

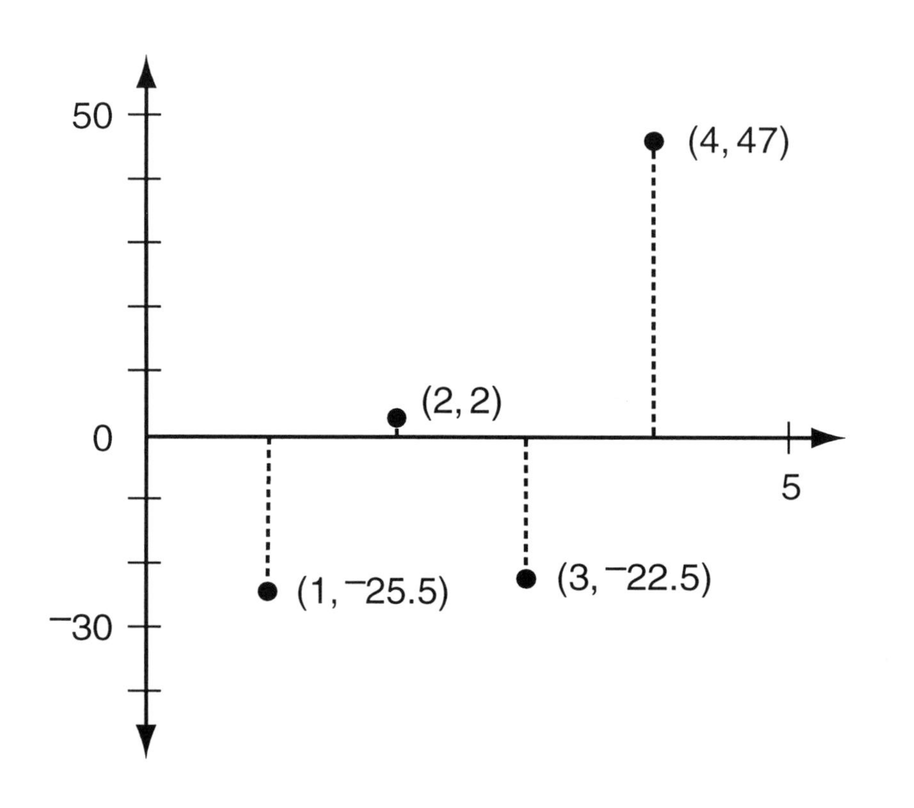

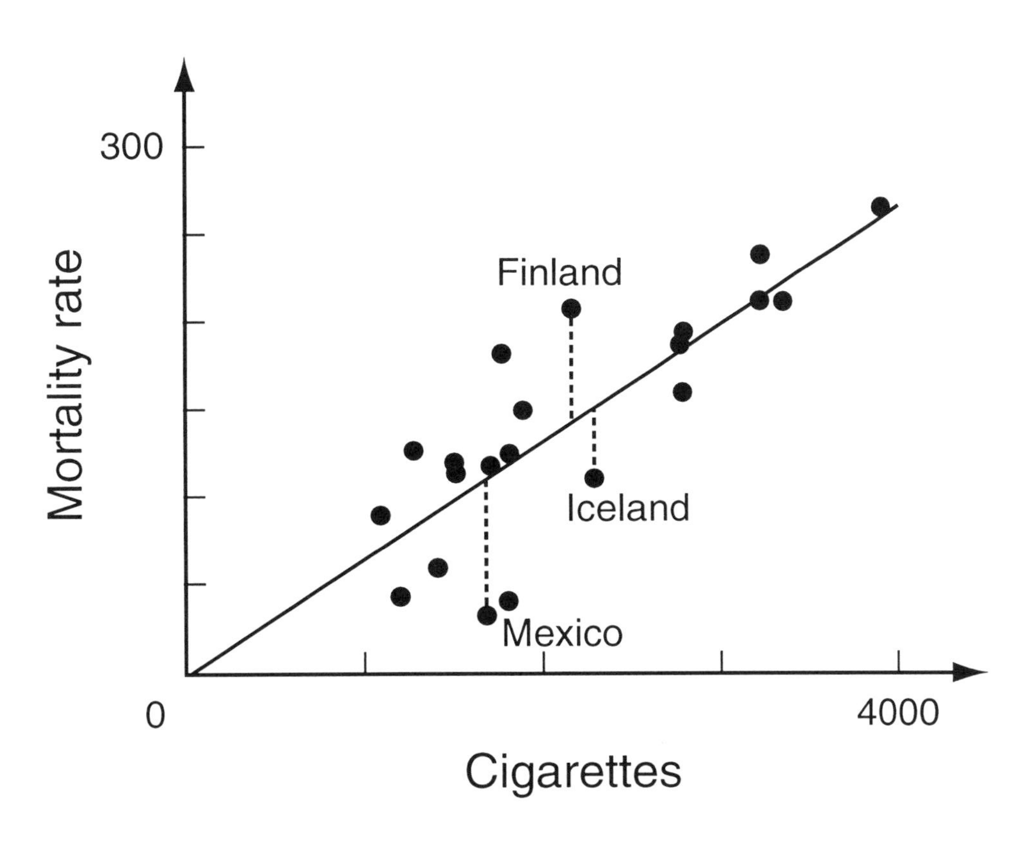
300
Mortality rate
Finland
Iceland
Mexico
0
4000
Cigarettes

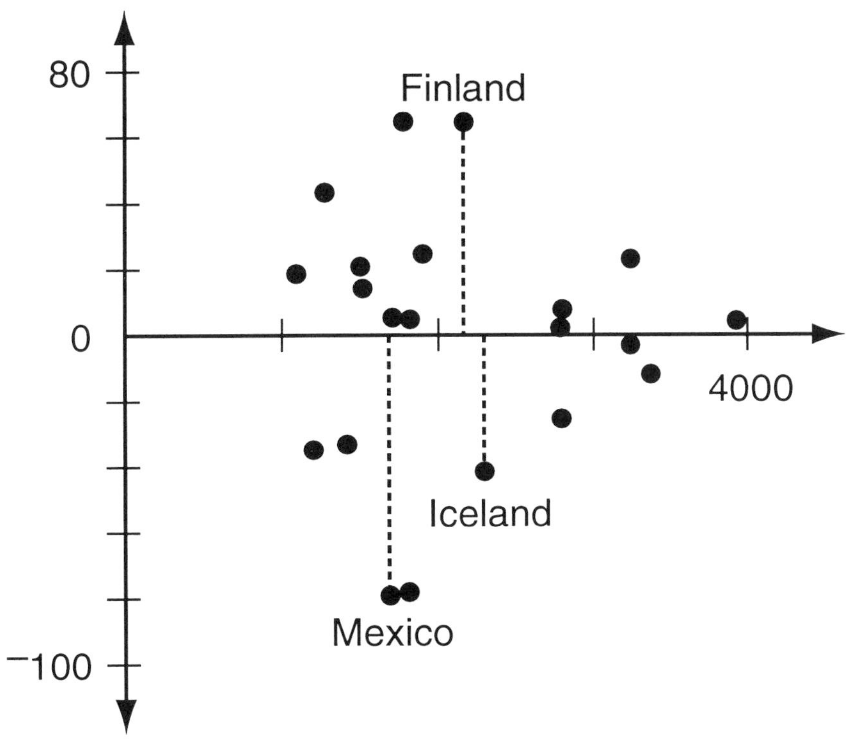
80
Finland
0
4000
Iceland
Mexico
−100

Residuals

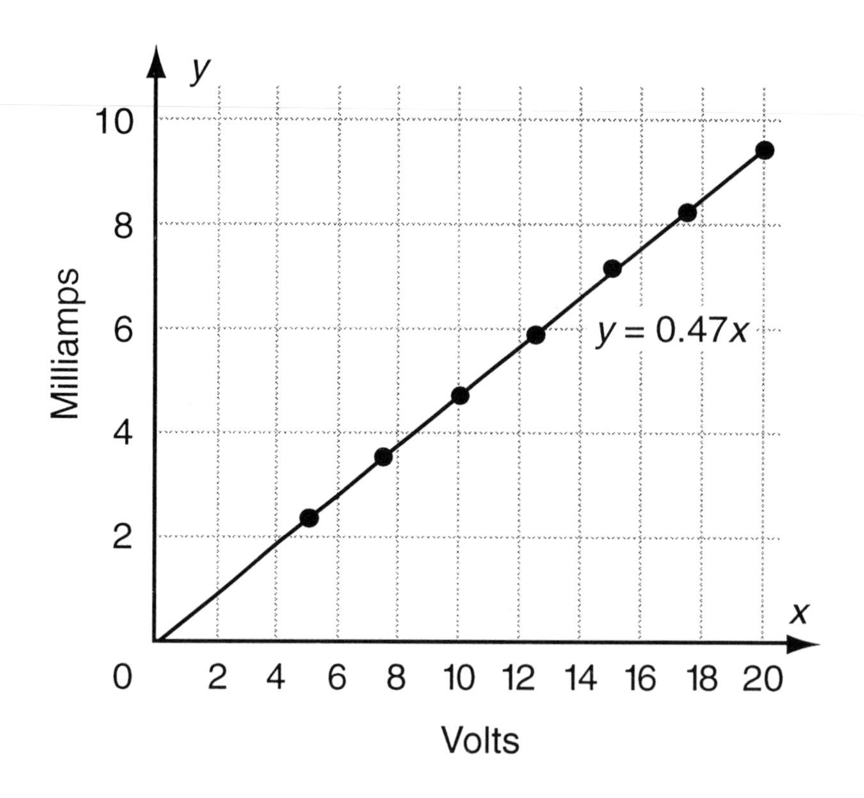
y
10
8
6
4
2
0
Milliamps
y = 0.47x
x
2 4 6 8 10 12 14 16 18 20
Volts

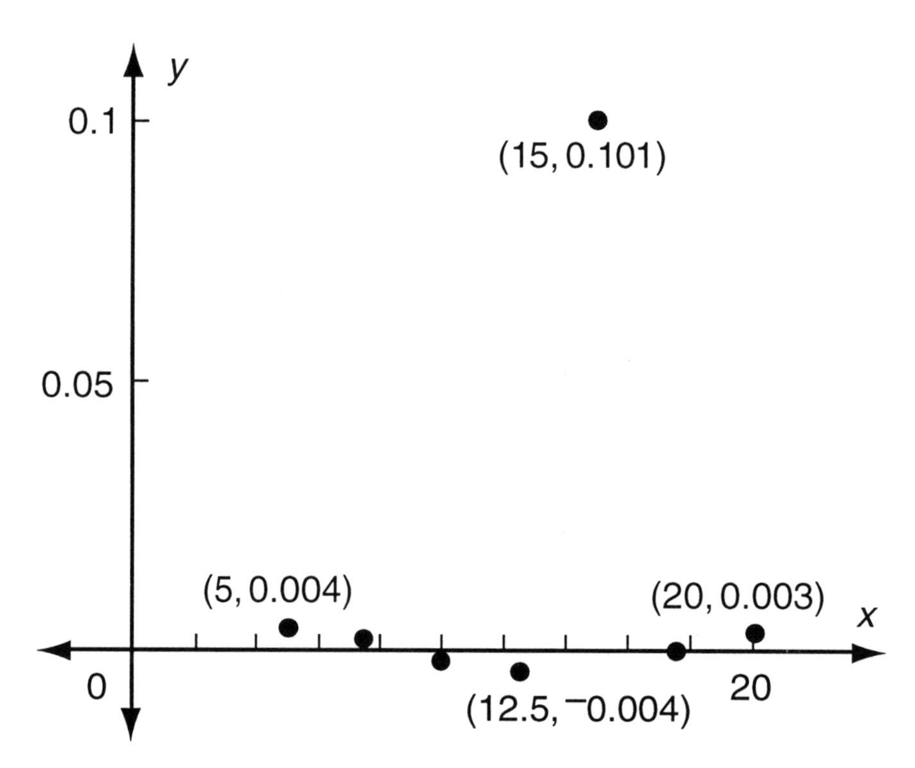
y
0.1
0.05
0
(15, 0.101)
(5, 0.004)
(20, 0.003)
x
(12.5, ⁻0.004)
20

Investigation 4.5.1: Airline Schedules

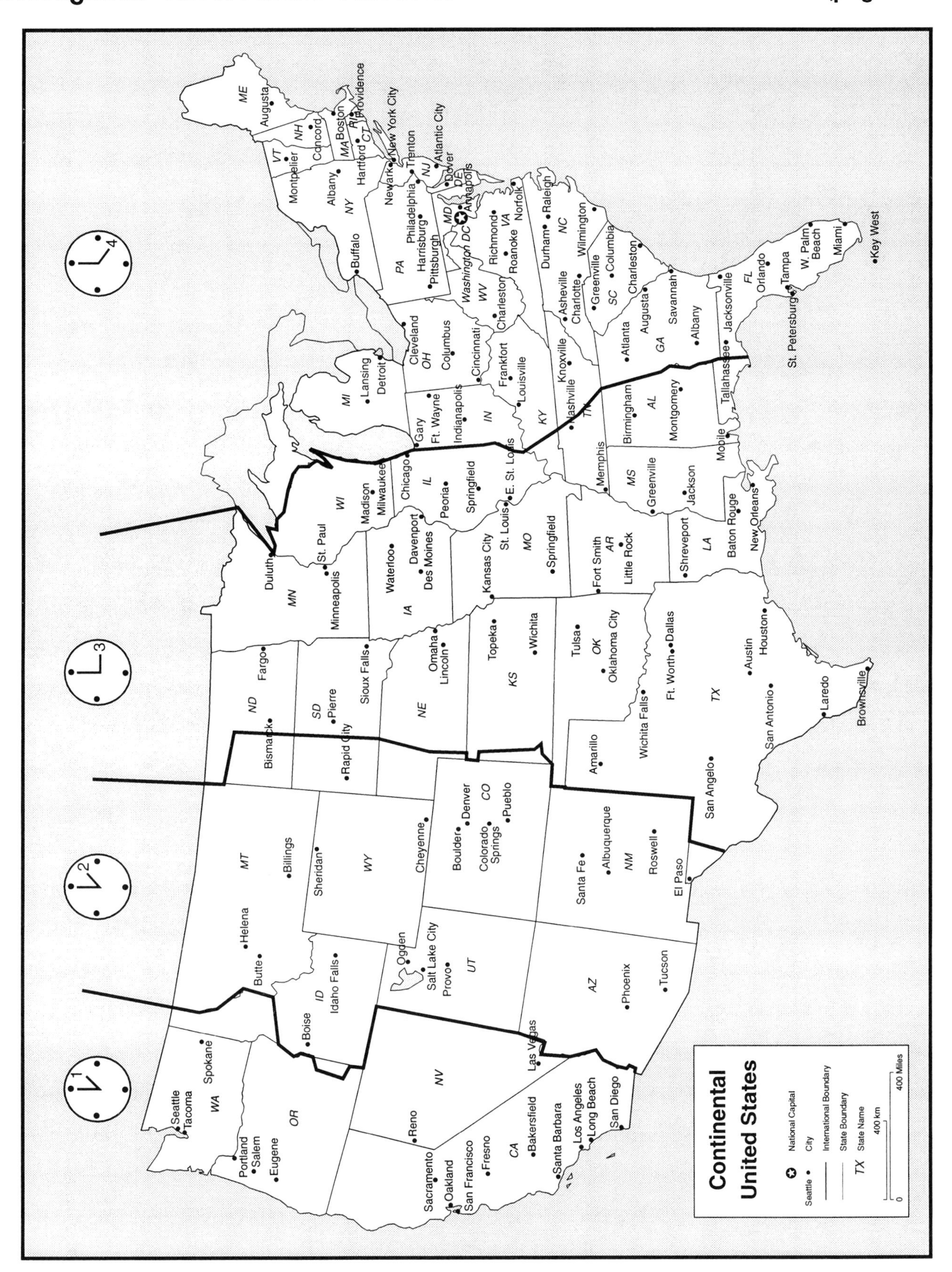

Investigation 4.5.1: Airline Schedules

Key

FM/TO—Originating city to destination city
DEP—Departure time from origination city shown in that city's local time
720a = 7:20 a.m. (a = a.m., p = p.m.)
ARR—Arrival time in destination city shown in that city's local time
MI—Approximate mileage

Destination Cities

Columbus, OH .... CMH
Champaign, IL .... CMI
Hancock, MI .... CMX
Charleston, WV .... CRW
Cancun, Mexico .... CUN
Cincinnati, OH .... CVG
Wausau/Stevens Point, WI .... CWA
Dayton, OH .... DAY
Washington, DC (Nat'l) .... DCA
Denver, CO .... DEN
Dallas/Ft Worth, TX .... DFW
Des Moines, IA .... DSM
Erie, PA .... ERI
Escanaba, MI .... ESC
Evansville, IN .... EVV
New York (Newark), NJ .... EWR
Fort Lauderdale, FL .... FLL
Flint, MI .... FNT
Frankfurt, Germany .... FRA
Fort Wayne, IN .... FWA
Grand Cayman, B.W.I. .... GCM
Grand Forks, ND .... GFK
Green Bay, WI .... GRB
Grand Rapids, MI .... GRR
Greenville/Spartanburg, SC .... GSP
Honolulu, HI .... HNL
Houston (Hobby), TX .... HOU
New York (Westchester County) .... HPN
Washington, DC (Dulles) .... IAD
Indianapolis, IN .... IND
Jacksonville, FL .... JAX
Osaka, Japan .... KIX
Lafayette, IN .... LAF
Lansing, MI .... LAN
Las Vegas, NV .... LAS
Los Angeles, CA .... LAX
Lexington, KY .... LEX
New York (LaGuardia), NY .... LGA
London (Gatwick), England .... LGW
Saginaw/Bay City/Midland, MI .... MBS
Kansas City, MO .... MCI
Orlando, FL .... MCO
Harrisburg, PA .... MDT
Chicago (Midway), IL .... MDW
Memphis, TN .... MEM
Mexico City, Mexico .... MEX
Miami, FL .... MIA
Milwaukee, WI .... MKE
Muskegon, MI .... MKG
Moline, IL .... MLI
Marquette, MI .... MQT
Madison, WI .... MSN
Minneapolis, St. Paul, MN .... MSP
New Orleans, LA .... MSY
Tokyo (Narita), Japan .... NRT
Chicago (O'Hare), IL .... ORD
Norfolk, VA .... ORF
West Palm Beach, FL .... PBI
Portland, OR .... PDX
Philadelphia, PA .... PHL
Phoenix, AZ .... PHX
Pittsburgh, PA .... PIT
Pellston/Mackinac Island, MI .... PLN
Providence/Newport, RI .... PVD
Raleigh/Durham, NC .... RDU
Richmond, VA .... RIC
Roanoke, VA .... ROA
Rochester, NY .... ROC
Fort Meyers, FL .... RSW
San Diego, CA .... SAN
South Bend, IN .... SBN
State College, PA .... SCE
Louisville, KY .... SDF
Seattle/Tacoma, WA .... SEA
Seoul, Korea .... SEL
San Francisco, CA .... SFO
San Juan, Puerto Rico .... SJU
Orange County, CA .... SNA
Sarasota/Bradenton, FL .... SRQ
St. Louis, MO .... STL
Syracuse, NY .... SYR
Toledo, OH .... TOL
Tampa, FL .... TPA
Taipei, Taiwan .... TPE
Traverse City, MI .... TVC
Knoxville, TN .... TYS
Fort Walton Beach, FL .... VPS
Halifax, NS, Canada .... YHZ
Youngstown, OH .... YNG
Ottawa, ON, Canada .... YOW
Regina, SK, Canada .... YQR
Montreal, PQ, Canada (Dorval) .... YUL
London, ON, Canada .... YXU
Toronto, ON, Canada .... YYZ

Investigation 4.5.1: Airline Schedules

Flight Schedule

FM/TO	DEP	ARR	MI
Detroit, MI	DTW		
CMH	655p	747p	156
CMH	830p	935p	156
CMH	1000p	1049p	156
CMI	920a	955a	298
CMI	1225p	100p	298
CMI	310p	345p	298
CRW	1045a	1215p	281
CRW	435p	605p	281
CRW	435p	605p	281
CRW	845p	1015p	281
CVG	700a	820a	229
CVG	925a	1050a	229
CVG	1200p	104p	229
CVG	130p	226p	229
CVG	305p	430p	229
CVG	440p	605p	229
CVG	455p	555p	229
CVG	840p	944p	229
CWA	145p	235p	363
CWA	510p	600p	363
CWA	830p	915p	363
DAY	925a	1035a	166
DAY	1225p	120p	166
DAY	130p	235p	166
DAY	135p	224p	166
DAY	140	229	166
DAY	505p	559p	166
DAY	830p	930p	166
DCA	710a	838a	405
DCA	920a	1040a	405
DCA	1035a	1156a	405
DCA	1040a	1201p	405
DCA	1210p	131p	405
DCA	140p	305p	405
DCA	305p	430p	405
DCA	435p	602p	405
DCA	436p	605p	405
DCA	645p	815p	405
DCA	835p	1004p	405
DEN	920a	1022a	1125
DEN	1215p	123p	1125
DEN	700p	803p	1125
DFW	700a	848a	986
DFW	940a	1135a	986
DFW	1215p	209p	986
DFW	310p	500p	986
DFW	505p	653p	986
DFW	645p	841p	986
DSM	1220p	113p	533
DSM	640p	729p	533
ERI	910a	1010a	163
ERI	130p	225p	163
ERI	450p	555p	163
ERI	830p	935p	163
ESC	930a	1115a	305
ESC	1215p	150p	305
EVV	910a	955a	364
EVV	320p	415p	364
EVV	650p	745p	364
EWR	700a	833a	488
EWR	900a	1031a	488
EWR	1035a	1210p	488
EWR	150p	324p	488
EWR	320p	504p	488
EWR	445p	625p	488
EWR	515p	655p	488
EWR	640p	821p	488
EWR	845p	1027p	488

FM/TO	DEP	ARR	MI
Detroit, MI	DTW		
FLL	730a	1033a	1127
FLL	910a	1213p	1127
FLL	1230p	327p	1127
FLL	450p	750p	1127
FLL	840p	1139p	1127
FNT	745a	820a	55
FNT	940a	1020a	55
FNT	1030a	1105a	55
FNT	1210p	1250p	55
FNT	1235p	115p	55
FNT	135p	210p	55
FNT	410p	445p	55
FNT	435p	510p	55
FNT	630p	705p	55
FNT	900p	940p	55
FNT	1000p	1035p	55
FRA	730p	825a	4161
FRA	730p	925a	4161
FRA	910p	1005a	4161
FRA	910p	1105a	4161
FWA	915a	900a	128
FWA	1235p	1225p	128
FWA	320p	320p	128
FWA	510p	510p	128
FWA	645p	645p	128
FWA	830p	825p	128
FWA	1010p	953p	128
GCM	435p	902p	1583
GFK	1235p	329p	782
GRB	925a	941a	287
GRB	1230p	1245p	287
GRB	500p	509p	287
GRB	705p	714p	287
GRB	830p	838p	287
GRB	1000p	1009p	287
GRR	915a	1008a	120
GRR	1036a	1120a	120
GRR	1215p	107p	120
GRR	315p	401p	120
GRR	450p	537p	120
GRR	645p	731P	120
GRR	830p	924p	120
GRR	1005p	1050p	120
GSP	715a	851a	508
GSP	135p	308p	508
GSP	445p	623p	508
GSP	825p	958	508
HOU	930a	1139a	1092
HOU	1230p	236p	1092
HOU	645p	846p	1092
HPN	725a	900a	505
HPN	140p	317p	505
HPN	455p	632p	505
HPN	845p	1017p	505
IAD	720a	841a	383
IAD	1045a	1205p	383
IAD	145p	307p	383
IAD	500p	625p	383
IAD	835p	1001p	383
IND	715a	723a	230
IND	935a	943a	230
IND	1225p	1230p	230
IND	135p	135p	230
IND	445p	451p	230
IND	640p	641p	230
IND	1005p	1006p	230
JAX	925a	1141a	814
JAX	1205p	224p	814

FM/TO	DEP	ARR	MI
Detroit, MI	DTW		
JAX	505p	725p	814
KIX	1250p	325p	6622
KIX	1250p	335p	6622
LAF	940a	1010a	224
LAF	1215p	1240p	224
LAF	310p	330p	224
LAF	650p	715p	224
LAN	920a	958a	74
LAN	1220p	100p	74
LAN	325p	401p	74
LAN	510p	550p	74
LAN	700p	740p	74
LAN	830p	913p	74
LAN	1000p	1040p	74
LAS	935a	1056a	1749
LAS	1215p	135p	1749
LAS	320p	431p	1749
LAS	705p	830p	1749
LAS	1010p	1127p	1749
LAX	925a	1110a	1979
LAX	1220p	217p	1979
LAX	325p	522p	1979
LAX	650p	838p	1979
LAX	1005p	1153p	1979
LEX	745a	920a	296
LEX	1210p	150p	296
LEX	430p	600p	296
LEX	900p	1030p	296
LGA	700a	838a	501
LGA	905a	1044a	501
LGA	1035a	1211p	501
LGA	1230p	209p	501
LGA	150p	332p	501
LGA	305p	446p	501
LGA	440p	624p	501
LGA	700p	844p	501
LGA	840p	1026p	501
LGW	850p	830a	3786
LGW	850p	930a	3786
MBS	915a	1004a	98
MBS	1210p	1258p	98
MBS	145p	226p	98
MBS	310p	359p	98
MBS	455p	540p	98
MBS	645p	730p	98
MBS	825p	914p	98
MBS	1000p	1041p	98
MCI	725a	822a	630
MCI	925a	1022a	630
MCI	1225p	127p	630
MCI	420p	519p	630
MCI	655p	757p	630
MCO	730a	1009a	957
MCO	900a	1142a	957
MCO	930a	1209p	957
MCO	1045a	127p	957
MCO	1200n	236p	957
MCO	130p	400p	957
MCO	300p	530p	957
MCO	325p	553p	957
MCO	445p	714p	957
MCO	500p	727p	957
MCO	700p	932p	957
MCO	850p	1125p	957
MDT	700a	929a	370
MDT	1035a	1215p	370
MDT	155p	313p	370
MDT	515p	635	370

Investigation 4.5.1: Airline Schedules

FM/TO	DEP	ARR	MI
Detroit, MI DTW			
MDT	830p	949p	370
MDW	705a	710a	229
MDW	940a	951a	229
MDW	1200n	1209p	229
MDW	310p	315p	229
MDW	500p	503p	229
MDW	640p	646p	229
MEM	700a	758a	610
MEM	1200n	1257p	610
MEM	1205p	102p	610
MEM	315p	406p	610
MEM	630p	723p	610
MEM	640p	730p	610
MEM	1005p	1049p	610
MEX	915a	1150a	1820
MIA	720a	1023a	1145
MIA	730a	1033a	1145
MIA	435p	736p	1145
MIA	500p	805p	1145
MKE	940a	950a	237
MKE	1225p	1235p	237
MKE	310p	315p	237
MKE	440p	442p	237
MKE	705p	712p	237
MKE	835p	842p	237
MKE	1000p	1000p	237
MKG	940a	1045a	161
MKG	100p	205p	161
MKG	500p	610p	161
MKG	845p	950p	161
MQT	910a	1100a	363
MQT	1205p	155p	363
MQT	420p	600p	363
MQT	850p	1045p	363
MSN	935a	951a	312
MSN	1220p	1234p	312
MSN	315p	330p	312
MSN	640p	653p	312
MSN	1000p	1009p	312
MSP	725a	817a	528
MSP	925a	1024a	528
MSP	1020a	1105a	528
MSP	1235p	131p	528
MSP	130p	215p	528
MSP	305p	355p	528
MSP	435p	529p	528
MSP	535p	629p	528
MSP	610p	705p	528
MSP	730p	828p	528
MSP	845p	937	528
MSP	1010p	1056	528
MSY	940a	1119a	926
MSY	1205p	144p	926
MSY	705p	834p	926
NRT	1230p	245p	6399
NRT	320p	635p	6399
ORD	700a	707a	235
ORD	800a	820a	235
ORD	935a	950a	235
ORD	1220p	1239p	235
ORD	325p	335p	235
ORD	430p	439p	235
ORD	605p	625p	235
ORD	650p	710p	235
ORD	850p	908p	235
ORD	1010p	1014p	235
ORF	710a	849a	529
ORF	140p	318p	529
ORF	455p	637p	529
ORF	820p	1002p	529
Detroit, MI DTW			
PBI	920a	1216p	1086
PBI	835p	1128p	1086
PDX	645p	834p	1953
PHL	705a	840a	453
PHL	1040a	1211p	453
PHL	145p	315p	453
PHL	305p	438p	453
PHL	445p	620p	453
PHL	830p	1007p	453
PHX	930a	1042a	1671
PHX	1220p	136p	1671
PHX	655p	803p	1671
PIT	715a	814a	201
PIT	1040a	1138a	201
PIT	1140a	1238p	201
PIT	130p	225p	201
PIT	315p	413p	201
PIT	630p	730p	201
PIT	820p	922p	201
PLN	930a	1055a	242
PLN	1235p	200p	242
PLN	450p	610p	242
PLN	855p	1015p	242
PVD	705a	847a	614
PVD	135p	315p	614
PVD	450p	633p	614
PVD	820p	1001p	614
RDU	710a	849a	502
RDU	145p	319p	502
RDU	505p	642p	502
RDU	840p	1017p	502
RIC	715a	843a	456
RIC	145p	316p	456
RIC	455p	628p	456
RIC	820p	950p	456
ROA	715a	905a	382
ROA	1035a	1220p	382
ROA	130p	315p	382
ROA	845p	1035p	382
ROC	840a	946a	296
ROC	145p	249p	296
ROC	630p	739p	296
ROC	820p	928p	296
RSW	920a	1209p	1081
RSW	1050a	139p	1081
RSW	1200n	248p	1081
RSW	310p	600p	1081
RSW	700p	950p	1081
RSW	825p	1115p	1081
SAN	930a	1115a	1956
SAN	655p	845p	1956
SBN	915a	905a	157
SBN	1230p	1224p	157
SBN	315p	320p	157
SBN	500p	450p	157
SBN	700p	700p	157
SBN	1005p	951p	157
SCE	1045a	1215p	301
SCE	130p	250p	301
SCE	430p	605p	301
SCE	840p	1010p	301
SDF	440p	550p	306
SDF	830p	1000p	306
SDF	1000p	1107p	306
SEA	930a	1127a	1927
SEA	1210p	153p	1927
SEA	310p	503p	1927
SEA	700p	855p	1927
SEA	1010p	1159p	1927
SEL	340p	710p	6625
Detroit, MI DTW			
SFO	935a	1138a	2079
SFO	1225p	231p	2079
SFO	320p	532p	2079
SFO	650p	849p	2079
SJU	910a	140p	1929
SJU	910a	240p	1929
SNA	925a	1115a	1960
SNA	645p	832p	1960
SRQ	1040a	121p	1023
SRQ	1225p	310p	1023
STL	720a	752a	440
STL	940a	1028a	440
STL	1205p	1245p	440
STL	320p	403p	440
STL	505p	544p	440
STL	655p	735p	440
SYR	725a	837a	374
SYR	1035a	1147a	374
SYR	205p	317p	374
SYR	520p	636p	374
SYR	615p	730p	374
SYR	830p	944p	374
TOL	930a	1015a	49
TOL	1235p	120p	49
TOL	150p	230p	49
TOL	430p	510p	49
TOL	630p	705p	49
TOL	845p	930p	49
TOL	1005p	1040p	49
TPA	730a	1010a	983
TPA	900a	1138a	983
TPA	910a	1148a	983
TPA	1215p	256p	983
TPA	650p	929p	983
TPA	845p	1128p	983
TVC	900a	1005a	207
TVC	1205p	103p	207
TVC	310p	404p	207
TVC	450p	605p	207
TVC	1000p	1115p	207
TVC	1005p	1100p	207
TYS	700a	900a	443
TYS	910a	1031a	443
TYS	450p	613p	443
TYS	700p	905p	443
YHZ	1040a	207p	1010
YHZ	450p	820p	1010
YNG	910a	1015a	154
YNG	330p	430p	154
YNG	705p	810p	154
YOW	730a	930a	439
YOW	130p	254p	439
YOW	450p	618p	439
YOW	840p	1008p	439
YUL	700a	837a	529
YUL	1035a	1210p	529
YUL	140p	316p	529
YUL	450p	630p	529
YUL	845p	1027p	529
YXU	910a	1010a	125
YXU	130p	230p	125
YXU	440p	540p	125
YXU	830p	925p	125
YYZ	720a	828a	214
YYZ	1045a	1150a	214
YYZ	150p	257p	214
YYZ	500p	615p	214
YYZ	840p	956p	214

Soda Machine Graph

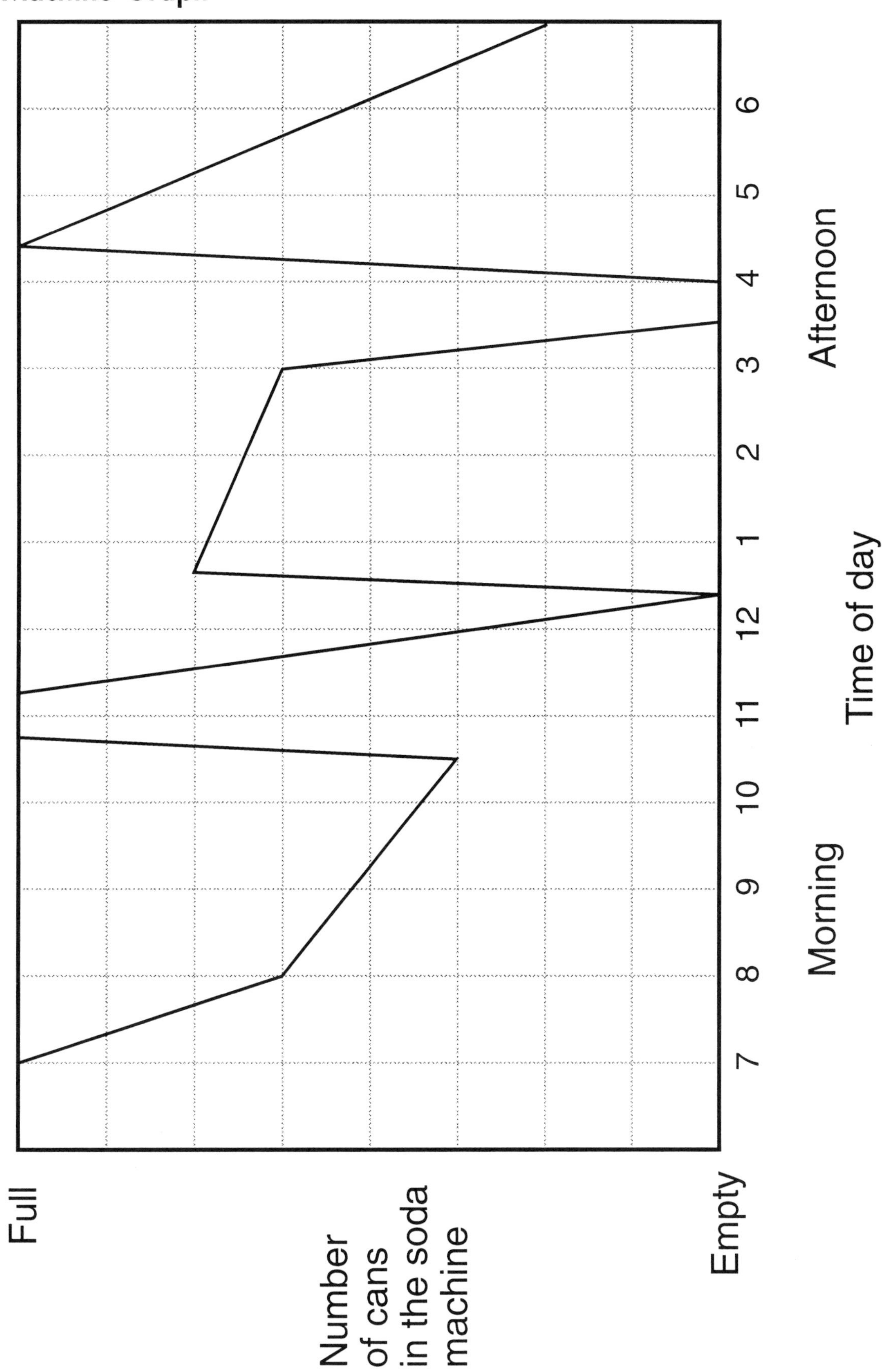

Section 5.1/Page 199 T

Examples 1 and 2

Example 1

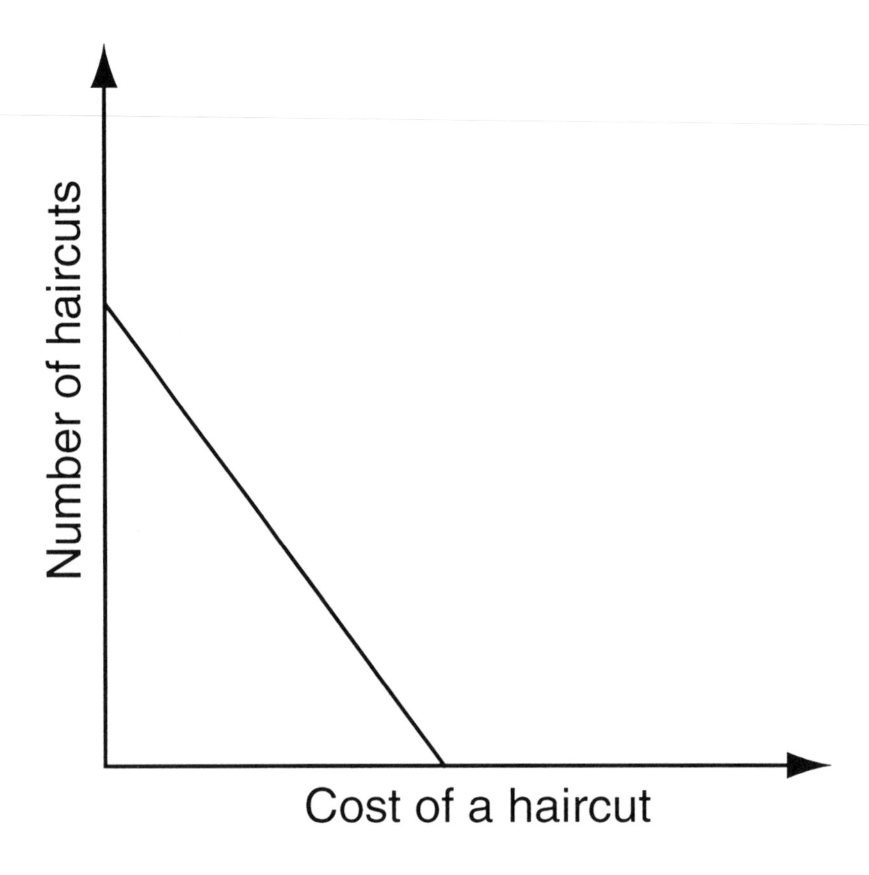

Example 2

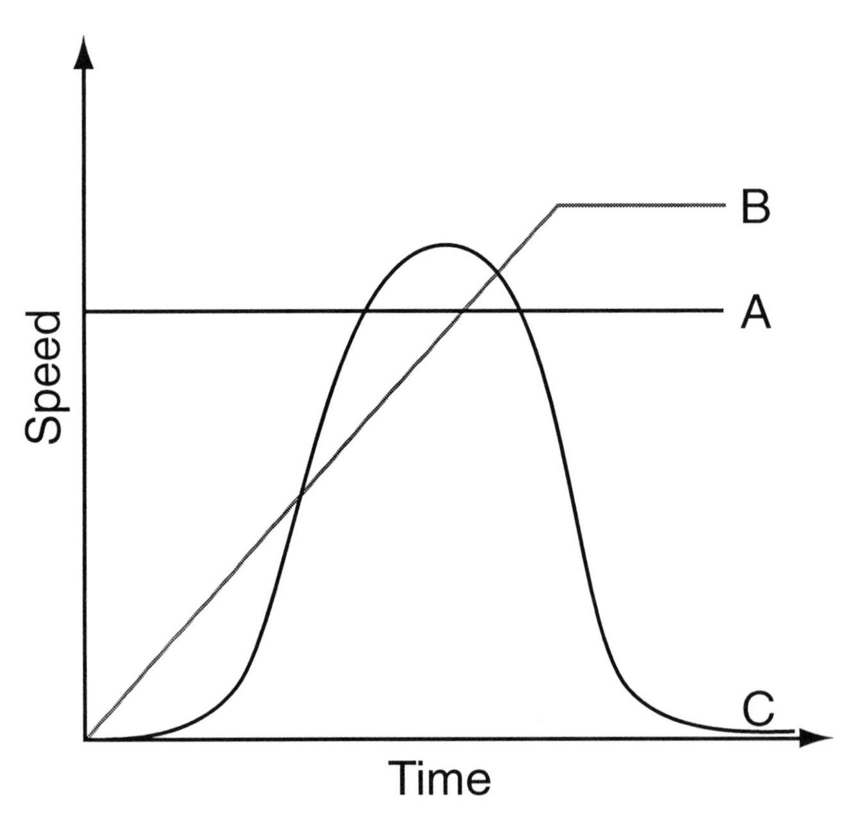

Problem 3: Roller Coaster

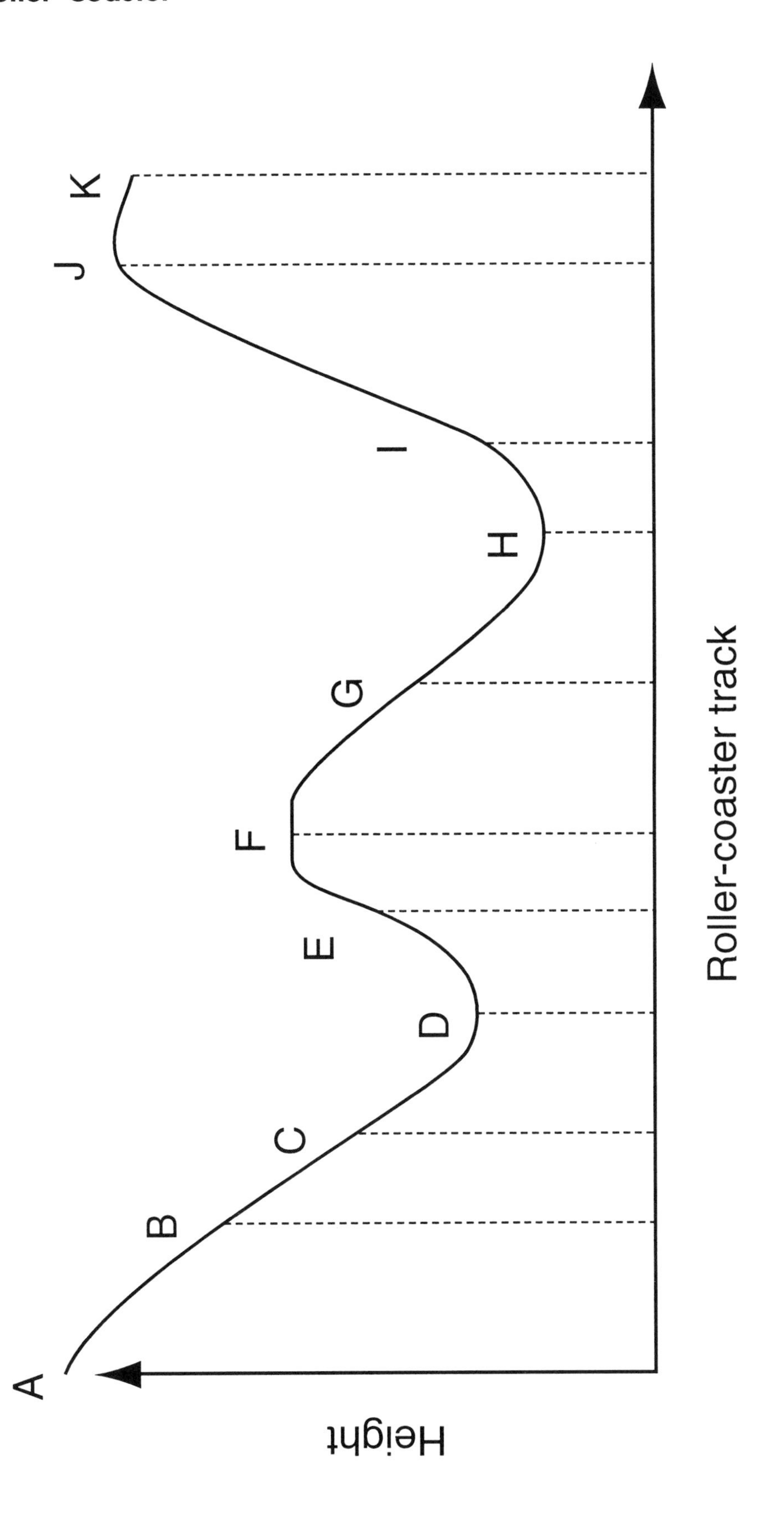

Web Graphs

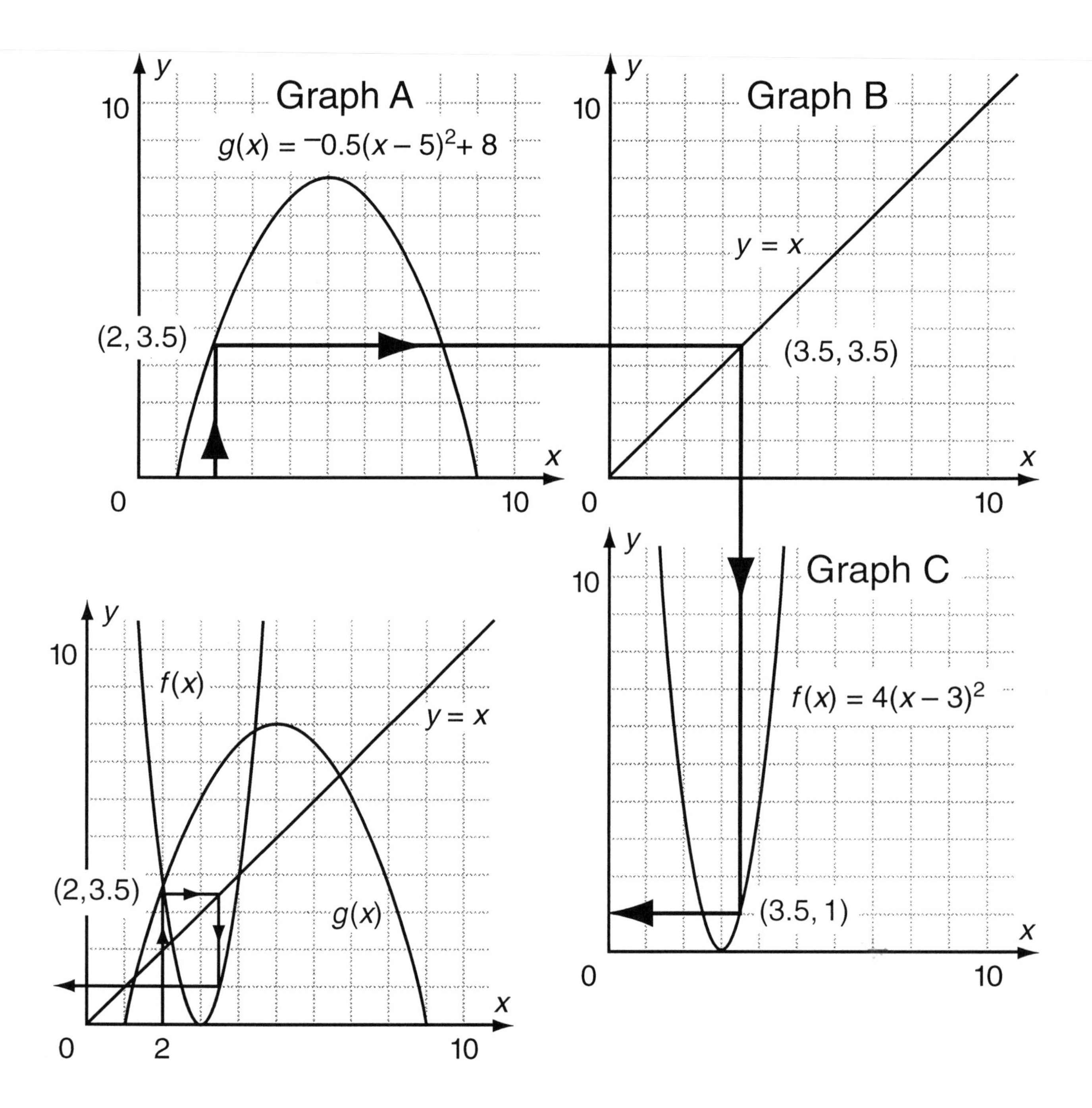
Graph A
$g(x) = {}^{-}0.5(x-5)^2 + 8$
(2, 3.5)
Graph B
$y = x$
(3.5, 3.5)
Graph C
$f(x) = 4(x-3)^2$
(3.5, 1)
f(x)
y = x
(2,3.5)
g(x)
x
y
0
2
10

Investigation 5.9.1: $f(f(f(f(\ldots f(x) \ldots))))$

$y = 2.5x(1 - x)$

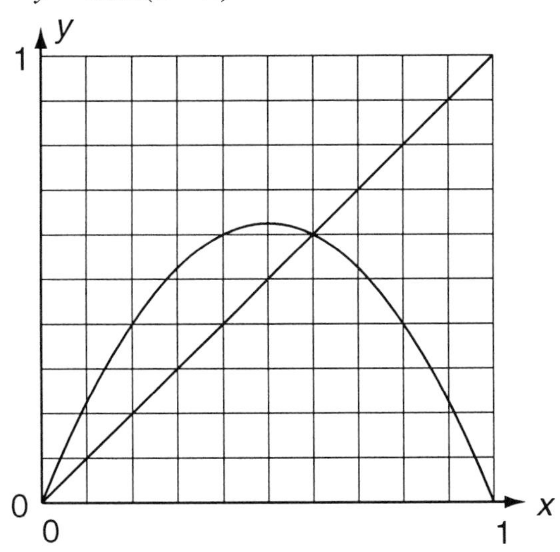

$y = 2.8x(1 - x)$

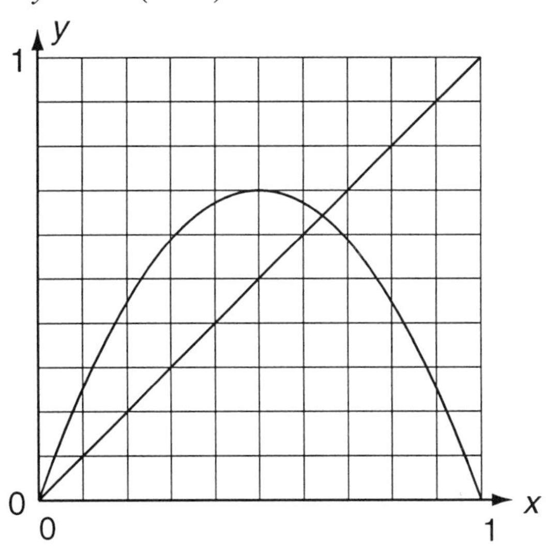

$y = 3.2x(1 - x)$

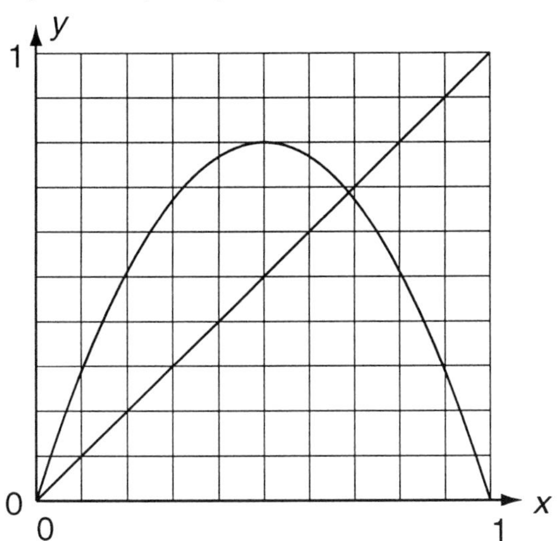

$y = 3.4x(1 - x)$

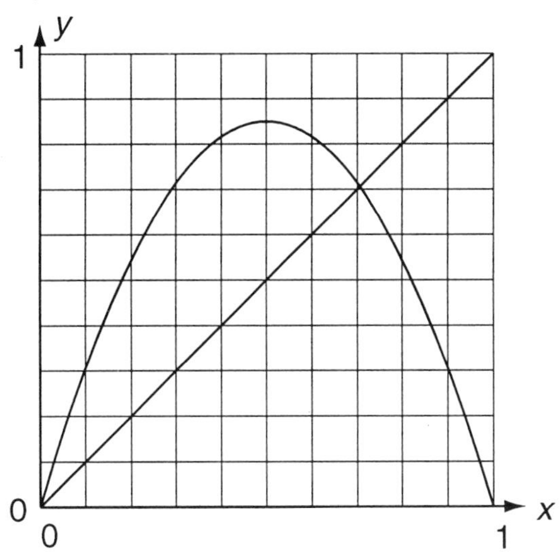

$y = 3.5x(1 - x)$

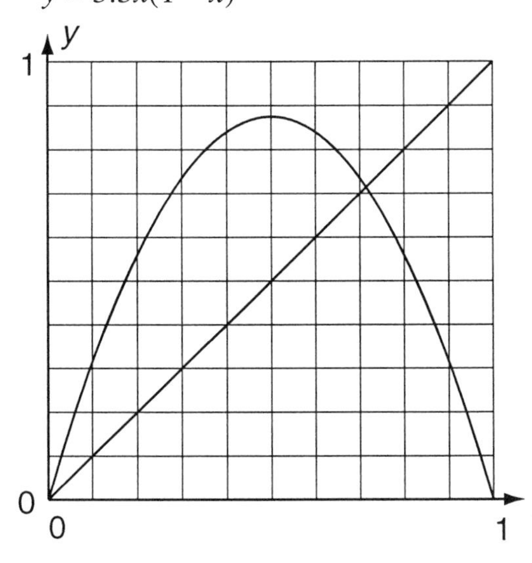

$y = 4x(1 - x)$

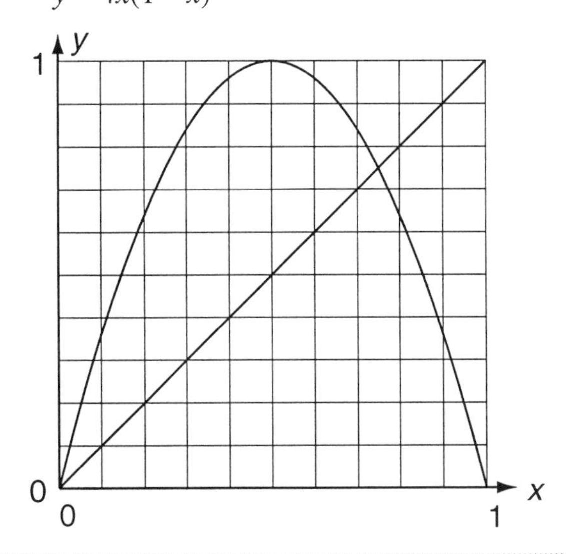

Paths

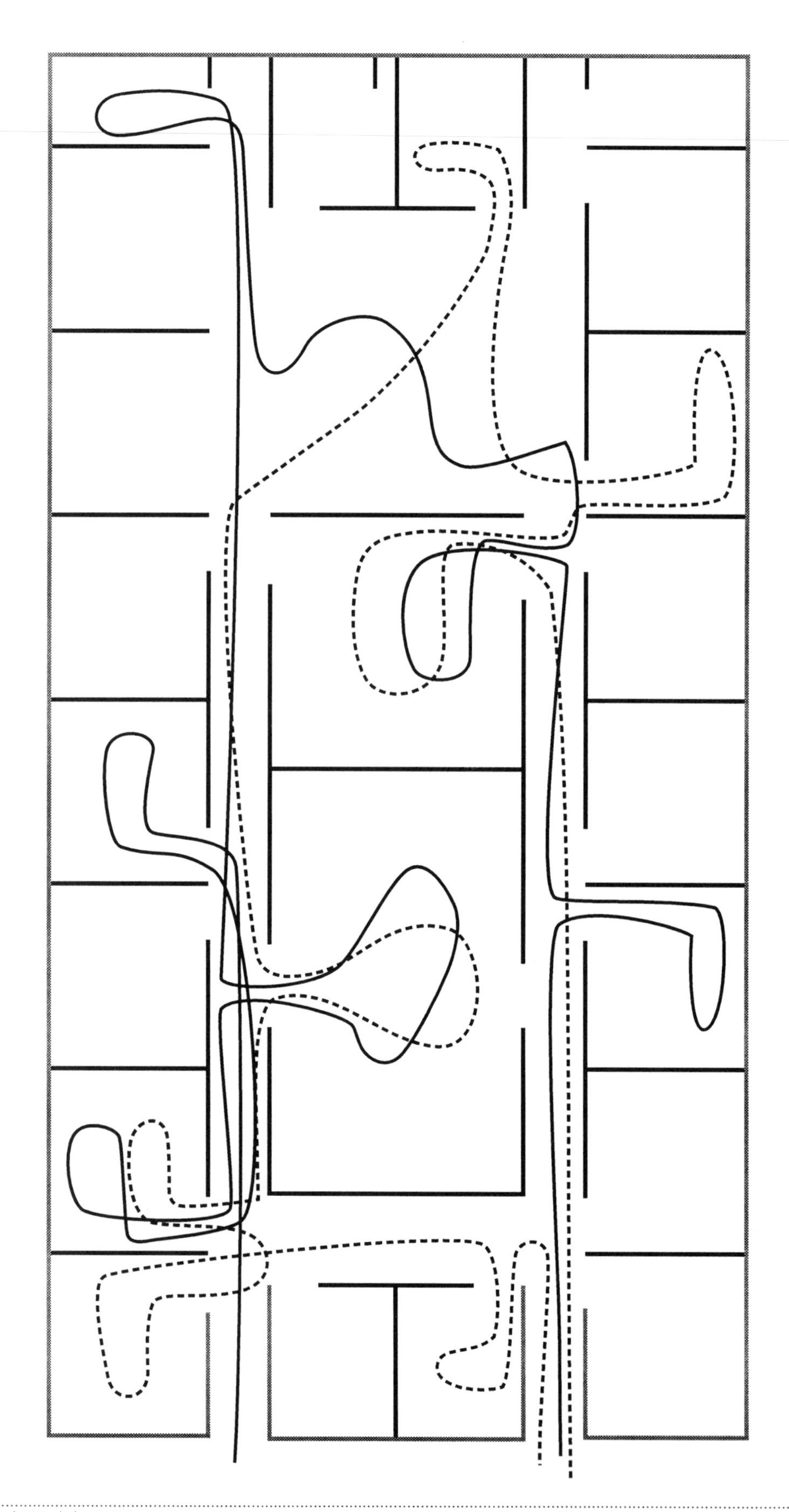

Gulf Map

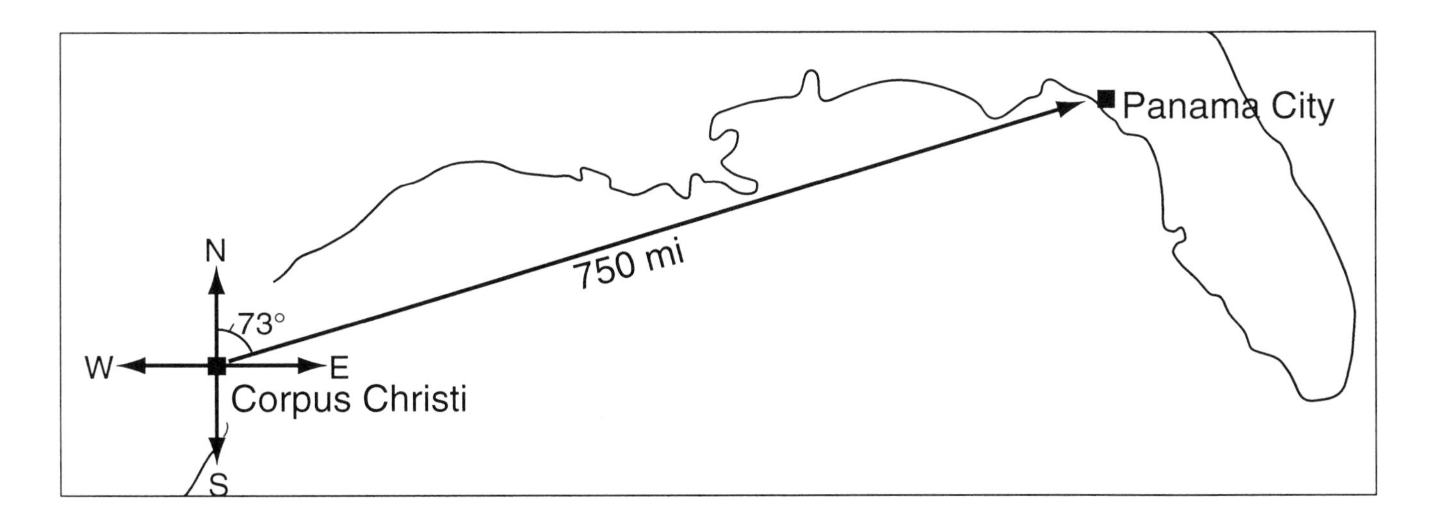

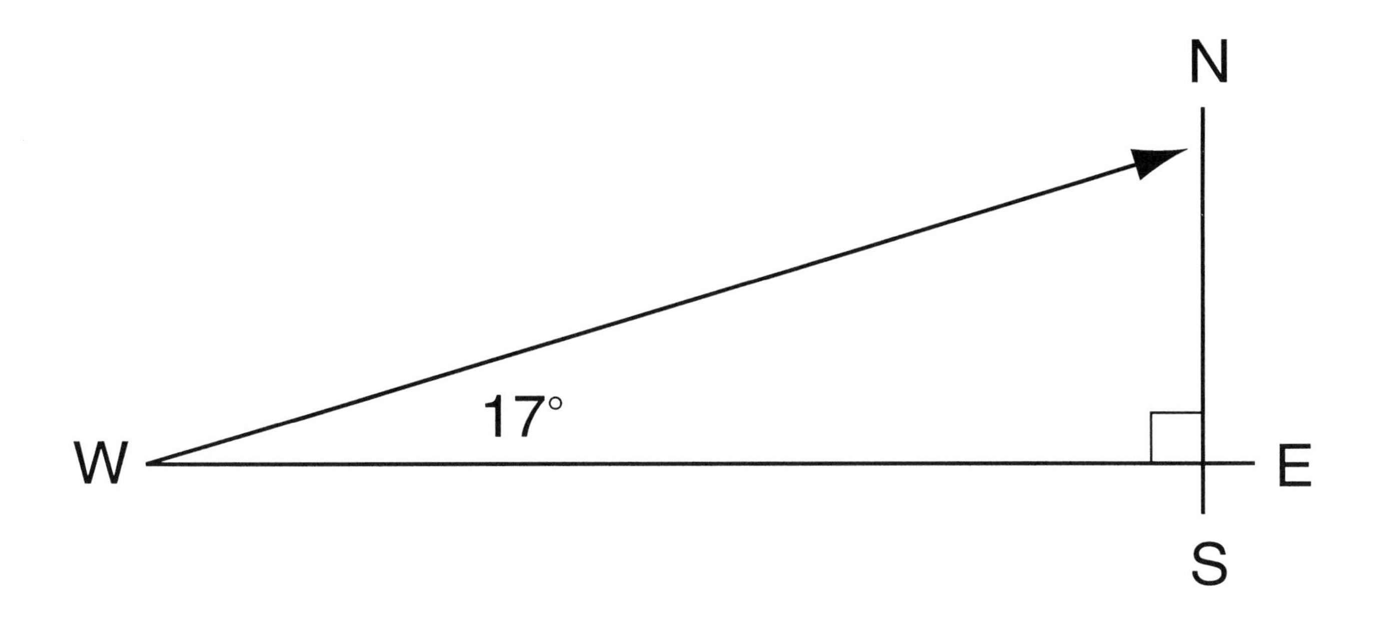

Investigation 6.3.2: Finding the Height of a Tree

Distance	Angle	Circumference	Height	Diameter

Circle Diagram

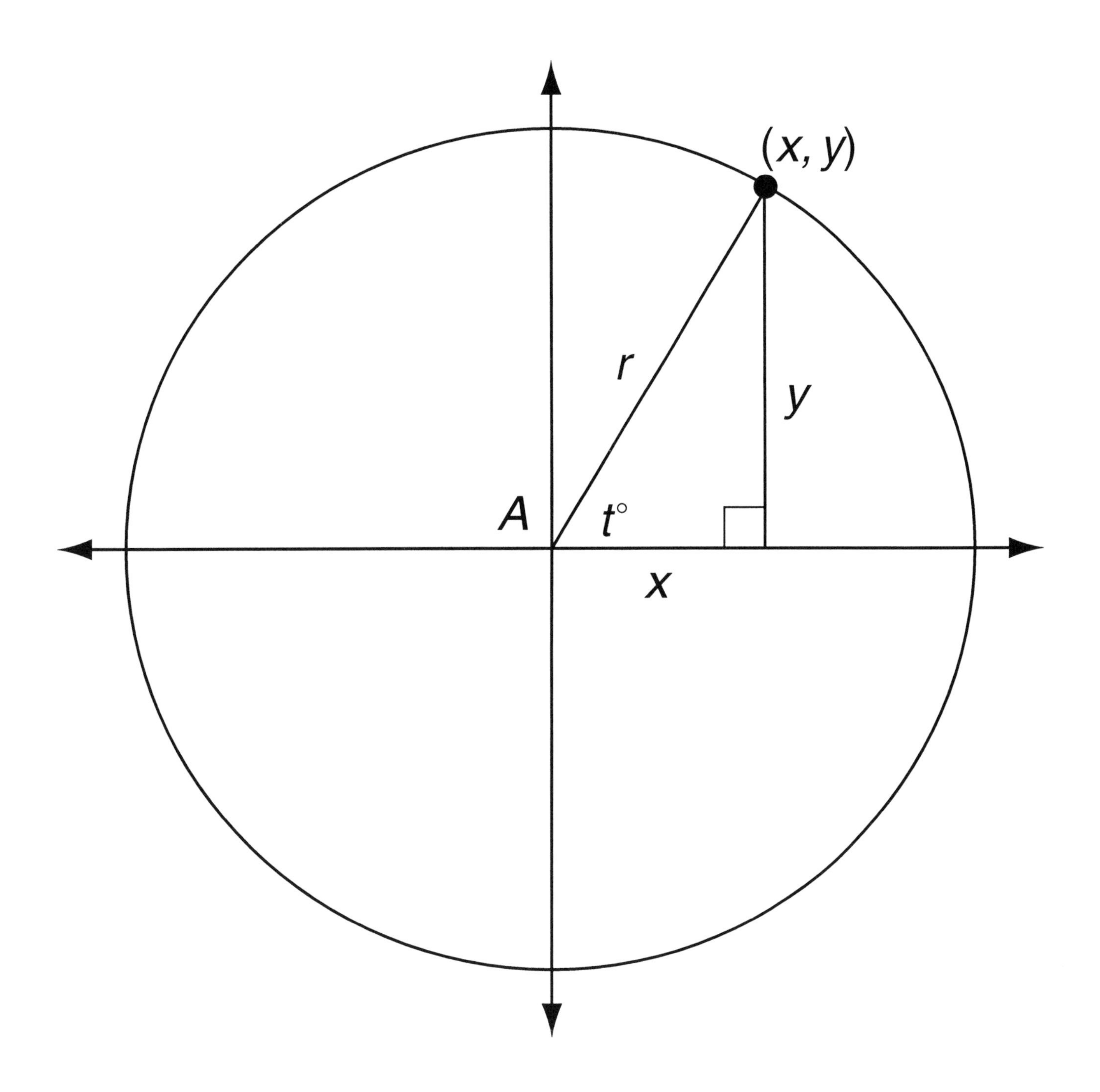

Unit Circle

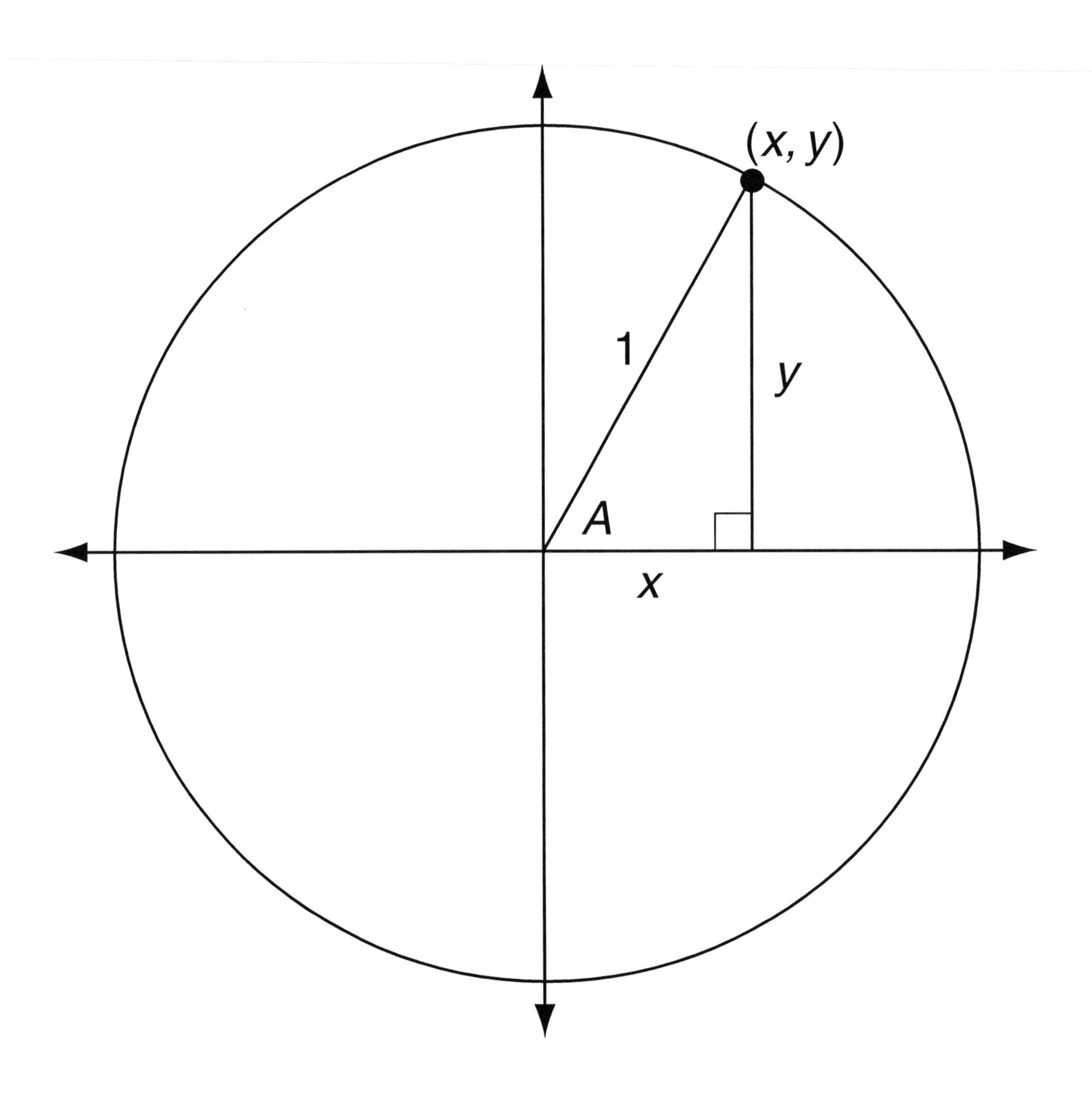

Toy Car Diagram

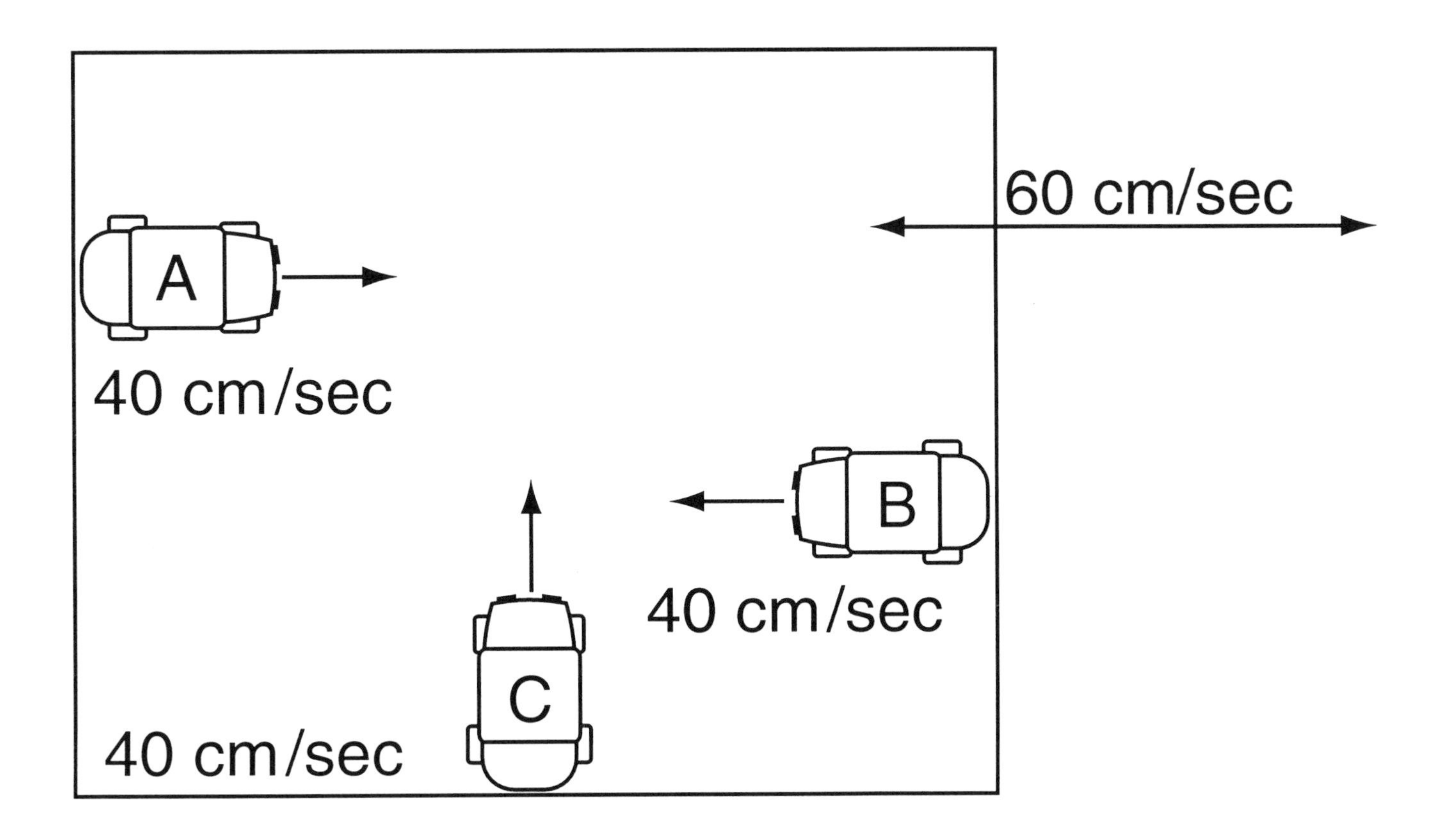

Investigation 7.1.1: Radioactive Squares

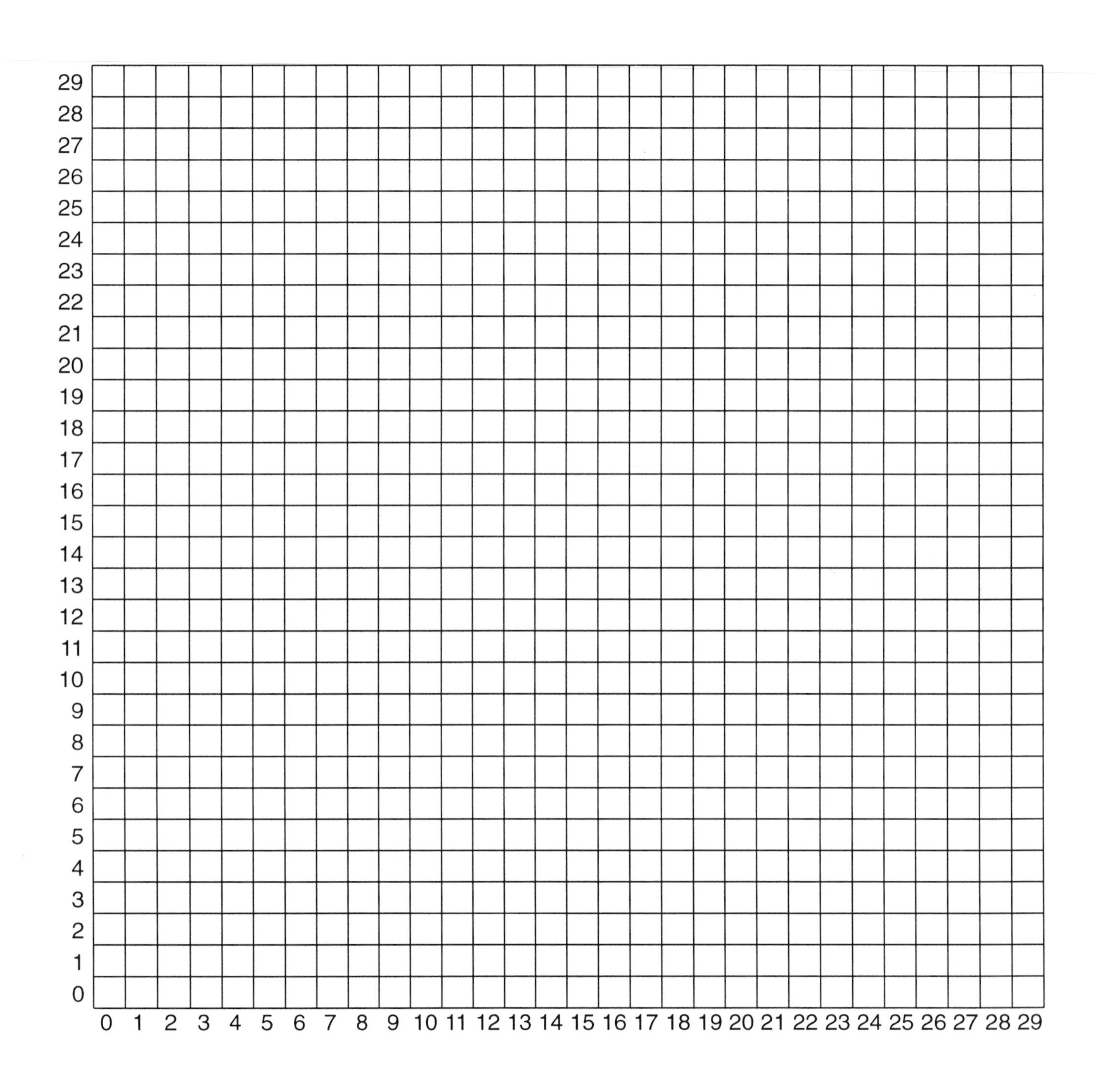

Investigation 7.7.2: Making a Logarithmic Ruler

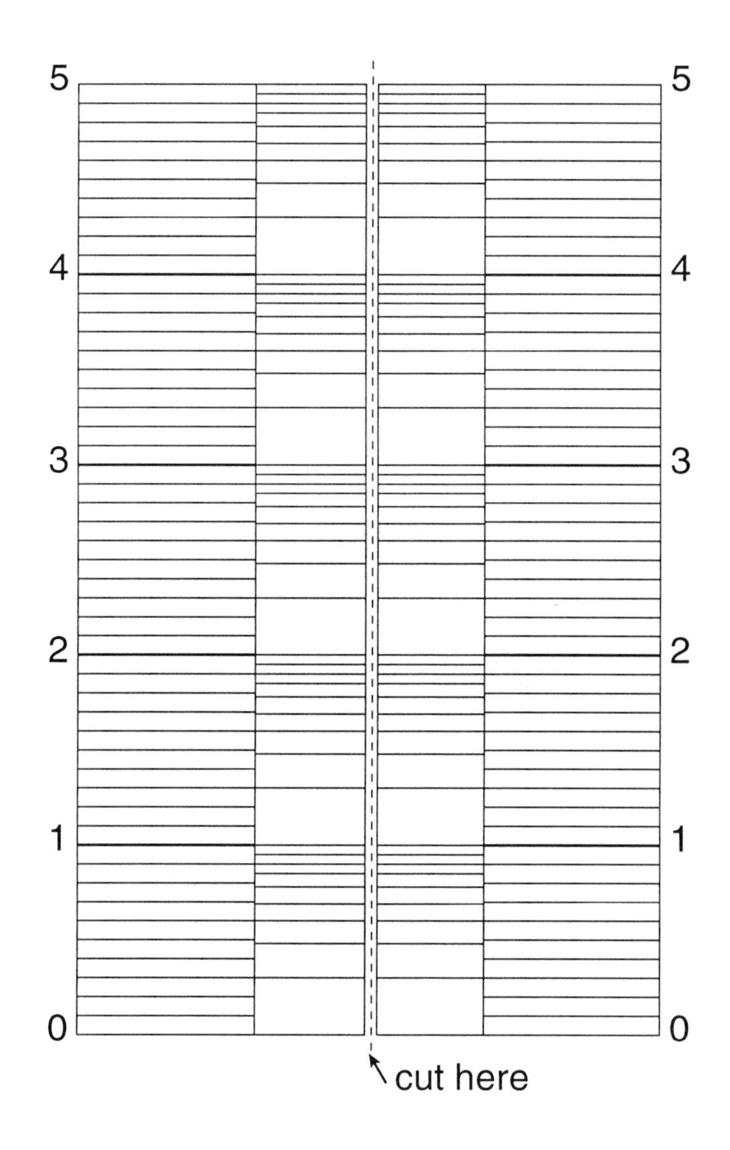

Semi-log Graph Paper

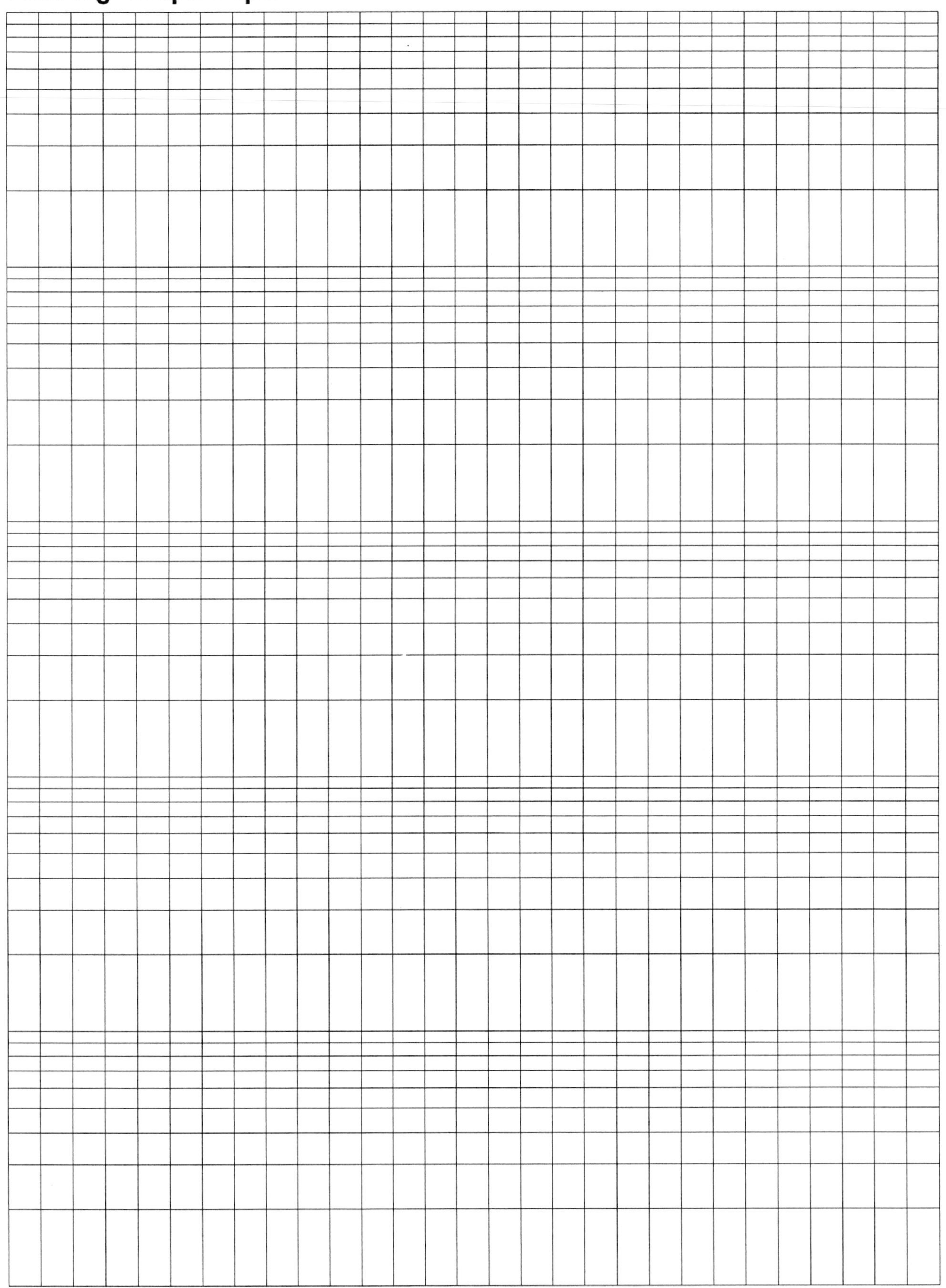

Extra Project: Fractal Dimensions

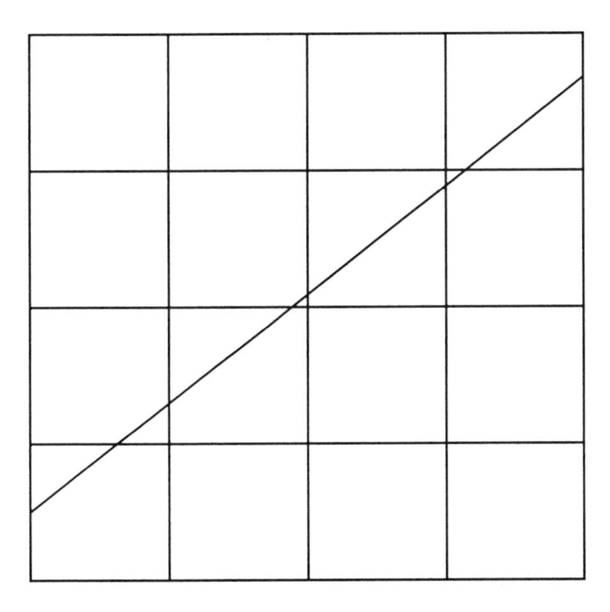

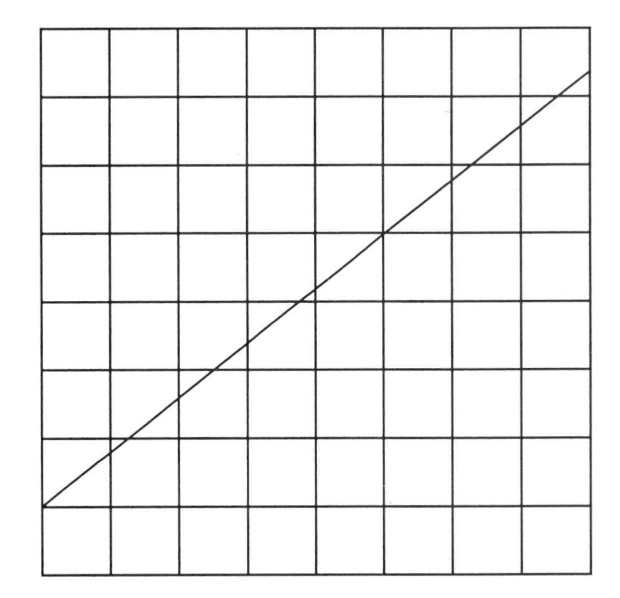

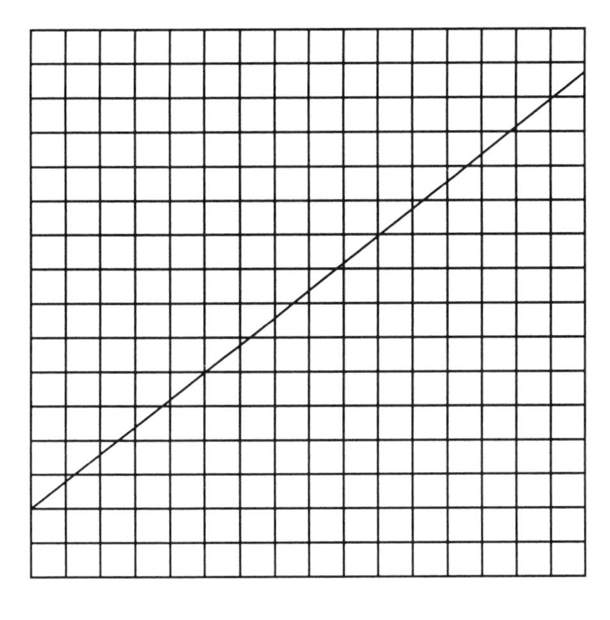

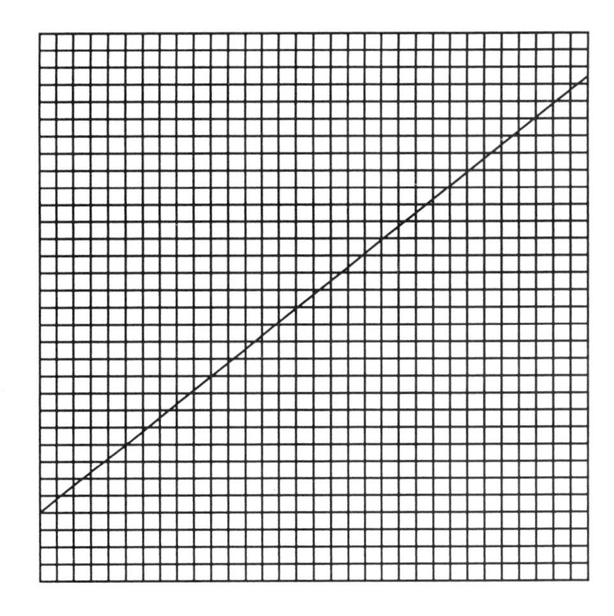

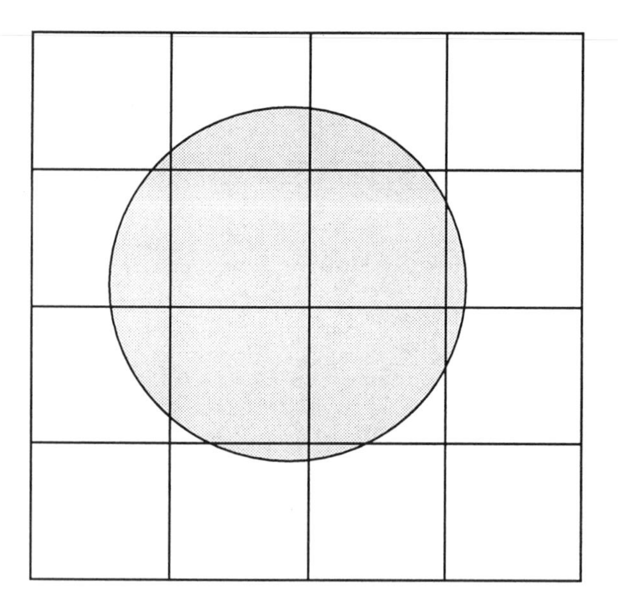

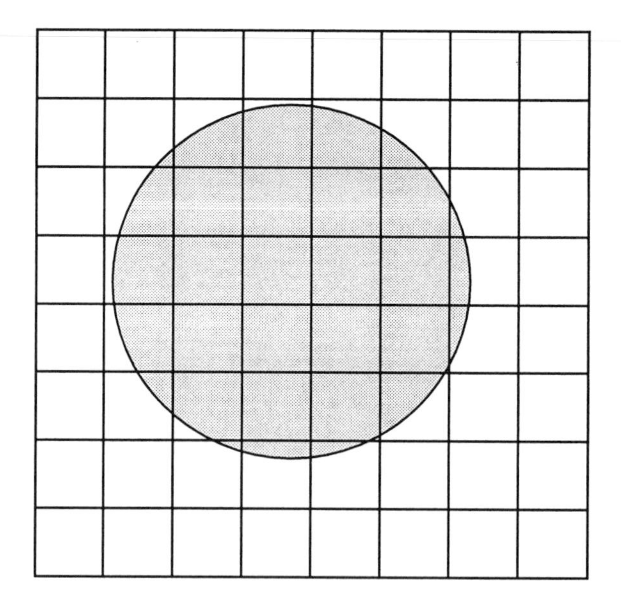

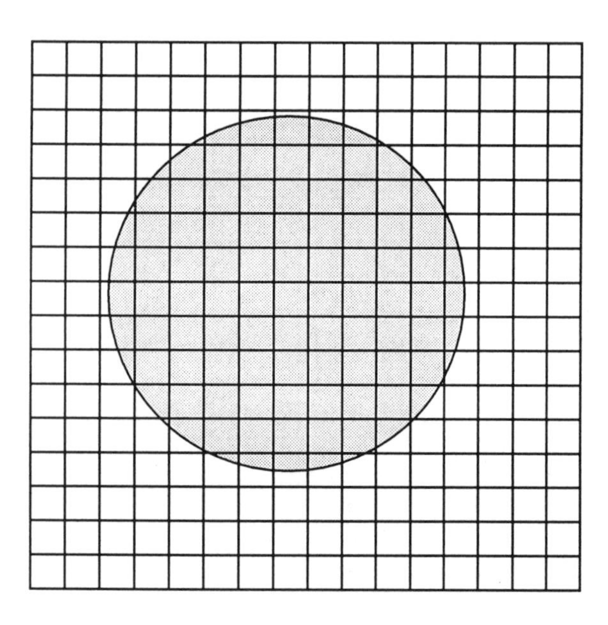

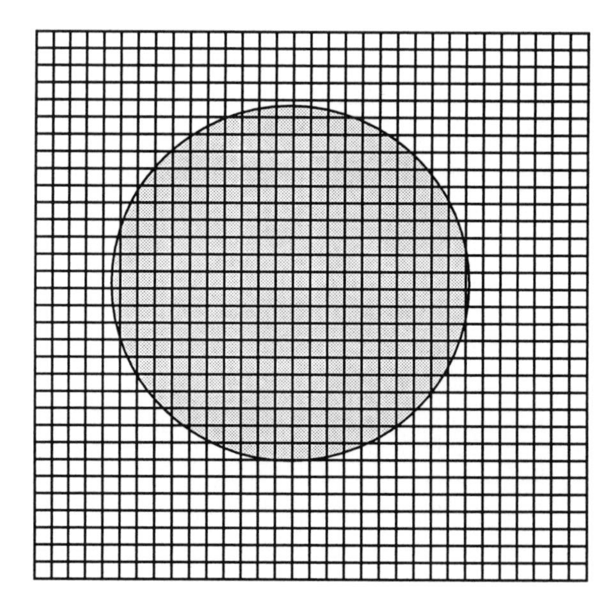

Extra Project: Fractal Dimensions

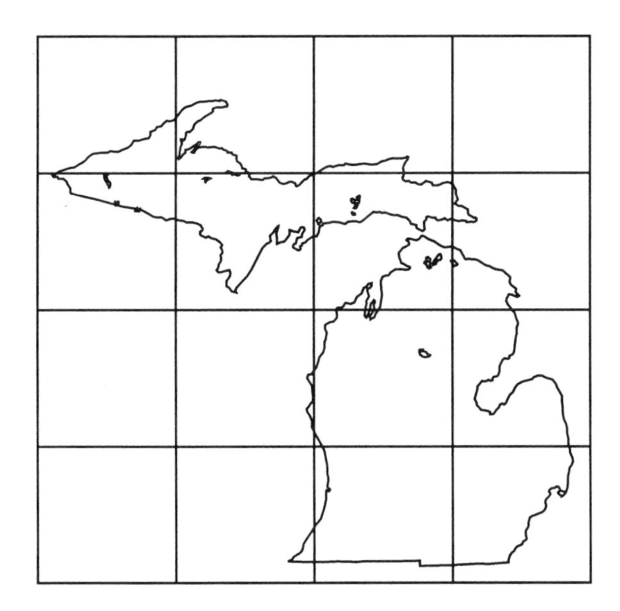

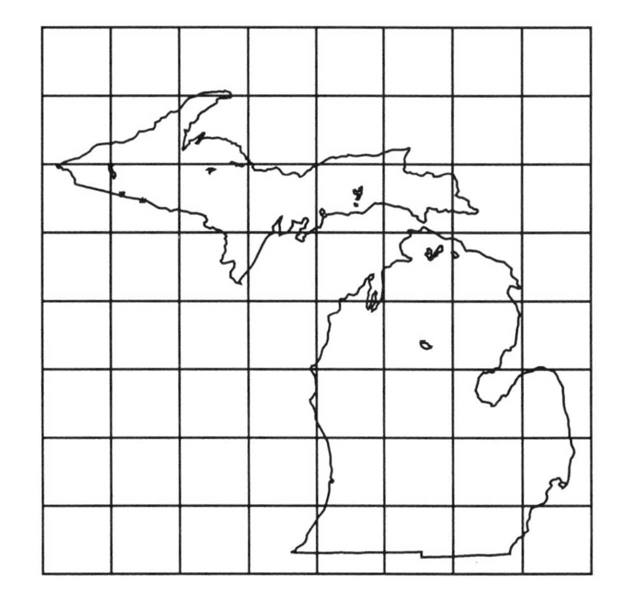

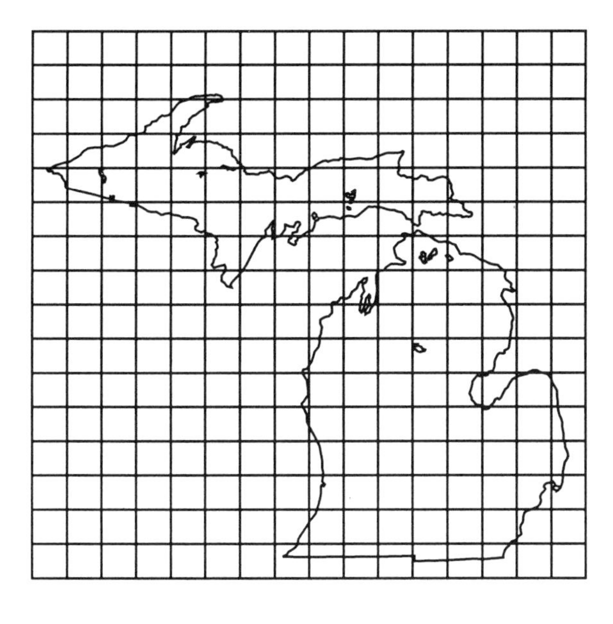

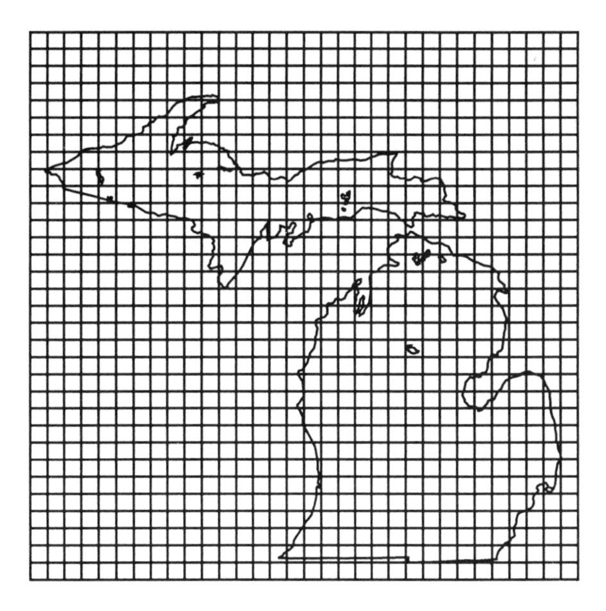

Example 2: Tree Diagram

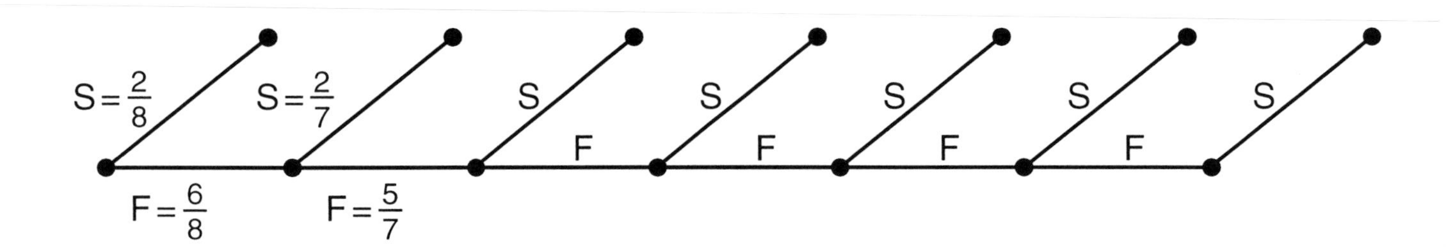

Section 8.4/Page 397 T

Investigation 8.4.1: Pennies on a Grid

Investigation 8.5.1: Conflict Resolution

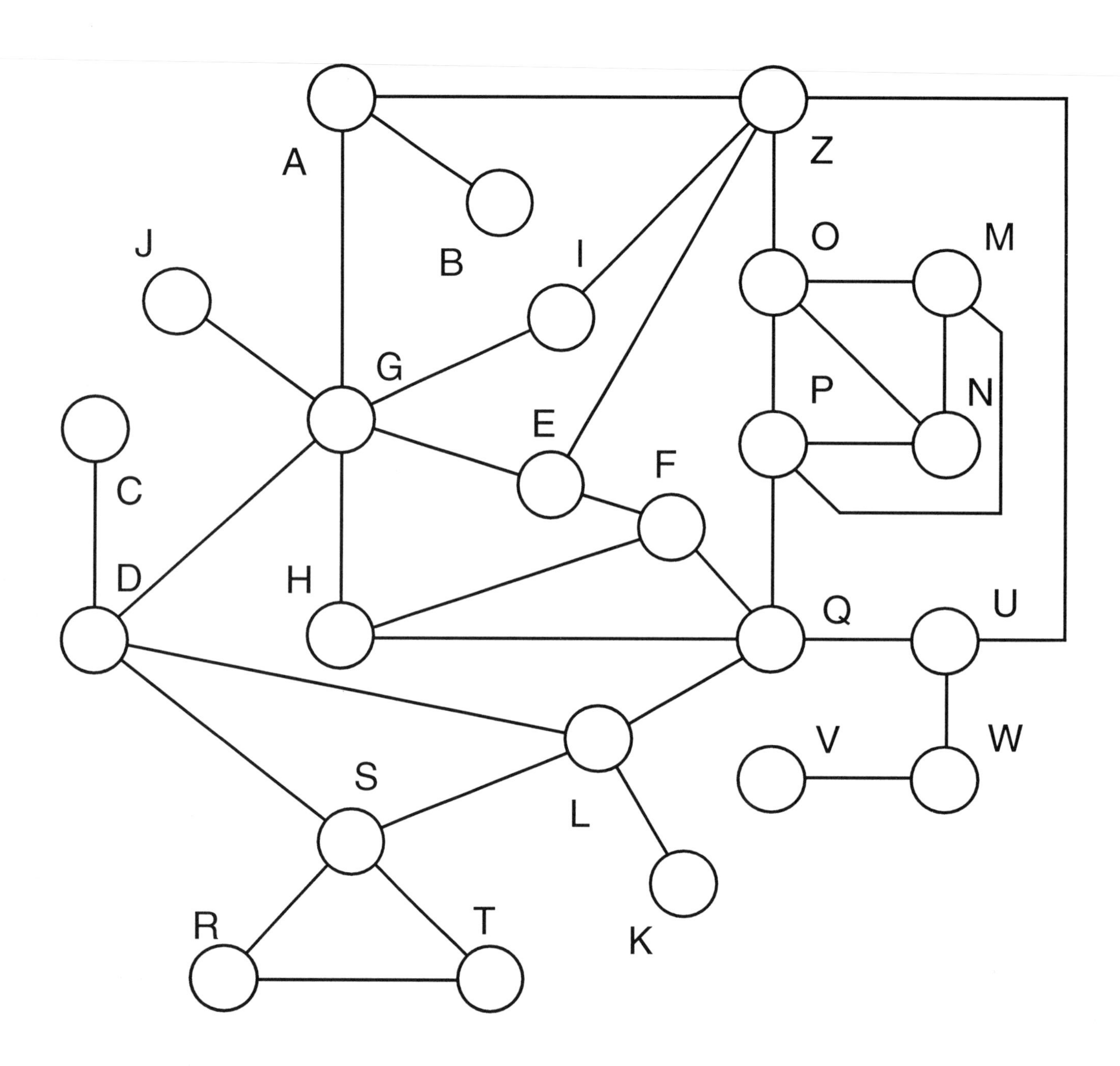

Problem 4

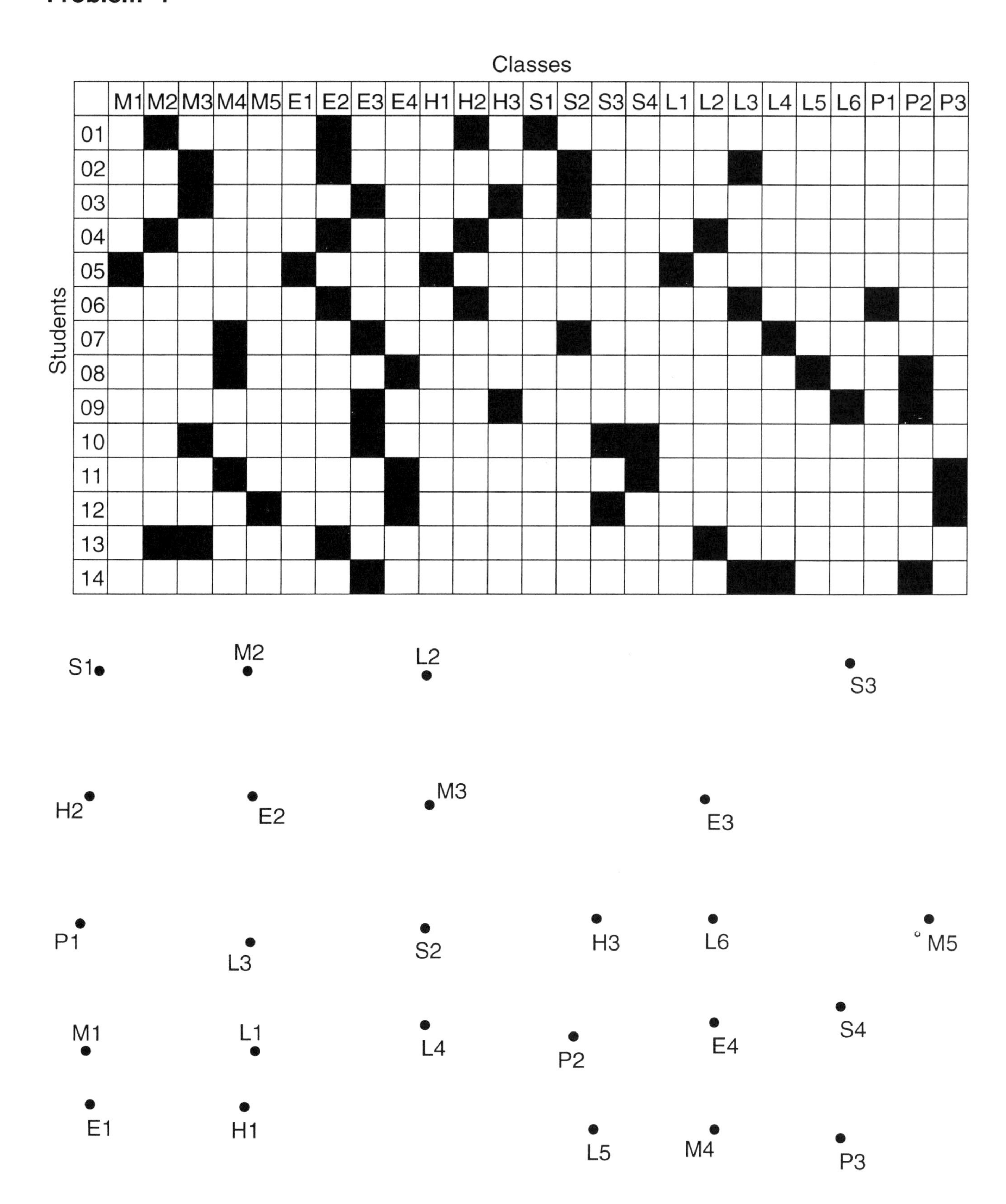
Classes
M1 M2 M3 M4 M5 E1 E2 E3 E4 H1 H2 H3 S1 S2 S3 S4 L1 L2 L3 L4 L5 L6 P1 P2 P3
Students
01
02
03
04
05
06
07
08
09
10
11
12
13
14
S1
M2
L2
S3
H2
E2
M3
E3
P1
L3
S2
H3
L6
M5
M1
L1
L4
P2
E4
S4
E1
H1
L5
M4
P3

Investigation 8.7.1: Transition Matrix

$$\begin{bmatrix} 1 & 0 & 0 & 0 & 0 & 0 \end{bmatrix} \begin{bmatrix} 0 & 1 & 0 & 0 & 0 & 1 \\ 1 & 0 & 0 & 1 & 0 & 1 \\ 0 & 0 & 0 & 0 & 1 & 0 \\ 0 & 1 & 0 & 0 & 1 & 1 \\ 0 & 0 & 1 & 1 & 0 & 1 \\ 1 & 1 & 0 & 1 & 1 & 0 \end{bmatrix} = \begin{bmatrix} 0 & 1 & 0 & 0 & 0 & 1 \end{bmatrix}$$

Random Number Table

78086	27605	80783	72059	05060	21366	84811	80730	77042	25406
36673	74153	37788	35736	83780	11566	25916	85274	27965	27549
09752	89231	06739	64351	80303	47999	15059	00677	46402	98961
58358	21124	08164	56928	95491	80511	23897	96281	19001	42952
89928	22964	26249	90286	41979	64737	99888	81369	22711	40318

49390	91663	94701	66328	08696	43795	13916	65570	73393	43882
22219	93199	21573	13645	72126	38799	89648	26301	80918	55096
28034	42119	88853	07211	56700	59113	84358	86127	94675	99511
58449	34746	64619	19171	63533	97899	84381	65023	80908	18694
10920	69975	82955	27251	43127	99059	25076	48299	71133	60036

36422	93239	76046	81114	77412	86557	19549	98473	15221	87856
78496	47197	37961	67568	14861	61077	85210	51264	49975	71785
95384	59596	05081	39968	80495	00192	94679	18307	16265	48888
37957	89199	10816	24260	52302	69592	55019	94127	71721	70673
31422	27529	95051	83157	96377	33723	52902	51302	86370	50452

07443	15346	40653	84238	24430	88834	77318	07486	33950	61598
41349	86255	92715	96654	49693	99286	83447	20215	16040	41085
12398	95111	45663	55020	57159	58010	43162	98878	73337	35571
77229	92095	44305	09285	73256	02968	31129	66588	48126	52700
61175	53014	60304	13976	96312	42442	96713	43940	92516	81421

16825	27482	97858	05642	88047	68960	52991	67703	29805	42701
84656	03089	05166	67571	25545	26603	40243	55482	38341	97781
03872	31767	23729	89523	73654	24625	78393	77172	41328	95633
40488	70426	04034	46618	55102	93408	10965	69744	80766	14889
98322	25528	43808	05935	78338	77881	90139	72375	50624	91385

13366	52764	02467	14202	74172	58770	65348	24115	44277	96735
86711	27764	86789	43800	87582	09298	17880	75507	35217	08352
53886	50358	62738	91783	71944	90221	79403	75139	09102	77826
99348	21186	42266	01531	44325	61942	13453	61917	90426	12437
49985	08787	59448	82680	52929	19077	98518	06251	58451	91140

49807	32863	69984	20102	09523	47827	08374	79849	19352	62726
46569	00365	23591	44317	55054	94835	20633	66215	46668	53587
09988	44203	43532	54538	16619	45444	11957	69184	98398	96508
32916	00567	82881	59753	54761	39404	90756	91760	18698	42852
93285	32297	27254	27198	99093	97821	46277	10439	30389	45372

03222	39951	12738	50303	25017	84207	52123	88637	19369	58289
87002	61789	96250	99337	14144	00027	53542	87030	14773	73087
68840	94259	01961	52552	91843	33855	00824	48733	81297	80411
88323	28828	64765	08244	53077	50897	91937	08871	91517	19668
55170	71962	64159	79364	53088	21536	39451	95649	65256	23950

Random Number Table

78086	27605	80783	72059	05060	21366
36673	74153	37788	35736	83780	11566
09752	89231	06739	64351	80303	47999
58358	21124	08164	56928	95491	80511
89928	22964	26249	90286	41979	64737
49390	91663	94701	66328	08696	43795
22219	93199	21573	13645	72126	38799
28034	42119	88853	07211	56700	59113
58449	34746	64619	19171	63533	97899
10920	69975	82955	27251	43127	99059
36422	93239	76046	81114	77412	86557
78496	47197	37961	67568	14861	61077
95384	59596	05081	39968	80495	00192
37957	89199	10816	24260	52302	69592
31422	27529	95051	83157	96377	33723
07443	15346	40653	84238	24430	88834
41349	86255	92715	96654	49693	99286
12398	95111	45663	55020	57159	58010
77229	92095	44305	09285	73256	02968
61175	53014	60304	13976	96312	42442

Example 1

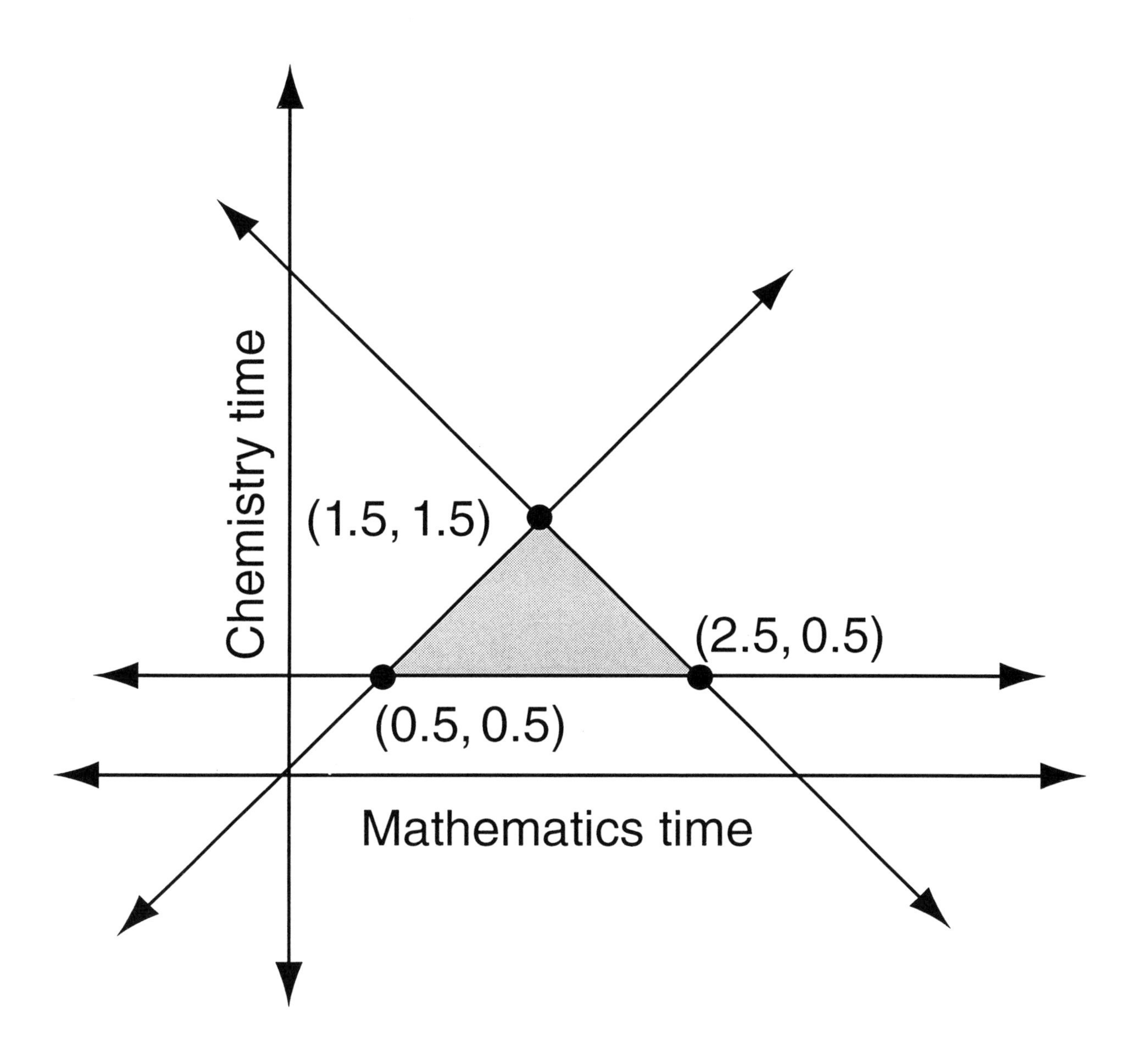

Example 2

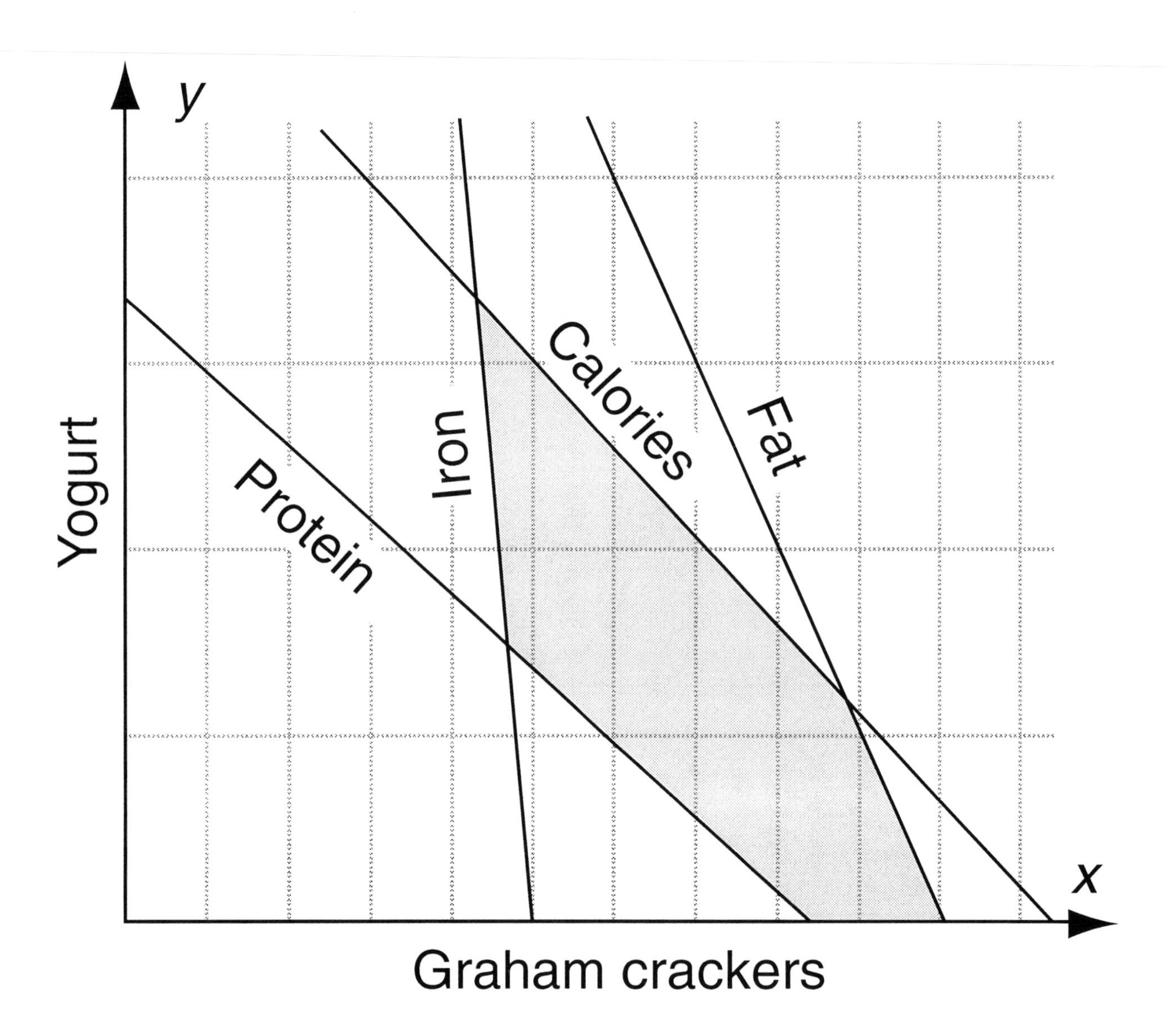

Investigation 10.1.1: Falling Objects

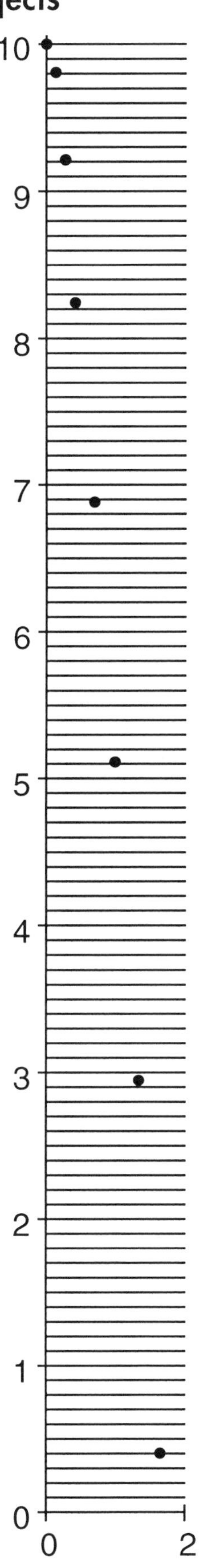

Tree Diagram

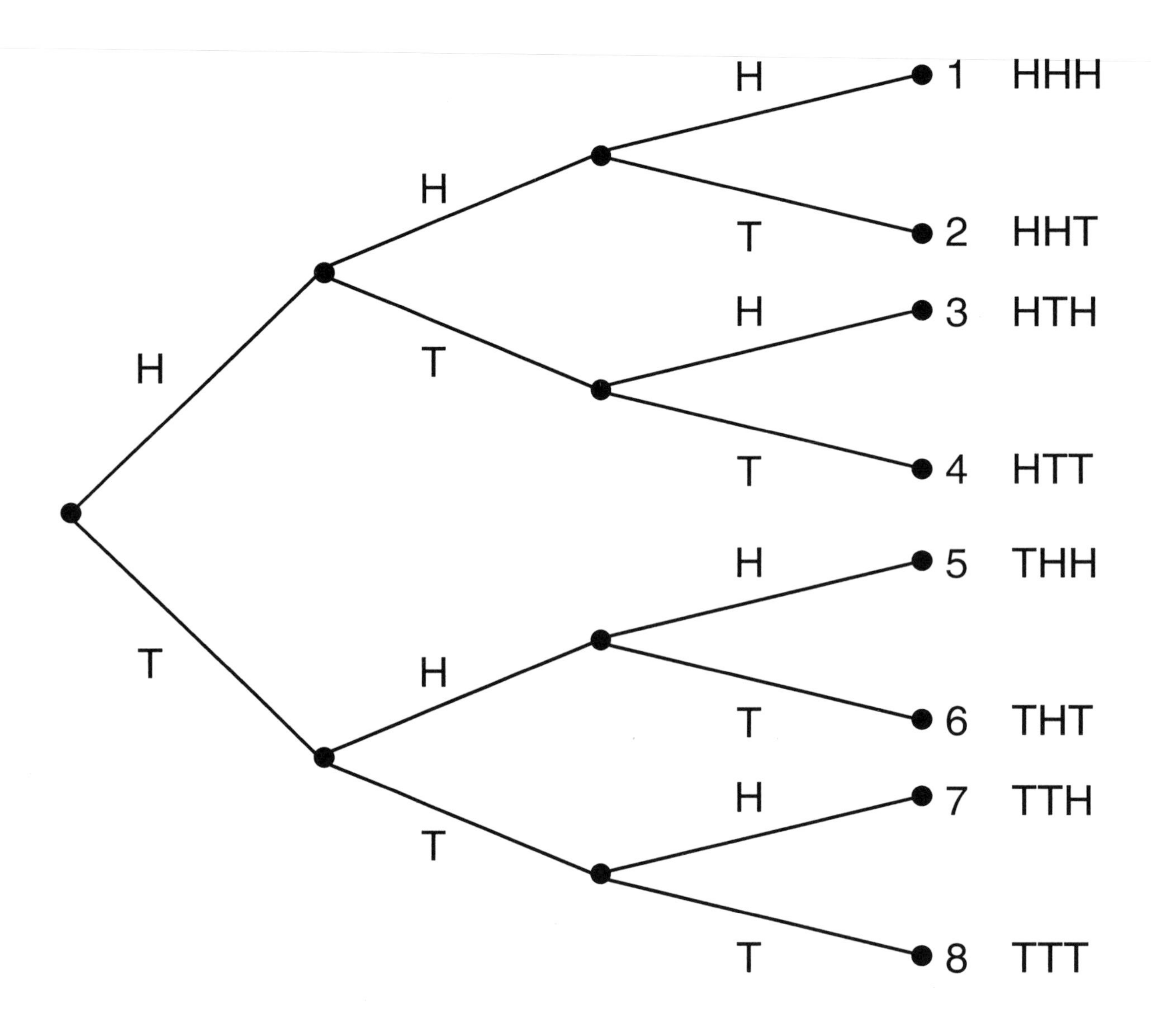

Means and the Normal Curve

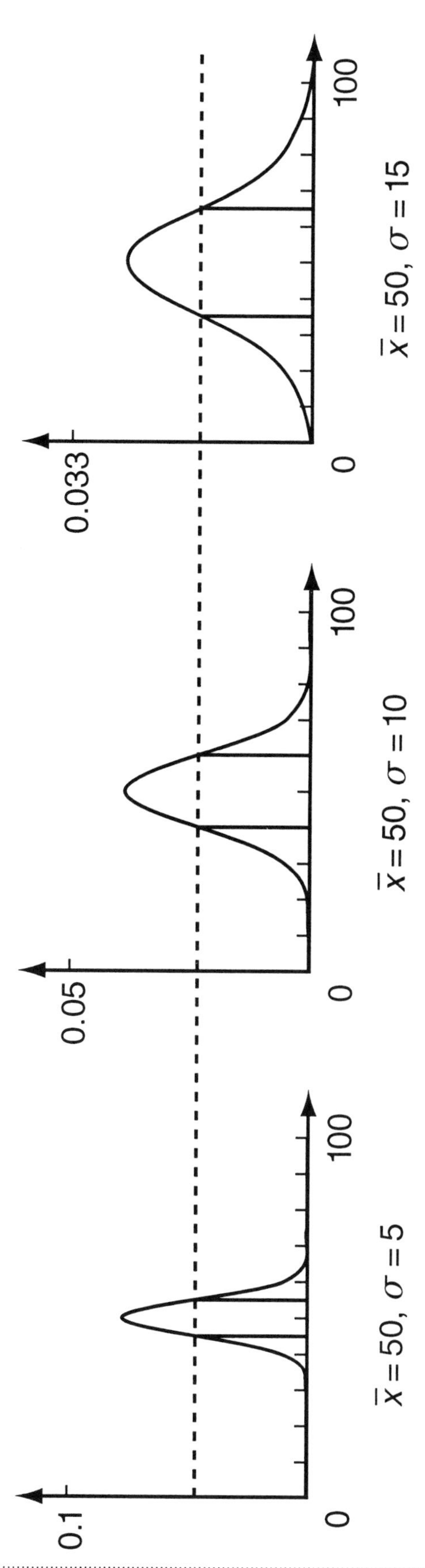

Investigation 12.1.2: Increase the Percentage

Number of light beans added (x)	0	10	20	30			...	x
Total number of light beans								
Total number of beans								
Percent of the total that are light (y)	30%							

Number of light beans removed (x)	0	5	10	15			...	x
Total number of light beans								
Total number of beans								
Percent of the total that are light (y)	30%							

Population Graphs

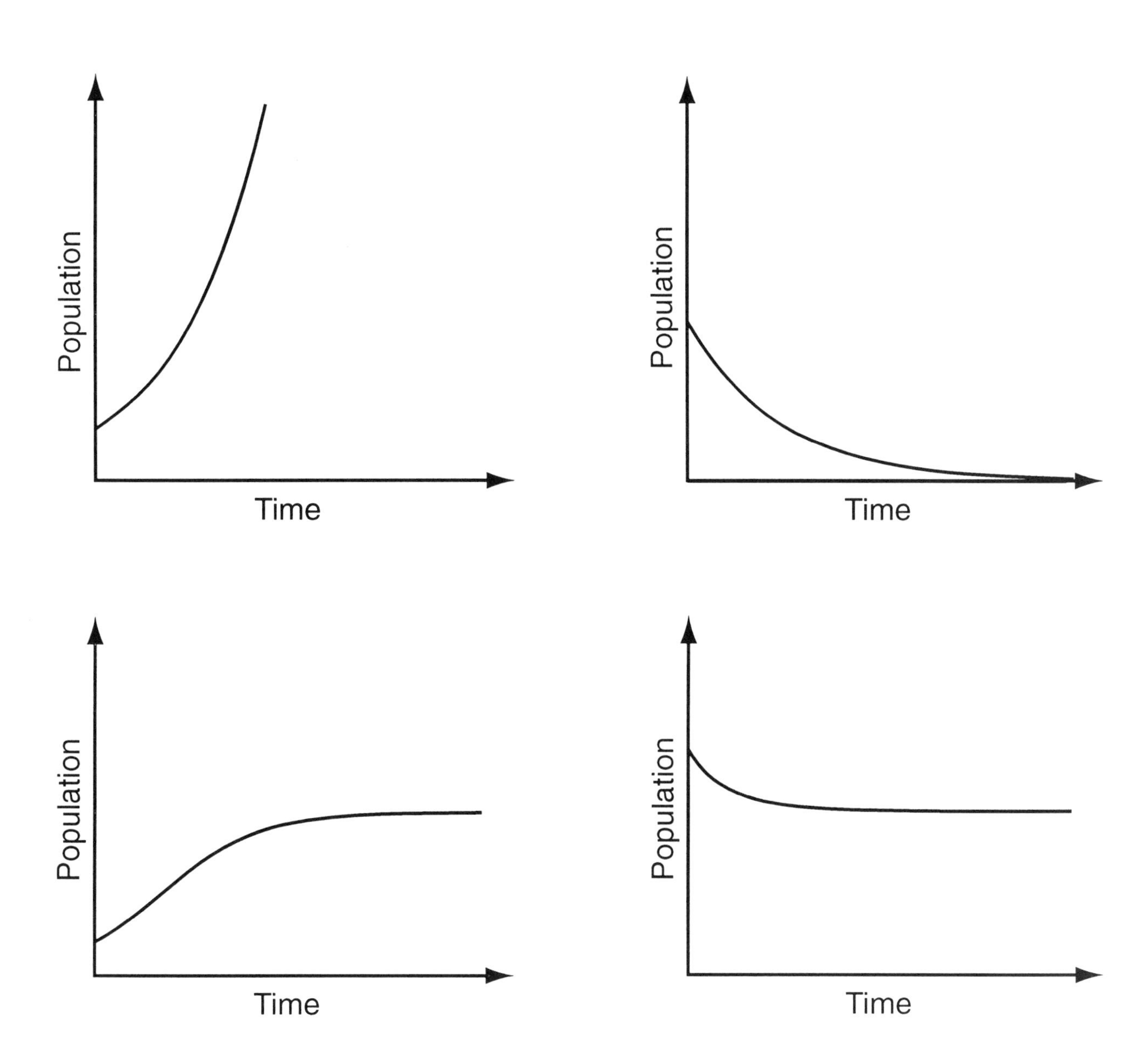

Section 13.6: Polar Graph Paper

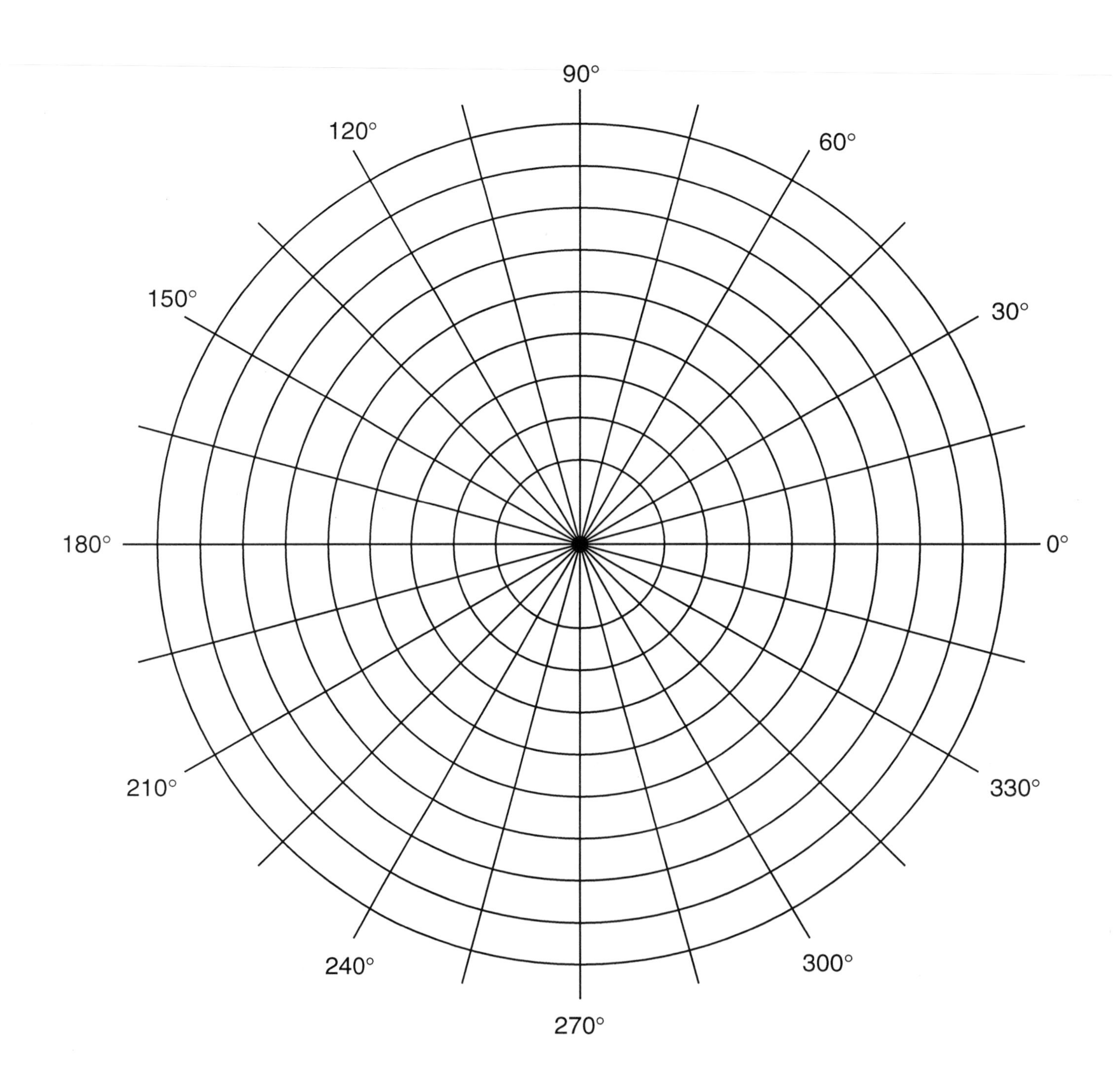

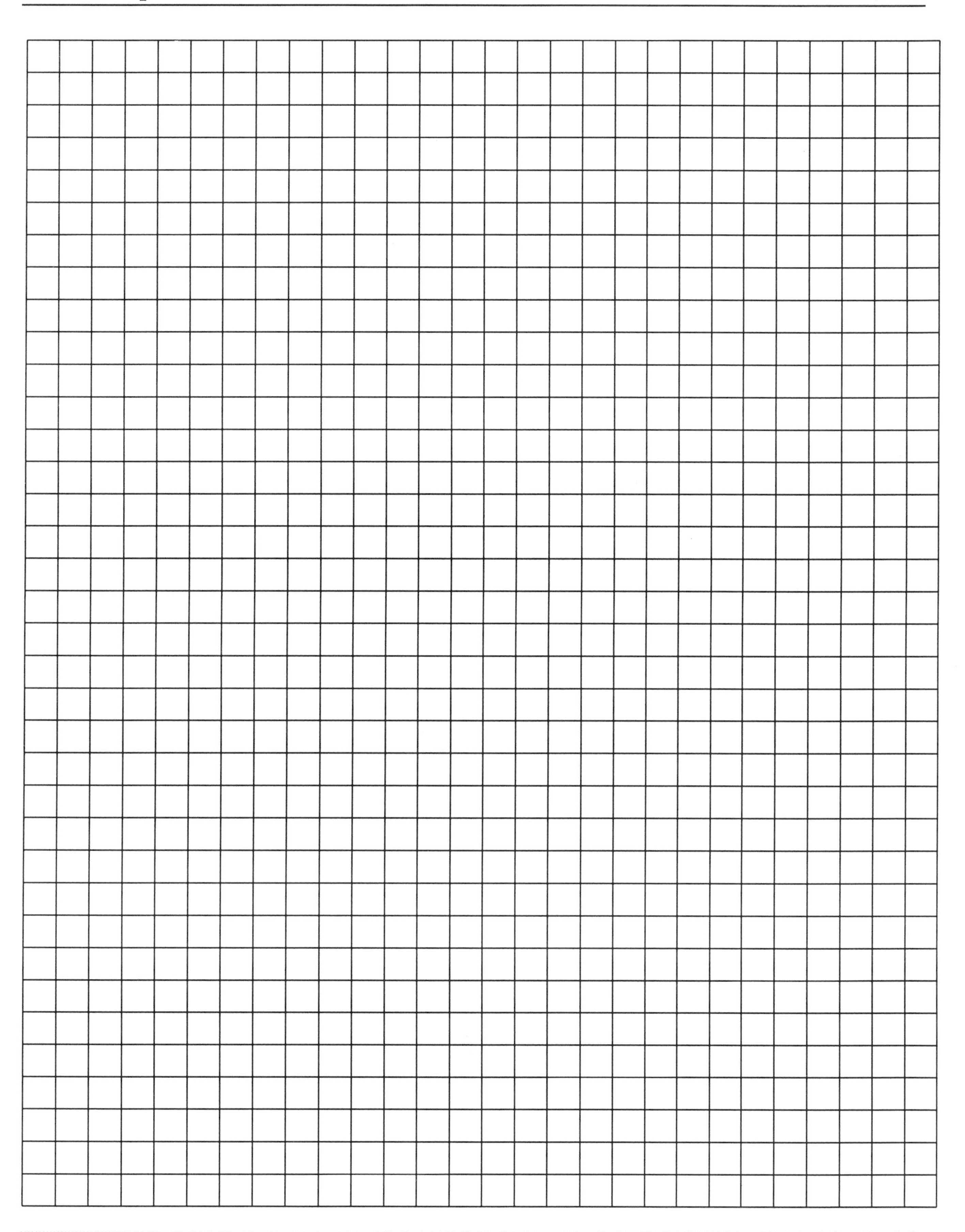

Grid Paper/2

T/W

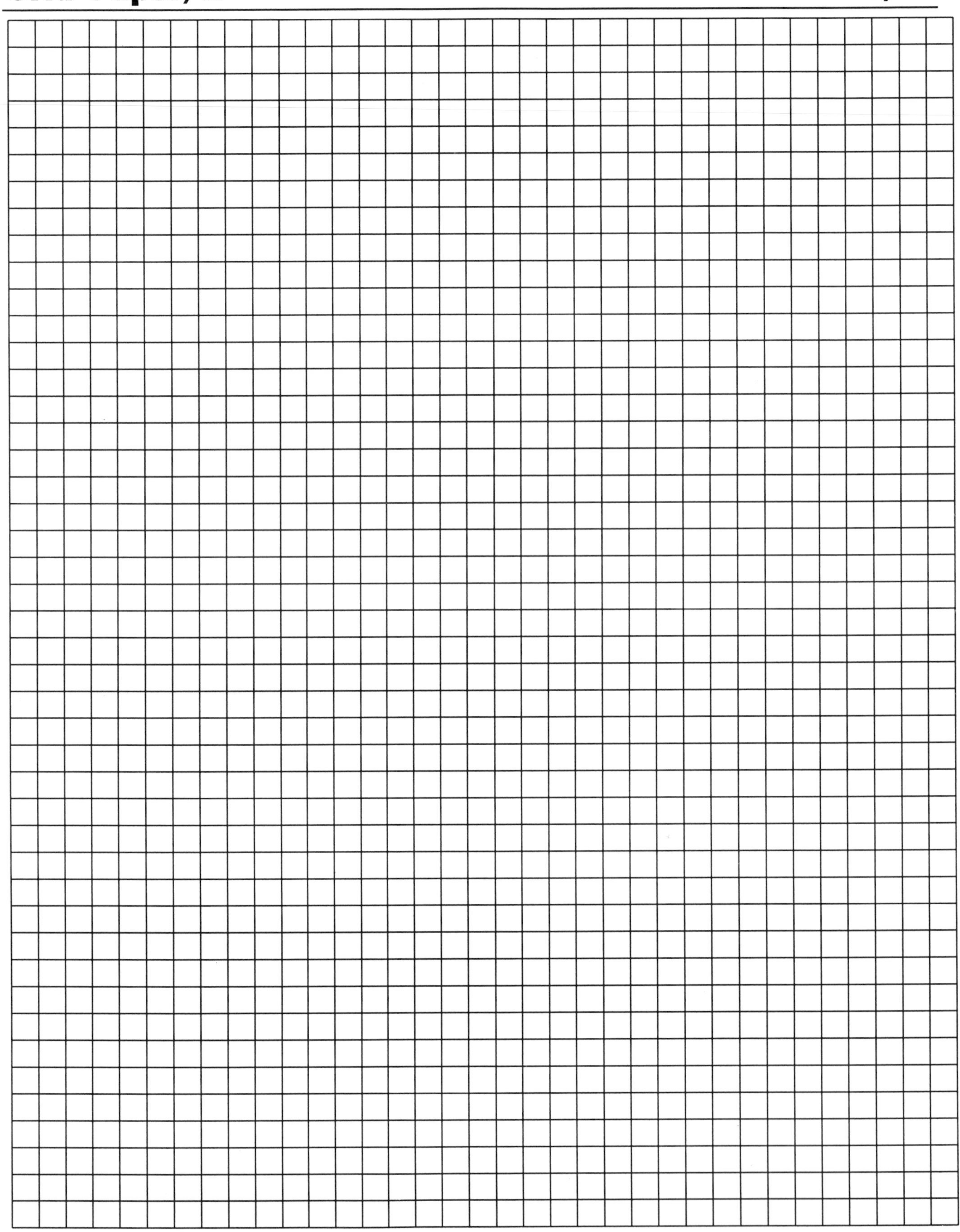

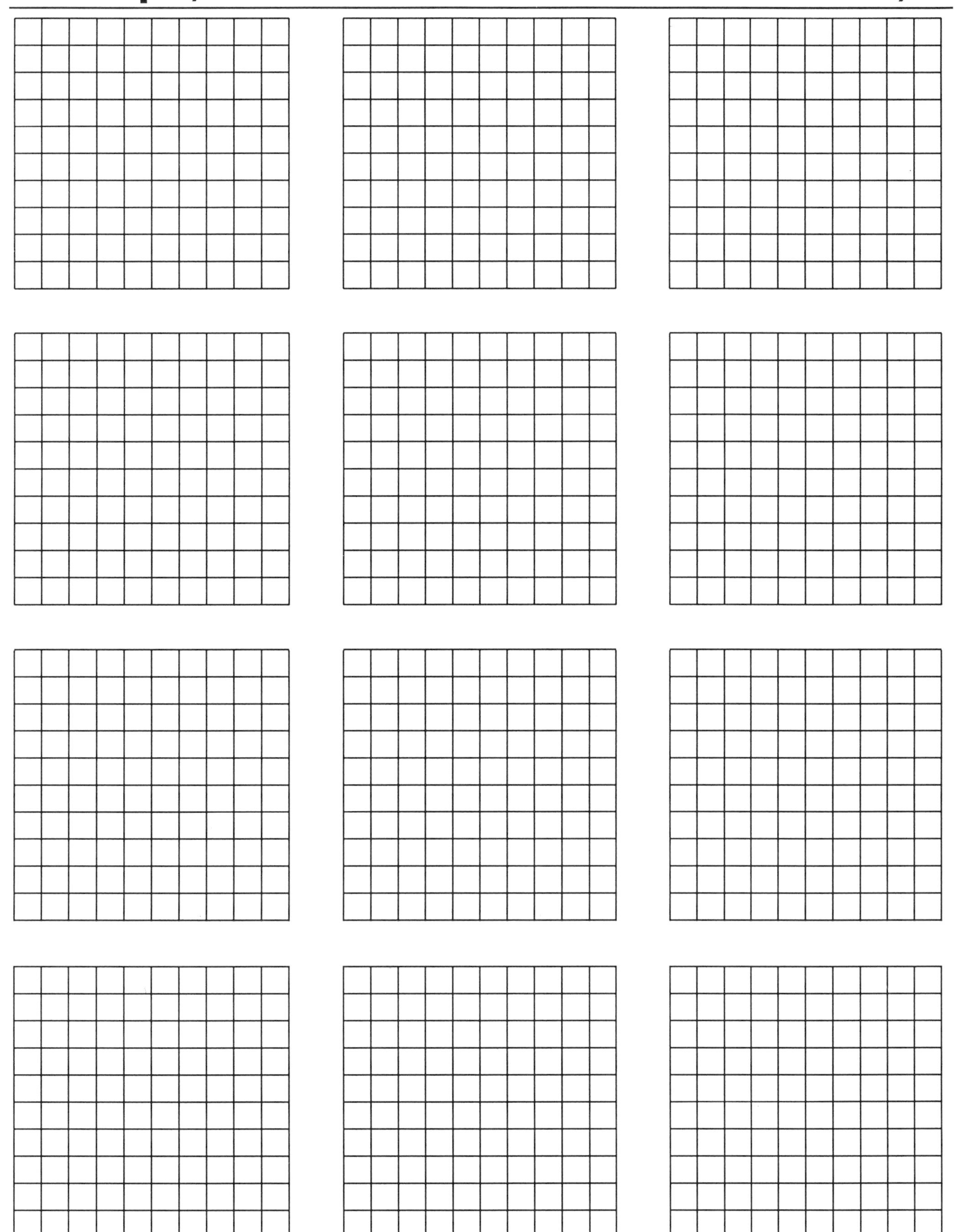

Introduction to the Supplementary Assessment Materials

In this section you will find assessment materials that complement the assessment suggestions provided in *Constructive Assessment in Mathematics: Practical Steps for Classroom Teachers* by David Clarke. For each chapter there are additional journal prompts, open-ended problems, projects, skill questions, and group problems. Answers are also provided for these problems. You could use the open-ended problems, projects, and group problems to replace projects or investigations in the book, as additional assignments, or for extra credit projects. The skills questions are appropriate for practical tests or quizzes. You can use these questions to supplement the quizzes provided in the *Quizzes, Tests, and Exams* book or as a reference for designing your own quiz.

Chapter 0: Introducing the Calculator

Journal Questions

For each of these questions, look for student answers that reflect thoughtful responses with explanations that support their thinking. You might find, at this early stage, that many students cannot respond clearly to these questions; they may not even know what they think! Because this may be the first time they have been asked these sorts of questions, their difficulty (and frustration) is understandable. Take this into consideration when you read the responses. Ultimately, you would want to look for growth from each student over the course of several attempts at responding to these types of questions. But students must be held accountable for intelligent answers. The extra time you spend now in reading student responses and writing pertinent comments will pay off later with papers that are easier to grade.

- What do you think is the purpose of Chapter 0? Be clear and support your response.

  Answers will vary.

- What are the important ideas or topics you learned in Chapter 0? Clearly explain each or give an example of each.

  Learning to work with your group and learning to use the graphing calculator.

- What ideas or topics were introduced in this chapter that you feel you do not quite understand yet or for which you do not see the purpose? Give examples.

  Answers will vary.

- What do you think is the role of the graphing calculator in your classroom? Be clear and explain your response.

  Answers will vary.

- What are the advantages of using the graphing calculator in your mathematics class? What are the disadvantages? Explain these completely.

  Answers will vary.

- What do you think is the purpose of working in groups in your classroom? Be clear and explain your response.

  Answers will vary.

- What are the advantages of working in groups in your mathematics class? What are the disadvantages? Explain these completely.

  Answers will vary.

Open-ended Problems

These problems can be very difficult for some students, especially if this is the first time they have seen such problems. That does not mean you should not ask them! The sooner students experience these types of problems, the sooner they will accept them and begin to consider them seriously for thoughtful responses. By reading the responses to these questions, you should be able to begin to distinguish students with a deeper understanding from those with a superficial understanding.

- Describe a problem that you think a graphing calculator will make easier to solve. Be clear as to why it will be easier with the graphing calculator than with a simpler calculator.

Answers will vary.

- Describe a problem that some people might *think* is easier to solve using a graphing calculator, but is actually just as easy to solve "by hand" or with a simpler calculator.

  Answers will vary.

- Write a problem that will utilize the graphing calculator appropriately. Explain how the graphing calculator is used and why it is necessary.

  Answers will vary.

Nonroutine Problems

These problems are classified as nonroutine because they require a little more thought on the part of the student and they require a written answer rather than a short, numeric answer. Emphasize to students the need to justify their responses. A student may respond with what you may consider a "wrong" answer, but give reasons with some merit. Read the justifications carefully to find out if the student solved a different problem because he or she worked from a different interpretation or assumption than was intended.

- Read each of the following problems carefully. *Do not solve any of the equations!* Decide whether or not you feel a graphing calculator would be a valuable tool in solving each of the problems, or if the problem can be solved "by hand" or with the aid of a simpler calculator. Be sure to justify your answer completely.

  a. If $a = {}^-2$ and $b = 3.1$, what is the value of $a - 3b$?

  b. Does the graph of $y = {}^-38.21x^2 - 6.54x + 72.1$ have any x-intercepts?

  c. A nonprofit organization has a balance of \$100,000 in its bank account at the beginning of the fiscal year. Each year the organization pays out 30% of its balance in donations. What is its balance at the end of the fiscal year?

  d. A nonprofit organization has a balance of \$100,000 in its bank account at the beginning of the fiscal year. Each year the organization pays out 30% of its balance in donations and brings in \$25,000 in contributions. What will happen to the organization's account in the long run?

  a. Simple or no calculator.

  b. Graphing calculator.

  c. Simple or no calculator.

  d. Graphing calculator.

- Find the most appropriate graphing window for the equation

  $$y = 0.1x^2 + 6x - 20.$$

  Justify why you believe it to be the "most appropriate" window.

  The x-intercepts are approximately $({}^-63.17, 0)$ and $(3.19, 0)$. The y-intercept is $(0, {}^-20)$. The vertex is $({}^-30, {}^-110)$. A suitable window is ${}^-80 \le x \le 50$, ${}^-125 \le y \le 80$.

- On a recent mathematics test, both Brutus and Olive were given the following expression to simplify using a graphing calculator:

  $$\frac{3 \cdot 8^2 - 5^2}{5^2 - 4^2}$$

Brutus arrived at an answer of 175 while Olive's answer was $18.\bar{5}$. Who was correct and what mistake did the other person make in entering the expression into the calculator? Explain completely.

Olive was correct. Brutus did not put parentheses around the numerator and the denominator.

Skill Questions: Appropriate for Quizzes or Tests

These problems, listed as "appropriate for quizzes and tests," should not make up the majority of your assessment items. They should be used as convenient items to check quickly for understanding or for attainment of skills. A traditional test made up almost entirely of these problems would lead students to believe that the nonroutine problems found in the text are really not that important because they won't "get tested on those." But certainly it is appropriate to give one or two of these kinds of problems on a 10- or 15-minute quiz to check that the students are progressing.

- In what order does your calculator perform mathematical operations?

  Parentheses, exponents, multiplication and division (left to right), addition and subtraction (left to right).

- If you wished to simplify $\frac{34 + 16^2}{3}$, how should you enter it into your calculator? Show the correct keystrokes.

  (34 + 16²)/3

- Show the order in which your graphing calculator will perform the operations in the following expressions.

  a. $\sqrt{19^2 + 325^3}$

  b. -87^2

  c. $\frac{123}{45(67)}$

  a. Square, cube, sum, then square root. $\approx$ 5859.05

  b. Square, then negate. $^-7569$

  c. Multiply denominator, then divide. $\approx$ 0.041

- Use your calculator to calculate the expressions 24/2(4) and 24/2 • 4.

  a. Describe and compare the two answers.

  b. If $x = {}^-4$, predict how your calculator will consider the expression $\frac{1}{2}x$. Verify your prediction and explain the results.

  a. Answers will vary depending on the calculator used.

TI-82

```
24/2(4)
                3
24/2*4
               48
```

TI-83

```
24/2(4)
               48
24/2*4
               48
```

b. Answers will vary depending on the calculator used.

TI-82		TI-83	
-4→X		-4→X	
	-4		-4
1/2X		1/2X	
	-.125		-2
(1/2)X		(1/2)X	
	-2		-2

- Use your graphing calculator to convert each of the following to a decimal number. Show your keystrokes.

a. $\frac{32}{56}$ b. $5\frac{7}{8}$

a. 32/56; $0.\overline{571428}$ **b. 5 + 7/8; 5.875**

- Use your graphing calculator to convert 0.538 to a fraction. Show your keystrokes.

On the TI-82 or TI-83: 0.538 [MATH] [1] (FRAC) = 269/500

- Describe how you would identify a fraction that is a repeating decimal.

Answers will vary.

- Show the keystrokes that would convert the following into scientific notation. Show each answer as it would be displayed on the calculator.

a. 65,001 b. 0.00004538

a. Answers will vary depending on the calculator used. $6.5001 \cdot 10^4$

b. Answers will vary depending on the calculator used. $4.538 \cdot 10^{-5}$

- Consider the expression $s\sqrt{\frac{Q - r^2}{d}}$. Evaluate this expression if $s = 123$, $Q = 234{,}000$, $r = 300$, and $d = 4 \cdot 10^{-5}$.

7,380,000

- Consider the expression $t\left|\frac{m+n}{a^2}\right|$. Evaluate this expression if $t = -8$, $m = -13$, $n = 2.2$, and $a = -4$.

−5.4

- Aaron can maintain a speed of 44 feet per second on his bicycle. Should he consider a career as a professional bike racer? Explain completely.

Yes, Aaron can cycle at 30 miles per hour, which is a reasonably fast speed to maintain.

Group Problem

This problem (adapted from *Mathematics for Elementary Teachers* by Kelly and Logothetti) is a difficult problem that most groups will simply explore with guess-and-check. This will force them to utilize the insights of all the people in the group and to cooperate in order to solve the problem. The calculator will also allow them to quickly check larger and larger problems. This problem, then, can be used to assess students' progress in their ability to work in groups as well as their problem-solving skills and calculator prowess.

- After a horrible storm at sea that destroyed the ship and killed most everyone on board, five sailors found themselves washed up on a deserted island, along with their pet monkey. Their first thoughts were to find food, and as they set out in search of island delicacies, they were lucky enough to find a grove of coconut trees. For the rest of the day they harvested coconuts, creating a large heap. After piling the coconuts, however, they were too tired to even think about eating, and they all fell fast asleep. After the first couple of hours of deep sleep, the first sailor woke up and began to think about their plight of being stranded on the island. "How long will the coconuts stay there?" he thought. After a few moments of contemplation, he sneaked over to the pile of coconuts, divided it up into five equal shares, with one coconut left over. Waking the monkey, he fed it the extra coconut, buried his share in an unmarked location, and then replaced the rest of the coconuts, hoping that the resulting heap would look the same to his shipmates. He then went back to sleep. No sooner was he sound asleep when the second sailor woke up, and he too began to worry about their situation. He quietly sneaked over to the pile of coconuts and repeated the first sailor's performance: he divided the coconuts into five equal piles with one coconut left over again, which he fed to the monkey. After burying his share, he replaced the coconuts and went back to sleep, hoping no one would be the wiser. Naturally, just after he dozed off into a deep sleep, the third sailor awoke and performed the same routine, with one coconut left over, which he stuffed into the monkey, and so on. After him, the fourth and fifth sailors did the same. The question is "What is the minimum number of coconuts in the original pile that would have allowed this process to take place?" Too tough? Try to solve the problem for three sailors and a monkey. Solve again, starting with four sailors and a monkey.

  Three sailors and a monkey: 25 coconuts; four sailors and a monkey: 253 coconuts; five sailors and a monkey: 3121 coconuts. If you want to give your students a real challenge, have them do the problem with six sailors and a monkey: 46,651 coconuts.

Chapter 1: Patterns and Recursion

Journal Questions

Look for students who have put some thought into their responses and can explain and support their thinking. Pay close attention to see if students are showing improvement in their ability to answer these types of questions.

- Some new ideas and concepts were introduced in Chapter 1. What do you think is the point of Chapter 1? What items are emphasized in this chapter? Be clear and justify your response.

  Answers will vary.

- Find three problems in the chapter that you feel are representative of the chapter. Write out the problem and the solution. For each problem, explain why you feel it is representative of the chapter.

  Answers will vary.

- Consider these different levels of understanding, along with their descriptions.

  Knowledge: To be at the knowledge level of understanding, a student can recall information at the appropriate time; he or she has been exposed to the information and can respond to questions or tasks about the information.

  How can a student demonstrate his or her knowledge? By recalling basic information: defining terms, listing characteristic ways of treating and presenting ideas, naming divisions or arrangements of a topic, listing criteria used to judge ideas, describing methods or techniques, or listing relevant principles and generalizations.

  Comprehension/Understanding: A student at this level comprehends and understands what is being communicated and makes use of the ideas but does not necessarily relate them to other ideas or materials. He or she may not yet understand the fullest meaning, but certainly has acquired the knowledge to advance.

  How can a student demonstrate his or her knowledge? Upon reading comprehension-level problems, a student at this level knows what is being asked and successfully works the problems, clearly lists the process used in working the problem, clearly describes the results of working the problem, draws conclusions based on the results of the problem, compares and contrasts two different problems, or restates an idea or principle in his or her own words.

  Application: At this level, a student can recognize the need to use an idea, method, or concept without being told to use it. He or she knows and comprehends the information and can apply it to a new situation, and can also recognize when a task is beyond his or her current competency.

  How can a student demonstrate his or her knowledge? By solving problems which require recognition of the appropriate concepts, theories, solution techniques, and so on, applying the laws of mathematics (as well as chemistry, physics, or engineering) to practical situations, or working *project type* problems.

  For each of the levels of understanding listed above, find an example or problem from your book or other work you have done so far this year, in which you can demonstrate that you are at that level of understanding for that problem. (For example, perhaps you are currently at the knowledge level for problems involving simplifying expressions. This would mean that you recall the order of operations and can simplify an expression when asked to do it, but could not go beyond this. Maybe you cannot find the mistake in another student's work.) Make sure you explain clearly why you believe you are at this level.

Answers will vary.

- What ideas or topics were introduced in this chapter that you feel you do not quite understand yet or for which you do not see the purpose? Give examples.

  Answers will vary.

- Consider again the role of the graphing calculator in this course for this chapter. Have you discovered new advantages or disadvantages of using the graphing calculator? If so, what are they? Has your perspective or feeling changed toward the use of the graphing calculator? Be clear and explain your response.

  Answers will vary.

- What graphing calculator skills have you mastered during this chapter? Explain thoroughly and use examples. What graphing calculator skills have you not yet mastered? Provide an example for which you need a calculator skill that you have not yet mastered.

  Answers will vary.

- Last chapter, you were asked to think about the purpose of working in groups in your mathematics class. Now, think about the role you played in your group. Were you a leader? A follower? Were you satisfied with the way you participated in your group? Will you change your role? Does it matter? Be clear and explain your response.

  Answers will vary.

- Have you discovered any new advantages of working in groups in your mathematics class? New disadvantages? Explain these completely.

- Think about a career that you would like to pursue. Do some research to find out about average earnings for this career, and create a realistic budget, including a savings plan. If you follow your plan, how much would you expect to save by age 40? By age 60? Justify your response by using mathematics from this course and others.

  Answers will vary.

Open-ended Problems

These problems are meant to be difficult and to leave the students "scratching their heads." That does not mean you should avoid these questions or similar ones! The format of the last two problems in this section is adapted from a paper by David Clarke (*Open-ended Tasks and Assessment: The Nettle or the Rose,* 1993) and the problems are to be done *without* additional resources. Students are to use only their previous knowledge, their graphing calculators, and their own resources. By reading their responses you will get a good insight into their reasoning capabilities and problem-solving skills.

- Chapter 1 is the study of patterns, recursion, sequences, and series. Your task is to convince the reader (you may choose a reader, but explain who your reader is) that you understand these ideas and how they can be used in real-life situations.

  Answers will vary.

- For the following problems, please follow this format.
  i. State the problem.
  ii. What do you already know that would help you solve this problem? Who (in your group) knows it and how does he or she know it?
  iii. What information do you need to assume? Why are you assuming it?
  iv. Record all your steps in solving the problem.
  v. State your answer clearly and completely.
  vi. How good is your answer? Remember: "A chain is only as strong as its weakest link!" What are your most unreliable approximations and weakest assumptions?
    1. What do you think will be the population of your town in the year 2025?
    2. What percentage of the people alive today (right now!) will be alive 10 years from now?

Projects

You should allow students at least two weeks, working entirely outside of class, to do the first project listed below.

The second project could be done as a group project and, depending on your particular class, you might offer some suggestions: Consider the decrease in seniors each year and the increase in freshmen each year. Consider only the net change, and so on. You may want to discuss the value of looking into the growth of the school district.

- Recently, an advertisement came through the mail offering a low-payment loan, which was said to be ideal for paying off high-interest-rate credit card debts or to consolidate all debts. The promoters claimed the selling point of this loan is the low monthly payments, which are always 2% of the loan balance. With even a mediocre credit history, an interested individual could borrow up to $5,000 instantly. The first monthly payment would only be $100, and the dollar amount of each payment after that would decrease, as long as you didn't borrow more money. The loan had no initial fees (another "plus") and charged an annual percentage interest rate of 21.9% compounded monthly.
  a. Present this information to at least five different people *not* in your mathematics class. Be sure at least two of them are out of high school. Ask them if they would be interested in such a loan offer. Carefully record their reasons why or why not.
  b. In the first part of a two-part paper, summarize what each of these five people said, including their reasons for whether or not they would choose such an offer. In the second part of the paper, analyze the proposal mathematically and offer your own conclusions as to whether or not this is a good offer.

  Answers will vary, but we hope students will realize what a horrible deal this is.

- By visiting your school's library, your city library, or by contacting any appropriate people, gather information on the population of your school and your school district for at least the last five years. Analyze the data and write several paragraphs explaining your careful mathematical analysis. Then, based on your analysis, make predictions as to your school's population growth over the next 20 years. Offer suggestions to your school board as to how to deal with any problems your predictions (if true) might forecast.

  Answers will vary.

Skill Questions: Appropriate for Quizzes or Tests

- Suppose that $1,000 is invested at 6.9% annual interest, compounded monthly.
  a. What is the balance after 5 years?
  b. Suppose $100 is added to the account every month. What is the balance after 5 years?

  a. $1,410.60 **b. $8,551.39**

- Suppose you want to buy a new stereo and finance or borrow $1,050. The 12-month loan has an annual interest rate of 14.5%.
  a. Write a recursive routine that provides the declining balances of the loan for a monthly payment of $100.
  b. Write out the first five terms of this sequence.
  c. What is the unpaid balance after 12 months?
  d. What is the real-world meaning of the last balance?
  e. Make the necessary adjustments to the monthly payment so that the loan can be paid off in 12 equal payments. What monthly payment works?
  f. What is the total cost of the new stereo paid over the 12 months?

  a. $u_1 = 1050, u_n = \left(1 + \frac{0.145}{12}\right)u_{(n-1)} - 100$

  b. 1050, 962.69, 874.32, 784.88, 694.37

  c. $29.38

  d. What is left to pay on the loan.

  e. $\approx$ **$102.51**

  f. $1,230.12

- The "biological" specimen *Geomeuricus sequencius* is 5 centimeters long when born. On the second day it grows 3 centimeters. The third day it grows 1.8 centimeters, and on each following day it grows 60% of the previous day's growth. What is the length of the critter after two weeks? What is the maximum length that it could grow?

  $\approx$ **12.49 centimeters; 12.5 centimeters**

- Write the first four terms for this sequence:

  $$u_n = \begin{cases} 1.5 & \text{if } n = 1 \\ 3u_{(n-1)} + 1 & \text{if } n > 1 \end{cases}$$

  1.5, 5.5, 17.5, 53.5

- Suppose a tree nursery manages 10,000 trees and each year sells 5% of the trees and plants 900 new ones.
  a. Determine the number of trees after 10 years.
  b. Determine the number of trees after 25 years.
  c. Determine the number of trees in the long run.

d. How many trees would the nursery need to plant yearly for the tree population to level out at 8000 trees?

a. $\approx$ **13,210** **b.** $\approx$ **15,781** **c. 18,000 trees** **d. 400**

- Given the sequence 2.5, 4.2, 5.9, 7.6, ...

a. What is the sixth term?

b. Write a recursive definition for the terms of this sequence.

c. Sketch a graph of these terms.

a. 11 **b.** $u_n = 2.5$ **for** $n = 1$, $u_n = u_{(n-1)} + 1.7$ **for** $n > 1$

c.

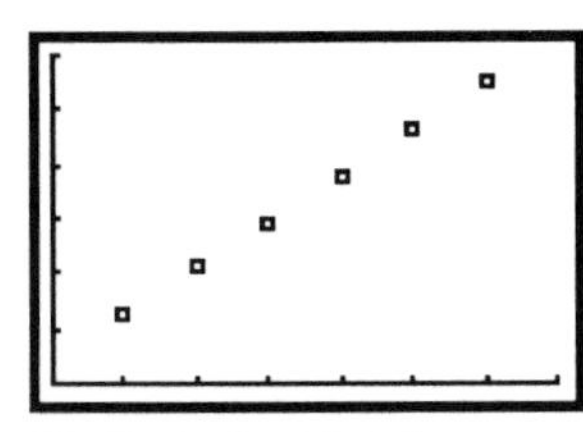

[0, 7, 1, 0, 12, 2]

- Consider the sequence generated by $u_n = 0.75 \bullet u_{(n-1)}$ with $u_1 = 4$.

a. What is S_8 for this sequence?

b. What is u_8 in this sequence?

c. What happens to the terms in the long run?

d. What happens to S_n in the long run?

a. 14.39819336

b. $4(.75)^7 \approx$ **0.5339355469**

c. Becomes smaller, tending to zero

d. Approaches 16.

- Find the sum of the first 80 even numbers, starting with 2. Show your method completely.

6480

- Find the sum of the first 60 multiples of 3. Be sure to show your work. If you use a program, please write it out.

5490

- The enrollment at a large university is currently 30,000. The school will graduate 20% of their students yearly and will enroll 7000 new students each year. What will be the enrollment 5 years from now? What will be the enrollment in the long run? Show your work.

$\approx$ **33,362, 35,000**

- A super-super-ball will rebound 85% of its height from which it is dropped. If a ball is dropped from 200 centimeters, how high will it bounce after the fifth bounce? What is the total distance the ball travels by the time it hits the floor the fifth time? What will be the total distance traveled by the time the ball comes to rest? Show all work, and state and explain any assumptions you make.

$\approx$ **88.74 centimeters,** $\approx$ **1283.45 centimeters,** $\approx$ **2466.67 centimeters**

Group Problems

The second problem is quite difficult and should be done in a group setting with the graphing calculators. The question leaves room for students to make some assumptions of their own, but be sure they realize what assumptions they have made and that their assumptions are made clear to the reader.

- Recently you opened a bank account at the Bank of Appropriate Numbers to start saving for the "incidentals" of college. The bank will pay an annual interest rate of 5%, compounded monthly. However there is a $5 monthly service charge. You would like to put some money in the account and leave it there to increase with the interest.

  a. If you start by investing $1,000, what will happen to your money in the long run?

  b. If you start by investing $2,000, what will happen to your money in the long run?

  c. Is there an initial amount of money you can invest that will keep your account at a constant value over a long period of time? Justify your answer. If so, what amount?

  a. Decreases about $0.83 each month. In the long run, you will have $0 in your account.

  b. It will grow about $3.33 each month. The balance will get larger without limit.

  c. $1,200

- The Fish and Wildlife Department has been taking a closer look at Lake Multiplicatus. Four years ago, a study at the lake revealed that there were approximately 3500 fish in the lake. At that time, the birth and death rates of the fish population were determined, and stocking and fishing limits were established. The biologist working for the Fish and Wildlife Department determined the birth rate to be 3%. In addition to the new births each spring, the park rangers stock the lake with 400 fish. The death rate of all these fish was found to be 4%. Lastly, the rangers decided to set the fishing limit for the entire lake at 350 fish per year. Approximately how many fish are in the lake now?

  The park rangers hope that the lake will sustain a healthy population of fish. If there are too many fish, the lake cannot support them and the fish will begin to die off. With a small fish population, other inhabitants of the lake (snails, algae, and so on) will grow beyond the lake's carrying capacity (that is, beyond the level at which the lake can sustain a healthy environment for animal life). Advise the rangers as to the fate of their lake by answering the following questions in a report to the rangers: Will the population of the fish grow beyond the capacity of the lake, which has been projected as 5500 fish? Will the fish population stabilize, thus providing a healthy lake? Or, will the fish population drop too low for the lake to remain healthy? Justify your position completely.

  There would be about 3559 fish now. The population eventually levels off at 5000.

Chapter 2: Sequences and Explicit Formulas

Journal Questions

Again, look for students who have put some thought into their responses and can explain and support their thinking. Pay close attention to see if students are showing improvement in their ability to answer these types of questions.

- Some new ideas and concepts were introduced in Chapter 2. What do you think is the point of Chapter 2? What items are emphasized in this chapter? Has the material you studied in this chapter helped you understand other material? Explain. Be clear and justify your responses.

  Answers will vary.

- Find three problems in the chapter that you feel are representative of the chapter. Write out the problem and the solution. For each problem, explain why you feel it is representative of the chapter.

  Answers will vary.

- What ideas or topics were introduced in this chapter that you feel you do not quite understand yet or for which you do not see the purpose? Give examples.

  Answers will vary.

- Consider again the role of the graphing calculator in this course for this chapter. Have you discovered new advantages or disadvantages of using the graphing calculator? If so, what are they? Has your perspective or feeling changed toward the use of the graphing calculator? (We hope that you will be aware of how you are improving with the use of the graphing calculator.) Be clear and explain your response.

  Answers will vary.

- What graphing calculator skills have you mastered during this chapter? Explain thoroughly and use examples. What graphing calculator skills have you not yet mastered? Provide an example for which you need a calculator skill that you have not yet mastered.

  Answers will vary.

- Have you discovered any new advantages of working in groups in your mathematics class? New disadvantages? Explain these completely.

  Answers will vary.

Open-ended Problems

- In Chapter 2 you study sequences and their explicit formulas. Your task is to convince the reader (you may choose a reader, but explain who your reader is) that you understand these ideas and how they are related.

  Answers will vary.

- Explain recursive and explicit formulas completely. Then compare and contrast the two terms.

  Answers will vary.

Projects

Problem 4 in Problem Set 2.6 could be used as a project. The construction of several stages takes a great deal of time and care and could not be done in a class period. If done outside of class, this project could take up to two weeks.

For the second project below, it may be necessary to have a whole class discussion about what stores or products should be considered. Frequency of sales might be worth considering and certainly the initial markup of the merchandise must be considered.

- Choose a topic in which you are interested and for which you can easily find data and information for the last 10 years. (For instance, you could choose "the population of the world" as a topic.) Using the data for the last 10 years, come up with a formula that you think best represents that data. Use your formula to make predictions about your topic. What are the consequences of your predictions? Present your mathematical calculations, findings, and predictions in a paper.

  Answers will vary.

- Think of all the different types of stores that are available to us: grocery, clothing, hardware, and so on. Choose a particular type of store that you frequent or that interests you. Suppose that the store you choose wishes to increase the number of people that shop there. The owners of the store realize that discounting prices on the merchandise (as is done during sales) brings in more customers. For instance, it may be that for each 5% markdown in price, the number of customers will increase 10%.

  Research the type of store that interests you. Come up with an optimum plan for the store, clearly stating your assumptions and showing your mathematics to support it, that will increase the store's number of customers without causing the store to go broke.

  Answers will vary.

- You have seen many applications involving geometric or exponential growth. Actually, many types of growth that appear geometric cannot continue forever, because they run out of room, or people, or resources. As you get close to this limit, things change and the percent increase begins to decline.

  The data given here is the number of new cases of AIDS diagnosed each year since 1980. Use x-values of 0 through 13 as you put this data into your calculator. Find a window that includes all the points. Sketch this graph on your graph paper. Try using an arithmetic or geometric sequence to fit the data as well as you can. Experiment with different starting values and rates until the graph contains at least one point near the beginning and one point near the end. Make separate graphs with each of these two sequences. (Use the same window as your first sketch.) If you connect the points of the sequence and the points of the data, you will find that neither of these two models really fit the data very well.

Year	Cases
1980	114
1981	352
1982	1,254
1983	3,670
1984	7,534
1985	14,701
1986	27,444
1987	53,226
1988	78,266
1989	107,728
1990	131,734
1991	163,502
1992	175,279
1993	194,668

The particular model described in the first paragraph is called a logistics model. A recursive form of this sequence looks like this:

$$u_n = u_{(n-1)}\left(1 + P\frac{(L - u_{(n-1)})}{L}\right)$$

You can see that this is like a geometric sequence, $u_n = u_{(n-1)}(1 + P)$, showing P percent growth. In the logistic sequence, this percent is multiplied by a factor that changes with the values of the sequence. Now you need to experiment with starting values, P and L, to match this sequence to the data. This will not be easy, so be organized and patient. If you are, eventually you will be successful. Make a sketch of your answer. Finally, try to find meanings for the values of P and L that relate to the data and the situation. What are the long-run implications of your model? What will happen 2 yr, 5 yr, and 10 yr into the future? In this case there is no way to follow up on this data, because by 1994 the medical community had gained a much better understanding of the disease and consequently redefined what it means to have AIDS. Therefore, the numbers from 1994 on do not include the same group of people.

Using the points (3, 3670) and (12, 175279) an arithmetic sequence would be $u_n = 19067n - 53533$. Using the same points, a geometric sequence would be $u_n = 1011(1.537)^n$. Using the logistic model, a reasonable fit may be obtained using $u_0 = 1200$, $P = 0.72$, and $L = 194{,}000$. P represents the unrestricted growth rate. L represents the long-run number of new cases per year. Using the values stated, the following predictions result:

Year	Cases	Year	Cases
1996	193,729	2002	194,000
1997	193,924	2003	194,000
1998	193,979	2004	194,000
1999	193,994	2005	194,000
2000	193,998	2006	194,000
2001	194,000	2007	194,000

Skill Questions: Appropriate for Quizzes or Tests

- For each of the following sequences, (i) identify it as arithmetic, geometric, both or neither, and (ii) find the explicit formula of the sequence, if possible.

  a. 91.3, 89, 86.7, 84.4, ...

  b. 576, 432, 324, 243, ...

  c. $\frac{1}{2}, \frac{2}{3}, \frac{3}{4}, \frac{4}{5}, \ldots$.

  a. arithmetic, $u_n = 93.6 - 2.3n$

  b. geometric, $u_n = 576(0.75)^{(n-1)}$

  c. neither, $u_n = \frac{n}{n+1}$

- Suppose that $1,500 is invested at 5.25% annual interest rate, compounded monthly.

  a. What is the balance after 5 years?

  b. Suppose $100 is added to the account every month. What is the balance after 5 years?

  a. ≈ $1,949.15 **b. ≈ $8,823.26**

- Write the first four terms for the sequence defined by $u_n = \frac{n(2n + 1)}{6}$.

$\frac{1}{2}, \frac{5}{3}, \frac{7}{2}, 6$

- Given the sequence 2.5, 2, 1.6, 1.28, ...
  a. What is the sixth term?
  b. Write an explicit formula for the terms of this sequence.
  c. Sketch a graph of these terms.

a. **0.8192**

b. **$u_n = 2.5(0.8)^{(n-1)}$**

c.

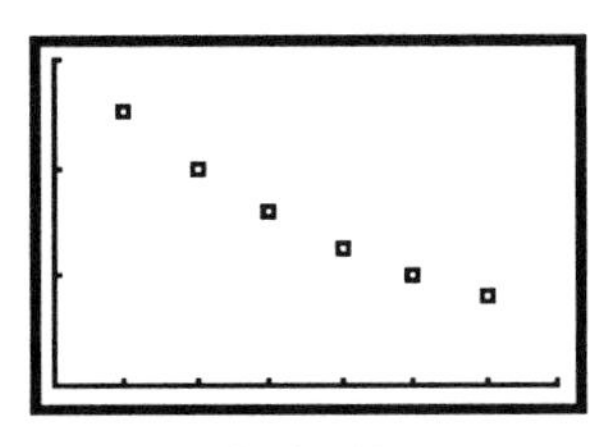

[0, 7, 1, 0, 3, 1]

- Examine the sequence represented on the graph at right.
  a. What are the next two **points** in the sequence pictured?
  b. What is the explicit formula for this sequence?
  c. What is the 40th term of this sequence?
  d. If the point (n, 1023) is on the graph of this sequence, what is n?

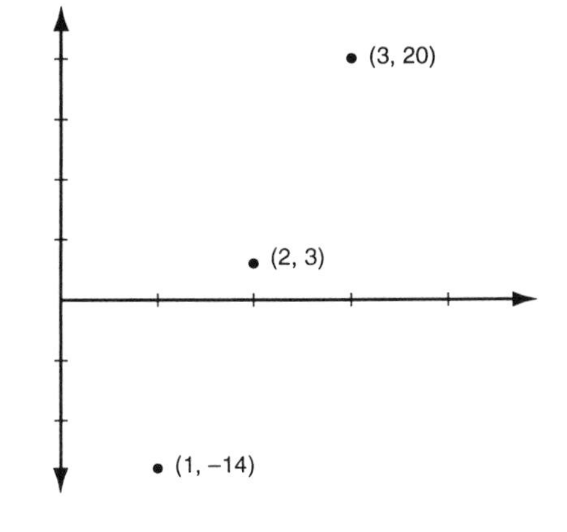

a. **(4, 37), (5, 54)** **b.** **$u_n = {}^{-}31 + 17n$**

c. **649** **d.** **$n = 62$**

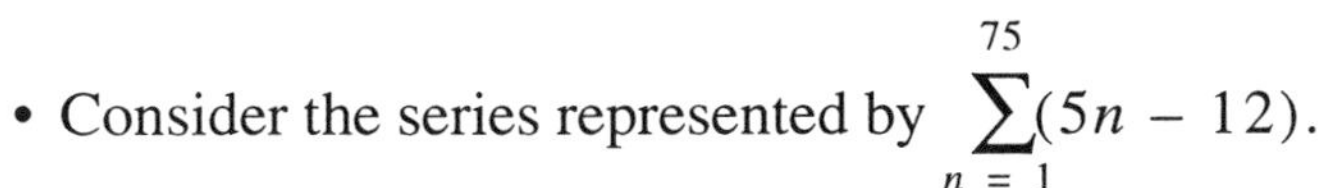

- Consider the series represented by $\sum_{n=1}^{75}(5n - 12)$.
  a. What are the first five terms of the sequence?
  b. Find S_{75} for this sequence.

a. **⁻7, ⁻2, 3, 8, 13** **b.** **14,238**

- Use an explicit formula to find the 13th term of the sequence beginning 2, 8, 32, 128, ... Show your work.

33,554,432

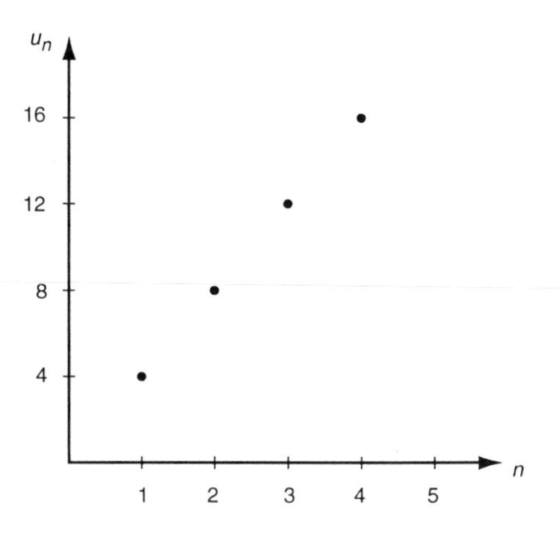

- Use the sequence pictured in the graph at the right to answer the questions below.
  - a. What sequence is pictured here? List the terms. Label it u_n.
  - b. What is u_3?
  - c. What is u_5? u_0?
  - d. What is the common difference?
  - e. What is the slope of the line through these points?
  - f. What is the u_n intercept?
  - g. What is the equation of the line through the points?
  - h. What is the formula of the sequence?

a. **4, 8 12, 16** **b.** **12** **c.** **20, 0**

d. **4** **e.** **4** **f.** **0**

g. $\boldsymbol{u(n) = 4n}$ **h.** $\boldsymbol{u(n) = 4n}$

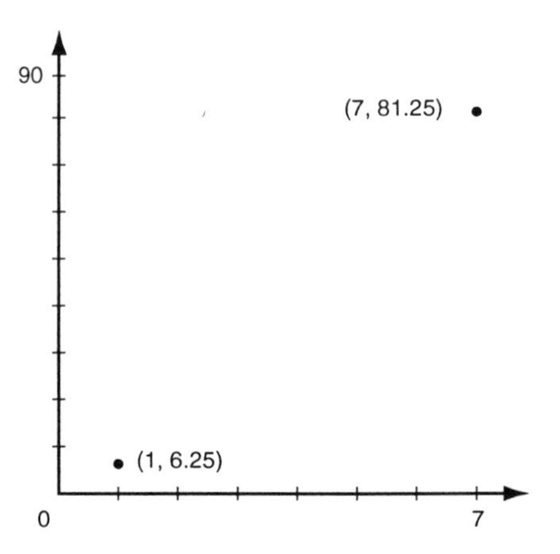

- In the graph at the right, the two points depict two terms of a particular arithmetic sequence. *Show more work than you think you need.*
  - a. Name the first seven terms of this sequence.
  - b. Write an explicit formula which describes this sequence.
  - c. Write an equation of the line which contains the two points pictured.
  - d. Find u_{80} using the formula developed in part b.
  - e. Find S_{80} using an explicit formula.

a. **6.25, 18.75, 31.25, 43.75, 56.25, 68.75, 81.25**

b. $\boldsymbol{u_n = {}^{-}6.25 + 12.5n}$

c. **Same as part b**

d. **993.75**

e. **40,000**

- Consider the sequence represented by $u_n = n^2 - 1$.
  - a. What are the first six terms?
  - b. Is this sequence arithmetic, geometric, both, or neither? Explain.
  - c. What is S_7? Explain completely how you found it.

a. **0, 3, 8, 15, 24, 35**

b. **Neither: no common difference, no common ratio.**

c. **133**

Group Problem

- Banks perform two key services for people: (1) they loan money to their customers and charge interest on those loans, and (2) they accept deposits for which the bank pays interest. As the bank lowers the interest rate they charge on loans, more customers will take out loans. At the same time, if the bank raises the interest rate they pay on deposits, more people will deposit money in the bank. Considering this information, what do you think are the ideal interest rates for the bank to charge and pay so that the bank can still make a profit and stay in business? You will need to make some assumptions in coming up with your plan for the bank. Be sure you carefully state each assumption; explain it completely and include why you are making it.

  Answers will vary.

- As you might know, Australia once had a real problem with rabbits! When rabbits were introduced into Australia in the late 1800s, there were no natural enemies on the continent. As a consequence, the number of rabbits quickly grew out of control.

  Suppose two rabbits, one male and one female, scampered on board a ship that was anchored at a European port. The ship set sail for Australia and when it anchored in late December, the two rabbits abandoned the ship to make their home on the island continent.

  Consider the following assumptions:

  i. The number of young produced in every litter is six, and three of those six are female.

  ii. The original female gives birth to six young on January 1, and produces another litter of six 40 days later and every 40 days thereafter as long as she lives.

  iii. Each female born on the island will produce her first litter 120 days after her birth, and then produces another new litter every 40 days thereafter.

  iv. The rabbits are on an island with no natural enemy and plenty of food. Therefore, in this first year, there are only births, and no rabbits die.

  What will be the total number of rabbits by the next January 1, including the original pair?

  Four different ways of finding and expressing the answers and means of calculating are given here: (1) a table showing the number of rabbits in each age category, (2) a verbal description of finding the next 40-day total, (3) a recursive formula, and (4) a calculator program for calculating and displaying the terms.

Day Number	1	41	81	121	161	201	241	281	321	361
Bearing age	2	2	2	8	14	20	44	86	146	278
80 days old	0	0	6	6	6	24	42	60	132	258
40 days old	0	6	6	6	24	42	60	132	258	438
Newborn	6	6	6	24	42	60	132	258	438	834
Total	8	14	20	44	86	146	278	536	974	1808

To find the next value, add the last value to three times the value from two terms earlier.

$$u_n = \begin{cases} 2 & n = 0 \\ u_{(n-1)} + 3u_{(n-3)} & n \geq 1 \end{cases}$$

```
Progrm:RABBIT
{2,2,2}→L1
For(N,4,12)
3L1(N-3)+L1(N-1)→L1(N)
Disp  L1(N):Pause
End
```

Chapter 3: Introduction to Statistics

Journal Questions

- Some new ideas and concepts were introduced in Chapter 3. What do you think is the point of Chapter 3? What items are emphasized in this chapter? What ideas seem particularly useful in the real world? Be clear and justify your response.

  Answers will vary.

- Find three problems in the chapter that you feel are representative of the chapter. Write out the problem and the solution. For each problem, explain why you feel it is representative of the chapter.

  Answers will vary.

- In Chapter 1 you were asked to consider three different levels of understanding: knowledge, comprehension/understanding, and application. Now we will present the next three levels.

  Analysis: To be at the knowledge level of understanding, a student can explain *why*. He or she can break down information into its parts in order to make the larger picture clear.

  How can a student demonstrate his or her knowledge? By analyzing results and breaking apart concepts, ideas, theories, equations, and so on, explaining the logical interconnections of the parts and developing detailed cause-and-effect chains.

  Synthesis: A student at this level has the ability to put together parts and elements into a unified organization that requires original thinking, and can recognize new problems and develop new tools to solve them.

  How can a student demonstrate his or her knowledge? By combining ideas into a statement, plan, product, or similar construct that is new for the student, and developing a program that includes the best parts of each of those ideas.

  Appreciation/Evaluation: At this level, a student has the ability to judge and appreciate the value of ideas, procedures, and methods using appropriate criteria.

  How can a student demonstrate his or her knowledge? By demonstrating the ability to make a judgment about something using some criteria or standard for making the judgment.

  Think of all the concepts presented so far this year. Make a list of the major topics that you have studied so far. For each topic, rate your level of understanding. Support your rating by explaining or demonstrating that you are at each level.

  Answers will vary.

- What ideas or topics were introduced in this chapter that you feel you do not quite understand yet or for which you do not see the purpose? Give examples.

  Answers will vary.

- What graphing calculator skills have you mastered during this chapter? Explain thoroughly and use examples. What graphing calculator skills have you not yet mastered? Provide an example for which you need a calculator skill that you have not yet mastered.

Answers will vary.

- Consider again the role of the graphing calculator in this course for this chapter. Have you discovered new advantages or disadvantages of using the graphing calculator? If so, what are they? Has your perspective or feeling changed toward the use of the graphing calculator? Be clear and explain your response.

  Answers will vary.

- Since the beginning of the school year, you have been working with your group, or perhaps you have worked with several different groups. How has your group work changed since the beginning of the school year? Has your role in your group changed? Explain completely.

  Answers will vary.

- Have you discovered any new advantages of working in groups in your mathematics class? New disadvantages? Explain these completely.

Open-ended Problems

- Chapter 3 is titled Introduction to Statistics. Your task is to convince the reader that you are gaining a basic understanding of statistics and how it can be used in real-life situations.

  Answers will vary.

- A May 1994 article in the *New York Times* revealed that Stanford University was reinstituting a failing grade after doing without one for many years.

  The article said that the *median* grade among the undergraduate students on campus is A–. What does this tell you?

  Of all the undergraduate students, one-half receive a grade below an A–, and (here's the surprising part) one-half receive a grade above an A–, that is, an A.

- In a box-and-whisker plot, point A represents Q1, the first quartile; point B represents the median; and point C represents Q3, the third quartile.

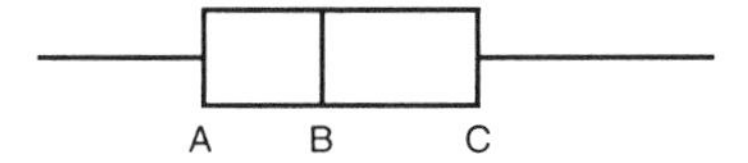

  Explain simply and completely enough so that an eighth-grader could understand the significance of each of these points.

  Answers will vary. Should contain something similar to the following: Line up all the data points from highest to lowest. The one in the exact middle is B. Now just look at all data points below B. The one in the exact middle of these is A. Now just look at all data points above B. The one in the exact middle is C.

  Is it possible for a box plot to look like the one below? Explain why or why not. Create a data set that corresponds to this box plot.

  Yes, if the median has the same value as Q1 (or Q3). For example, if the data is 14, 17, 20, 20, 20, 20, 21, 24, 27, 27, 28, then Q1 = the median = 20.

- While editing his school newspaper on a computer, I. M. Ditzy made a grave error! He accidentally deleted all of the text of the article about the following graph.

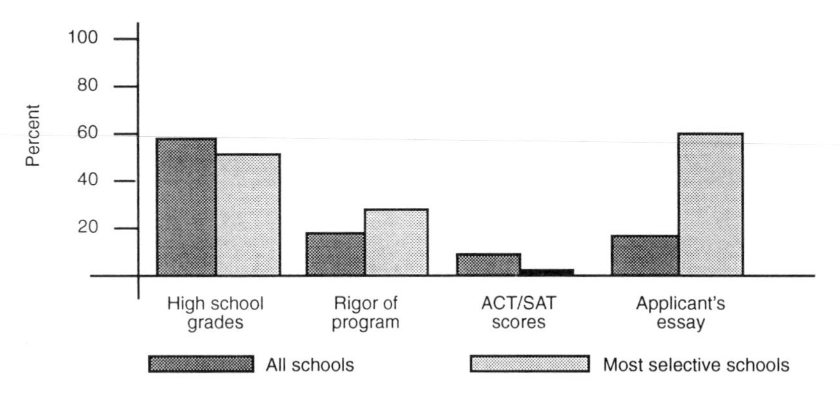

Help I. M. Ditzy out by writing the article to accompany this graph. The article must contain at least three paragraphs.

Answers will vary. The key is for the students to realize that this graph represents what different colleges look at when reviewing applications. Specifically, the order of importance for all schools is high school grades, rigor of program, and applicant's essay (tie), and ACT/SAT scores, while the order of importance for the most selective schools is essay, grades, rigor of program, and test scores.

- For each problem below, please follow this format.
  - i. State the problem.
  - ii. What do you already know that would help you solve this problem? Who (in your group) knows it and how does he or she know it?
  - iii. What information do you need to assume? Why are you assuming it?
  - iv. Record all your steps in solving the problem.
  - v. State your answer clearly and completely.
  - vi. How good is your answer? Remember: "A chain is only as strong as its weakest link!" What are your most unreliable approximations and weakest assumptions?

    1. What do you think is the mean age of the population of your town? What is the median age?

       Answers will vary.

    2. On the average, how many traffic tickets (per student) do you think students at your school have received?

       Answers will vary.

Projects

Each of the following projects could be done during Chapter 3. The students will be able to do more analysis, however, if these are completed during Chapter 4. The best approach, though, might be to assign the project(s) during Chapter 3, but not have it due until the end of Chapter 4. This will allow students to choose the approach they wish to take for the problem.

These projects could be divided up among the students or groups in the class, or students could choose which one they wish to work on. Or, perhaps, if the group format is used, each group could choose two projects. Then after having completed both projects, students could compare and contrast the two, explaining which one is more reliable. Another alternative is to ask students to create their own survey on a topic of their choosing.

- Survey everyone in your class: How many children are in each person's family? Analyze this data, find an appropriate way to represent it, then interpret the data. Use this information to make predictions about your student body. What are the strengths and weaknesses of your predictions?

  Answers will vary.

- Survey everyone in your class: How much money does each person have on him or her right now? Analyze this data, find an appropriate way to represent it, then interpret the data. Use this information to make predictions about your student body. What are the strengths and weaknesses of your predictions?

  Answers will vary.

- Survey everyone in your class: How many As, Bs, Cs, Ds, and Fs did each student have on his or her last report card? Analyze this data, find an appropriate way to represent it, then interpret the data. Use this information to make predictions about your student body. What are the strengths and weaknesses of your predictions?

  Answers will vary.

- Survey everyone in your class: How many letters are in each person's whole name? Analyze this data, find an appropriate way to represent it, then interpret the data. Use this information to make predictions about your student body. What are the strengths and weaknesses of your predictions?

- Find an article in your city newspaper that uses a significant amount of data and statistics, but contains no graphs. Rewrite the article, representing as much of the information as you can graphically (that is, with histograms, box plots, and so on). Conclude your article by describing the insights you have gained from the graphs. Indicate to the reader what graph and where to look in order to "see" your conclusions. Submit a copy of the original article with your improved version.

  Answers will vary.

Skill Questions: Appropriate for Quizzes or Tests

- The monthly normal temperatures below are based on records for the 30-year period 1951 to 1980, inclusive. The temperatures are in Fahrenheit degrees.

City	J	F	M	A	M	J	J	A	S	O	N	D
San Francisco, CA	49	52	53	55	58	61	62	63	64	61	55	49
Springfield, MO	32	36	45	56	65	73	78	77	70	58	45	36

Source: National Climatic Data Center, NESDIS, NOAA, U.S. Dept. of Commerce.

a. What do you think is meant by "monthly normal temperature"? Explain.

b. Find the mean temperature for each city. What does this tell you? Explain.

c. List the five summary points for each city and sketch a box plot for each city on the same scale. What does this graph tell you? Explain.

d. Find the interquartile range (length of the box) for each city. What does this tell you? Explain.

a. Answers will vary. It's probably the average of the highs and lows for each of the 30 days over all 30 years.

b. **SF ≈ 56.83; S, MO ≈ 55.92**

c. **SF: Min = 49, Q1 = 52.5, Median 56.5, Q3 = 61.5, Max = 64; S, MO: Min = 32, Q1 = 40.5, Median = 57, Q3 = 71.5, Max = 78**

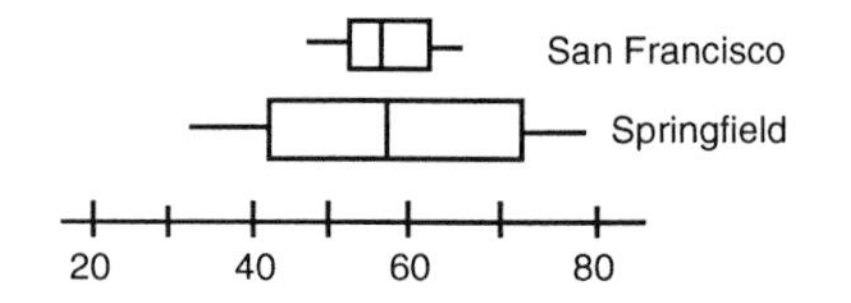

d. **San Francisco, 9; Springfield, 31**

- The table below shows the average salary per player (in dollars) paid by each National Football League team during 1992.

Team	Average salary
Atlanta	564,100
Buffalo	564,355
Chicago	460,060
Cincinnati	513,085
Cleveland	468,675
Dallas	466,980
Denver	450,640
Detroit	470,095
Green Bay	493,035
Houston	544,430
Indianapolis	674,405
Kansas City	447,075
LA Raiders	570,145
LA Rams	483,910

Team	Average salary
Miami	627,140
Minnesota	477,420
New England	437,625
New Orleans	566,570
NY Giants	561,700
NY Jets	486,180
Philadelphia	475,015
Phoenix	412,185
Pittsburgh	358,625
San Diego	412,505
San Francisco	613,420
Seattle	411,615
Tampa Bay	379,660
Washington	529,035

Source: *The Milwaukee Journal*, January 4, 1993.

a. Find the mean and median for this set of data.

b. Make a box plot of this data (use graph paper). Clearly label the important points.

c. The top box plot shows the salary information for teams along the east coast. The box plot at the bottom shows the salary information for teams in the midwest. State at least three conclusions you can make from studying these plots.

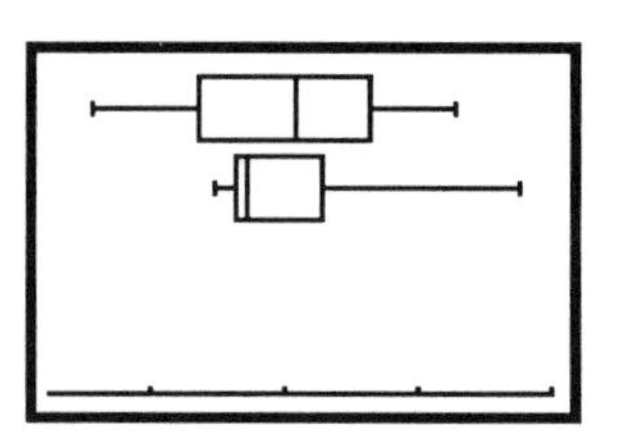

[325000, 700000, 100000, 0, 3, 0]

d. Suppose that currently several players for Seattle earn twice the team average. How do you think the median Seattle team salary compares to the mean Seattle team salary of $411,615? Explain why you think this.

e. Make a histogram on graph paper showing the data for all of the teams. Clearly and neatly label the axes.

f. On your histogram, label the bar that contains the median, with the letter A.

g. Is it possible to compute the mean player salary based on this data? Why or why not?

a. **mean = $497,131.61, median = $480,665**

b. **For the box plot, min = 358,625, Q1 = 448,857.5, Q3 = 562,900, and max = 674,405.**

c. **Answers will vary.**

d. Answers will vary. A key point is that if "several" refers to more than half of the team members, then the median is higher; if "several" is only a couple of team members, then the median is lower.

e. and f.

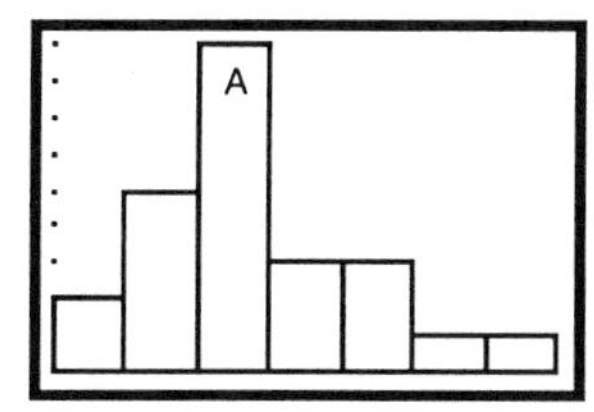

[3550000, 700000, 50000, 0, 9, 1]

g. No, because you don't know how many players are on each team.

- Your friend's younger sister just received her scores on a standardized test she took at school. She scored in the 89th percentile, but she does not understand what that means. Explain it to her completely.

She scored better than 89% of others who took the test.

- The table below shows the high school graduation rate and rank of all 50 states and the District of Columbia in 1991.

	Graduation Rate	Rank
Alabama	65.6	44
Alaska	72.3	33
Arizona	72.4	32
Arkansas	76.6	21
California	67.7	42
Colorado	74.5	26
Connecticut	78.6	16
Delaware	68.0	40
D.C.	59.5	50
Florida	61.2	48
Georgia	64.0	46
Hawaii	76.1	23
Idaho	79.7	12
Illinois	77.5	18
Indiana	75.3	25
Iowa	85.9	4
Kansas	81.1	10
Kentucky	70.0	36
Louisiana	54.3	51
Maine	79.0	14
Maryland	73.1	29
Massachusetts	79.7	12
Michigan	69.9	37
Minnesota	89.5	1
Mississippi	61.7	47
Missouri	72.5	31

	Graduation Rate	Rank
Montana	84.9	5
Nebraska	86.3	3
Nevada	77.4	20
New Hampshire	76.2	22
New Jersey	82.1	8
New Mexico	69.5	38
New York	64.4	45
North Carolina	68.4	39
North Dakota	86.7	2
Ohio	72.3	33
Oklahoma	75.5	24
Oregon	71.6	35
Pennsylvania	78.5	17
Rhode Island	73.6	27
South Carolina	61.2	48
South Dakota	84.2	6
Tennessee	67.8	41
Texas	65.9	43
Utah	79.0	14
Vermont	80.9	11
Virginia	73.6	27
Washington	73.1	29
West Virginia	77.5	18
Wisconsin	82.5	7
Wyoming	81.7	9

Source: National Center for Education Statistics, U.S. Dept. of Education.

a. Calculate the mean graduation rate for all 50 states and the District of Columbia.

b. Calculate the mean absolute deviation. What does this number tell you?

c. How does your state compare to the mean? Explain.

a. 74.13%

b. 6.2583; it is a measure of the spread of the data.

c. Answers will vary.

- The table below shows the average number of pupils per teacher and the average pay per teacher for the 1991–1992 school year.

State	Pupils per teacher	Average pay per teacher
Alabama	17.8	$26,951
Alaska	16.7	44,718
Arizona	19.3	31,176
Arkansas	17.0	27,070
California	22.8	40,192
Colorado	17.9	33,072
Connecticut	14.0	46,971
Delaware	16.8	34,548
Florida	17.6	31,070
Georgia	18.5	29,509
Hawaii	18.5	34,528
Idaho	19.4	26,334
Illinois	16.8	36,461
Indiana	17.5	34,809
Iowa	15.7	29,202
Kansas	15.2	30,731
Kentucky	17.2	30,870
Louisiana	16.6	25,948
Maine	14.0	30,097
Maryland	16.9	38,728
Massachusetts	15.1	37,256
Michigan	19.2	41,149
Minnesota	17.2	34,451
Mississippi	17.9	24,367
Missouri	15.8	28,895
Montana	15.8	$27,590
Nebraska	14.7	27,231
Nevada	18.6	33,857
New Hampshire	15.5	33,170
New Jersey	13.8	41,027
New Mexico	17.6	26,389
New York	15.4	43,335
North Carolina	16.8	28,791
North Dakota	15.3	24,495
Ohio	17.3	33,243
Oklahoma	15.6	25,339
Oregon	18.6	34,100
Pennsylvania	16.8	38,715
Rhode Island	14.6	36,417
South Carolina	16.9	28,068
South Dakota	14.8	23,291
Tennessee	19.4	28,621
Texas	15.8	29,041
Utah	24.9	26,339
Vermont	13.8	33,646
Virginia	15.7	31,657
Washington	20.2	34,823
West Virginia	15.3	27,366
Wisconsin	15.7	35,227
Wyoming	15.6	30,425

Source: National Center for Education Statistics, U.S. Dept. of Education; National Education Assn. of Teachers.

a. Calculate the mean, median, and standard deviation of the number of pupils per teacher for all 50 states.

b. Calculate the mean, median, and standard deviation of the average pay per teacher for all 50 states.

c. Draw two histograms representing the information about the states. What does each graph tell you? Explain.

d. Based on the information above, does one state seem better than the others? Does one (or two) seem particularly worse? Explain in a paragraph or two. Carefully use statistical information to support your conclusions.

a. mean = 16.918, median = 16.8, s.d. ≈ 2.13

b. mean = 32,226.12, median 31,123, s.d. ≈ 5517.38

c. pupils per teacher **average salary**

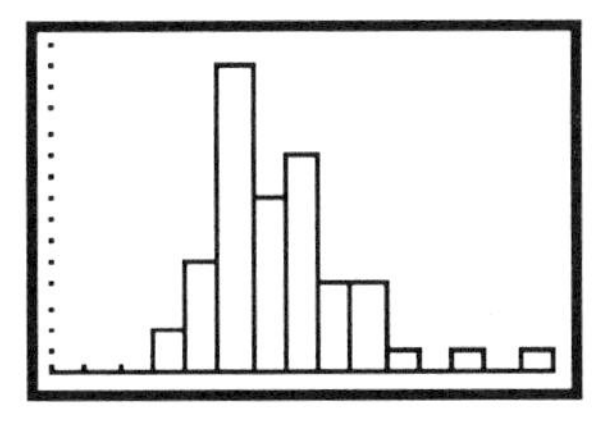

[10, 25, 1, 0, 15, 1]

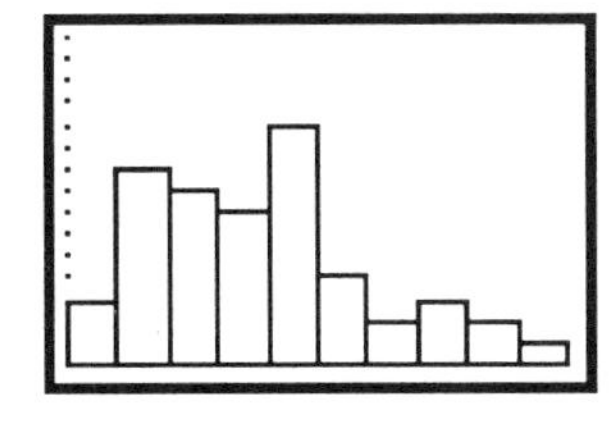

[22500, 47500, 2500, 0, 15, 1]

d. Answers will vary. Good responses may take into account the cost per student.

Group Problem

The following is a guided exploration that could be used as a prelude to Chapter 4.

- Listed below are the skyscrapers in the United States, in order of height, that are at least 72 stories tall.

Building	Stories	Height (feet)
Sears Tower	110	1454
World Trade Center	110	1377
Empire State	102	1250
Amoco	80	1136
John Hancock	100	1127
Chrysler	77	1046
First Interstate	73	1017
Texas	75	1002
Columbia Seafirst	76	943
Water Tower Plaza	74	859
Westin Peachtree	73	754
Detroit Westin	73	712

a. What is the dependent variable, stories or height? Explain. How many data points are there?

b. Sort the ordered pairs in order of their x-coordinates (from smallest to largest). Divide the data into three equal groups.

c. Find the median x-coordinate of each group.

d. Similarly sort the y-coordinates from smallest to largest and divide into three groups.

e. Find the median y-coordinate of each group.

f. The median point for each group has now been found. Average the coordinates of the three median points to find the coordinates of the centroid.

g. Find the slope of the line connecting the first and third median points.

h. Find the equation of the line with this slope that contains the centroid. This line is the *median-median line*.

i. What is the real-world meaning of the slope? The y-intercept?

j. Use the median-median line to predict the height of an 88-story building. Explain the reasonableness of this prediction.

a. Dependent: height; independent: stories; 12 data points.

b.

First group:		Second group:		Third group:	
Westin Peachtree	**73**	**Texas**	**75**	**John Hancock**	**100**
Detroit Westin	**73**	**Columbia Seafirst**	**76**	**Empire State**	**102**
First Interstate	**73**	**Chrysler**	**77**	**World Trade Center**	**110**
Water Tower Plaza	**74**	**Amoco**	**80**	**Sears Tower**	**110**

c. First group median = 73, second group median = 76.5, third group median = 106

d.

First group:		Second group:		Third group:	
Detroit Westin	**712**	**Texas**	**1002**	**Amoco**	**1136**
Westin Peachtree	**754**	**First Interstate**	**1017**	**Empire State**	**1250**
Water Tower Plaza	**859**	**Chrysler**	**1046**	**World Trade Center**	**1377**
Columbia Seafirst	**943**	**John Hancock**	**1127**	**Sears Tower**	**1454**

e. First group median = 806.5, second group median = 1031.5, third group median = 1313.5

f. (85.17, 1050.5) **g.** $\frac{169}{11}$ **h.** $y - 1050.5 = \frac{169}{11}(x - 85.17)$

i. The number of feet per story is approximately 15.

j. Using the equation in part h, the height is approximately 1094.13.

- A cycling magazine wants to establish that cycling is an excellent way to improve a person's fitness and health. The magazine runs a full-page advertisement asking readers who ride their bikes regularly to write in and describe the quality of their health and fitness. Of the 2145 readers who reply, 96% report good to excellent health and fitness.

  a. Is this a reasonable way for the magazine to establish that cycling is beneficial to health and fitness? Explain completely. If you do not think so, give suggestions.

  b. Do you think that 96% is probably higher than, lower than, or about the same as the actual percent of people who find cycling beneficial to health and fitness? Explain.

a. Answers will vary.

b. Higher. People who subscribe to the magazine are interested in cycling regularly and are more likely to be interested in staying fit.

- A researcher for a university wants to find out how much the average high school student studies on any given school day. To avoid bias, she does not want only volunteers filling out surveys, so she devises a plan. For two weeks, Monday through Friday, she will station herself outside a high school library. Every fourth person who enters the library she will ask to sign in and sign out, thus giving her the time these students spent in the library. She wants to publish the results of her survey in an article entitled "Average High School Student Spends Hours Studying."

  Do you think this was a good way to set up the research? Explain completely. If you think this was not such a good way, offer suggestions to help her improve the validity of the results.

  Answers will vary. Going to the library may not be something an average student does.

Chapter 4: Data Analysis

Journal Questions

- In Chapter 4, you continued your study of statistics. What do you think is the point of Chapter 4? What is different about this chapter from the last? What ideas seem particularly useful in the real world? Be clear and justify your response.

  Answers will vary.

- Find three problems in the chapter that you feel are representative of the chapter. Write out the problem and the solution. For each problem, explain why you feel it is representative of the chapter.

  Answers will vary.

- So far this year, you have considered six different levels of understanding: knowledge, comprehension/understanding, application, analysis, synthesis, and appreciation/evaluation.

  Find your prior list of the major ideas and concepts you have studied so far and add any new ideas and concepts from this chapter. Fill in your topics in the table at the right, and rate your level of understanding. Be prepared to support your rating by explaining or demonstrating that you are at each level.

  Answers will vary.

Topic	knowledge	comprehension/ understanding	application	analysis	synthesis	appreciation/ evaluation

- What ideas or topics were introduced in this chapter that you feel you do not quite understand yet or for which you do not see the purpose? Give examples.

  Answers will vary.

- Find a problem that you cannot solve. Write out the problem and as much of the solution as you can. Then, clearly explain what it is that is keeping you from solving the problem. Be as specific and clear as you can.

  Answers will vary.

- What graphing calculator skills have you mastered during this chapter? Explain thoroughly and use examples. What graphing calculator skills have you not yet mastered? Provide an example for which you need a calculator skill that you have not yet mastered.

  Answers will vary.

- Consider again the role of the graphing calculator in this course for this chapter. Have you discovered new advantages or disadvantages of using the graphing calculator? If so, what are they? Has your perspective or feeling changed toward the use of the graphing calculator? Be clear and explain your response.

  Answers will vary.

- Since the beginning of the school year, you have been working with your group, or perhaps you have worked with several different groups. We have asked you to think about how your groups have worked together and about your role in your group. Reread what you have written so far. What role would you like your group to play in the classroom? What role would you like to play in your group? Explain completely.

  Answers will vary.

- Have you discovered any new advantages of working in groups in your mathematics class? New disadvantages? Explain these completely.

  Answers will vary.

Open-ended Problems

- Chapter 4 is titled Data Analysis. Your task is to convince the reader that you understand what "data analysis" means and how it can be used in real-life situations.

  Answers will vary.

The next problem is adapted from the NCTM Addenda Series/Grades 9–12: Data Analysis and Statistics.

- In a certain country the defense budget was $30 million for 1980. The total budget for that year was $500 million. The following year the defense budget was $35 million, while the total budget was $605 million. Inflation during the period between the two budgets was 10%.
  a. You are invited to offer a presentation for a pacifist society. You want to explain that the defense budget has decreased this year. Explain how this could be done.
  b. You are invited to offer a presentation at a military academy. You want to explain that the defense budget has increased this year. Explain how this could be done.
  c. What do your responses to the last two problems tell you about the use of statistics? Explain.

  a. Answers will vary. Key point: in 1980 defense budget was 6%; it dropped to 5.8% in 1981.

  b. Answers will vary. Key point: $30 million increased to $35 million, which is about a 17% increase; this is more than inflation.

  c. Answers will vary.

- For each problem below, please follow this format.
  i. State the problem.
  ii. What do you already know that would help you solve this problem? Who (in your group) knows it and how does he or she know it?
  iii. What information do you need to assume? Why are you assuming it?
  iv. Record all your steps in solving the problem.
  v. State your answer clearly and completely.
  vi. How good is your answer? Remember: "A chain is only as strong as its weakest link!" What are your most unreliable approximations and weakest assumptions?

  1. How many calories does the average 16-year-old consume in one day?

     Answers will vary.

  2. What will be the average life expectancy in the year 2025?

     Answers will vary.

- In a recent article by Sonya Ross (Associated Press), she states: "The world's big cities are growing by a million people a week and will hold more than half the Earth's population within a decade, the World Bank said Monday."

  a. Find a way to represent this information graphically, so as to stress the significance of this statement.

  The article went on: "The study found urban populations are growing by 3.8% a year, and projected that by 2020, 3.6 billion people will inhabit urban areas while about 3 billion will remain in rural areas."

  b. Based on this growth rate and projection, what is the urban population now?

  c. The article also says: "In 1990, there were 1.4 billion people living in the world's urban areas." Does this fit the data given above? Explain.

  d. "By the year 2000," the article continues, "there will be 391 cities with more than 1 million residents, up from 288 in 1990. Of those, 26 will be megacities, with more than 10 million people; 13 of those megacities, the study said, will be in Asia." Graphically represent this growth rate data.

  e. Give at least three reasons why people are concerned about the world's population growth. (The article, dated September 20, 1994, gives two reasons.)

  a. Answers will vary. **b. $\approx$ 1.5 billion in 1997**

  c. No, the data and rate imply a population of approximately 1.16 billion in 1990.

  d. Answers will vary. **e. Answers will vary.**

Projects

Remember that any of the projects in Chapter 3 can be done in this chapter as well.

- For this project, you will be using statistics and data analysis to answer a question. The question is up to you!

  a. Come up with a question or problem to which you have a "guess" as to the answer, but you are not certain your answer is correct. It should be something in which you are interested and to which you would like to know the answer. For instance, you could ask: "Do shorter people run more slowly?" "Do more students smoke in schools with smoking areas than in schools that don't allow smoking on campus?" "Does eating a good breakfast affect your grades in school?" or any other question for which data can be gathered.

  b. Clearly state the problem or question, being as specific as you can. Write a paragraph containing this problem statement and what you think the answer is (your hypothesis). Also include how you plan to research your question.

  c. Find out as much as you can about the question: Has someone already done research on this question? Does the question really have an answer? Collect as much research as you can on your topic. Be sure to include a bibliography in your project report.

  d. Design the study and develop techniques and measuring instruments that will provide objective data pertinent to your hypothesis.

  e. Collect the data.

  g. Interpret the results and draw conclusions. Use charts, tables, histograms, box plots, stem-and-leaf plots, correlation lines, and so on—whatever is appropriate to display the data—in your project report on the results.

  Answers will vary.

- Find an article in your city newspaper that uses a significant amount of data and statistics. Rewrite the article, representing as much of the information as you can graphically (that is, with histograms, box plots, and so on).

  Answers will vary.

These projects are best done in groups. That way, each group can have each of the four group members try the experiment (perhaps several times) so that the group can collect sufficient data.

- For the following projects:
  i. Record the data neatly and clearly.
  ii. Describe the experiment.
  iii. Explain the factors you considered when setting up the experiment.
  iv. Summarize the results of the experiment. Use graphs and statistical values.
  v. Analyze the results.
  vi. Interpret the results.
  vii. What variables might affect your results? Explain.
  viii. Does your data contain any outliers? Explain these.
  ix. Based on your results, make predictions.
    a. For how many seconds can you balance a ball on your head?
    b. How far can you roll a penny before it falls over?
    c. Roll a die once and record the outcome. How many more rolls does it take for you to get the same number?

    Answers will vary.

Skill Questions: Appropriate for Quizzes or Tests

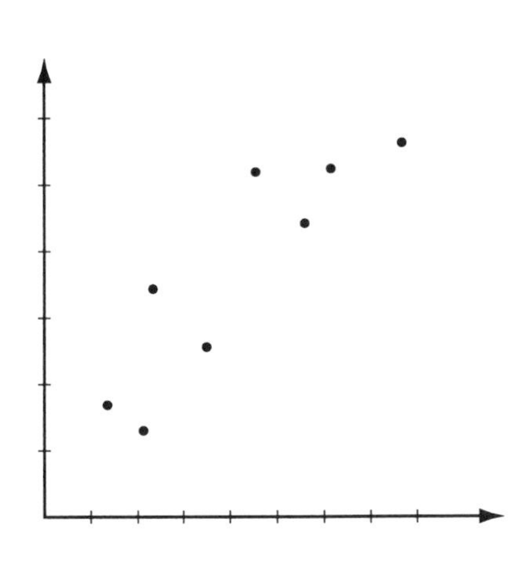

- Consider the set of data graphed at the right. (Each tick mark represents 1 unit.)
  a. Draw the line of best fit (by sight).
  b. What is the y-intercept of your line?
  c. What is the slope of your line?
  d. What is the equation of your line?

  a. Answers will vary.

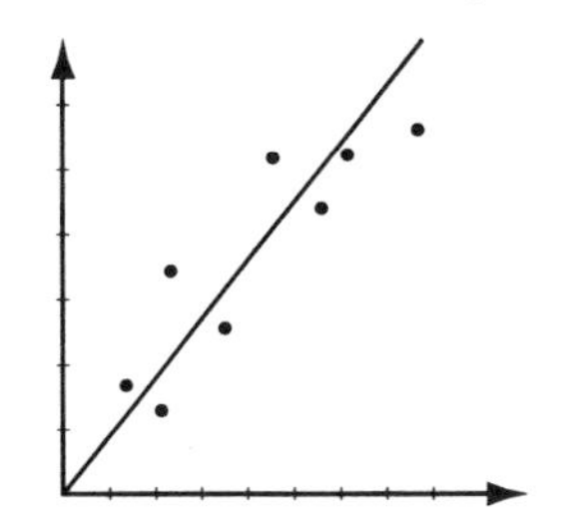

  b. Answers will vary. (≈ 0)

  c. ≈ 0.9 **d. $y \approx 0.9x$**

- Find the slope of the line between (−5, 2) and (1, −4).

  ⁻1

- Find the equation of the line with slope 5 and passing through the point (3.5, −2).

  $y = 5x - 19.5$

- What is the y-intercept for the line whose equation is $y = {}^-3.4x - 29.3$?

  (0, ⁻29.3)

- For each line shown below, state whether the slope is positive, negative, zero, or undefined.

a.

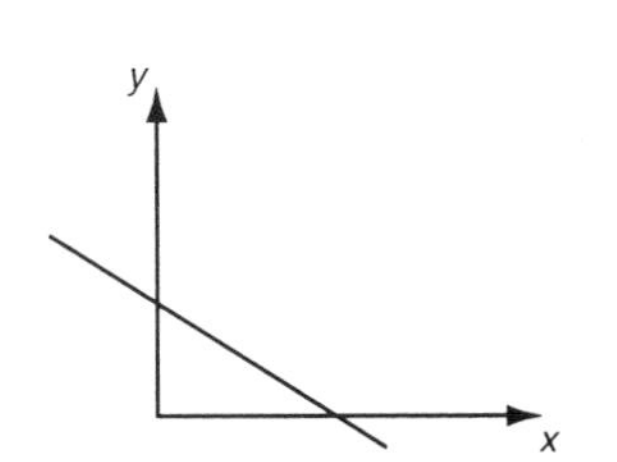

b.

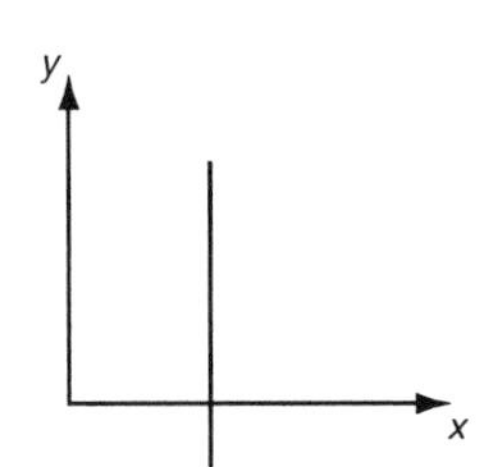

c.

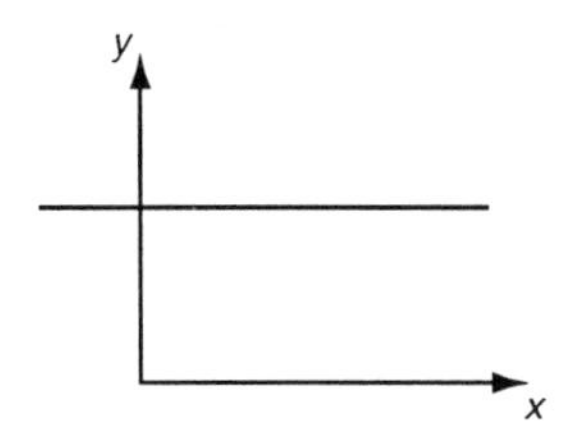

a. negative **b. undefined** **c. zero**

- Which scatter plot shown below has the strongest positive linear association? Which has the strongest negative linear association? Justify your answers.

a. b.

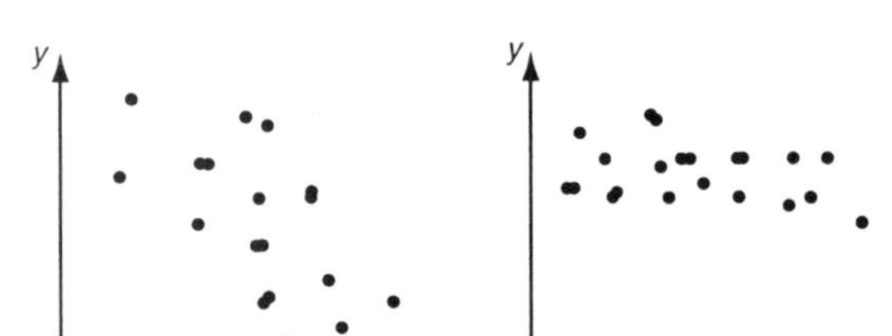

c. d.

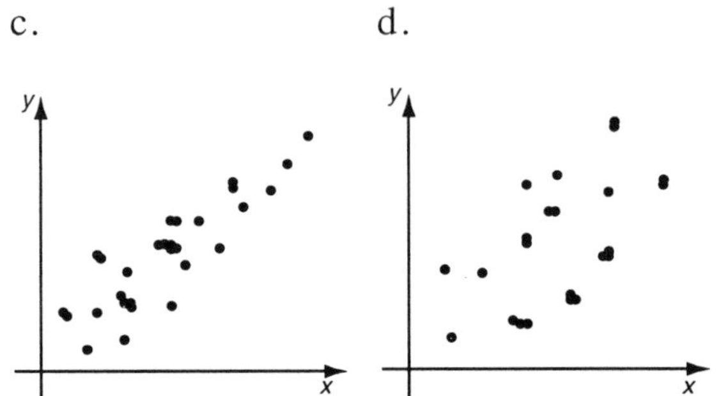

Graph c has the strongest positive linear association, and graph a has the strongest negative linear association.

- The graph below compares children's heights at age 16 with their heights at age 8.

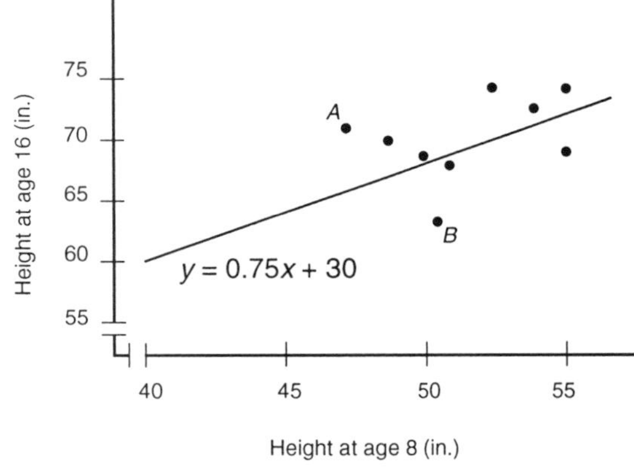

a. Estimate the residuals at points A and B.

b. Using the model $y = 0.75x + 30$, predict the height at age 16 of a child who is 52 inches tall at age 8.

a. A: ≈ 6.75; B: ≈ ⁻5.25 **b. 69 inches**

- Scientists have monitored the number of chirps per minute made by crickets and the corresponding temperature.

Number of chirps per minute	136	165	98	110	150	210	84	158	221	178
Temperature in degrees Fahrenheit	72	84	68	75	80	94	60	75	92	89

a. Make a scatter plot of the data (chirps, temperature). Find the equation of the least-squares regression line and the correlation coefficient.

b. Graph the least-squares regression line and the scatter plot. What does r tell you about the relationship between the temperature and the frequency of chirps made by crickets? Explain completely.

c. How well does the line seem to summarize the points?

d. If a cricket chirps 90 times per minute, what is the predicted temperature?

e. What is the real-world meaning of the slope?

f. What is the real-world meaning of the y-intercept?

a. $y = 0.23x + 44.48$, $r = 0.94$

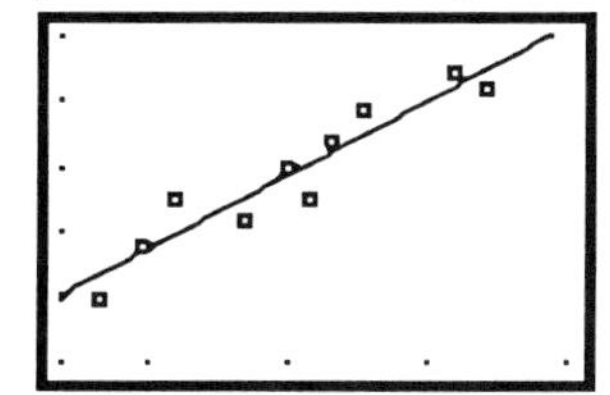

[70, 250, 50, 50, 100, 10]

b. The correlation coefficient r is fairly close to 1, so the fit is fairly good.

c. According to r, fairly well.

d. ≈ 65°

e. The change in the number of chirps per minute per degree change in temperature.

f. The temperature when there are zero chirps.

- The statistics for the rebounds and total points scored for the Detroit Pistons' 1988–1989 season are given in the following table.

Player	Rebounds	Total Points
Aguirre	386	1511
Thomas	273	1458
Dumars	172	1186
Johnson	255	1130
Laimbeer	776	1106
Rodman	772	735
Edwards	231	555
Mahorn	496	522
Salley	335	467
Long	77	372

a. Enter the data as (rebounds, total points). Find the equation of the least-squares regression line and the correlation coefficient.

b. Graph the least-squares regression line and the scatter plot. How does the picture reinforce the message given by the correlation coefficient? Explain completely.

a. $y = 0.12x + 860.01$, $r = 0.066$

b. The points are spread out, so the line is not close to them.

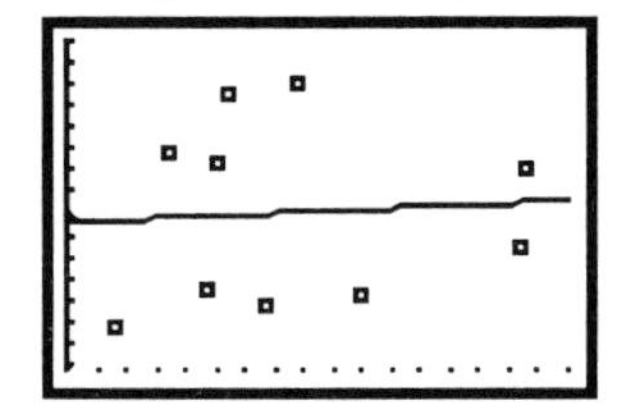

[0, 850, 50, 175, 1700, 100]

- A local pizzeria kept track of their yearly pizza sales from 1983 to 1987. The numbers are shown in the table below.

Year	1983	1984	1985	1986	1987
Pizzas	750	780	795	860	870

This data can represented by the equation $y = 32x - 62709$.

a. Draw a graph of the information in the table above and include the graph of the equation.

b. What is the real-world meaning of the slope?

c. Based on this model, how many pizzas would you expect to be sold in 1994?

d. Does the equation seem to be a realistic model of this situation? Explain completely.

e. What is the sum of the residuals for this data?

a.

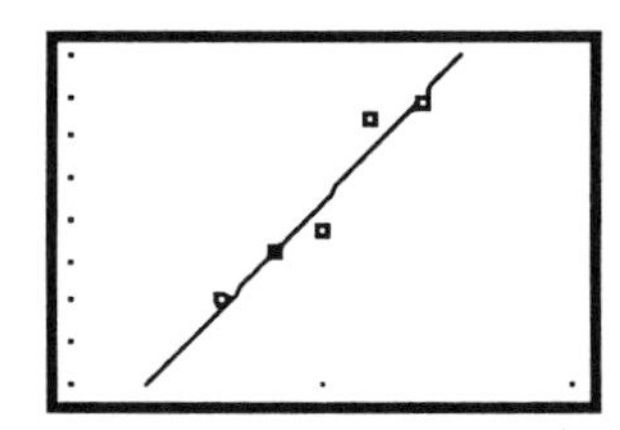

[1980, 1990, 5, 700, 900, 25]

b. Increase in pizzas per year.

c. $\approx$ **1099**

d. The equation will show a continual increase year after year, but we would actually expect there to be some leveling off.

e. 0

- Which three points would you use to find the median-median line for the data given below?

x	4.0	5.2	5.8	6.5	7.2	7.8	8.3	8.9	9.7	10.1	11.2	12.9	12.5	13.1
y	23	28	29	35	35	40	42	50	47	52	60	58	62	64

(5.8, 29), (8.6, 44.5), and (12.9, 60)

- Write the equation of the line parallel to the graph of $y = 0.35x - 5.7$ and passing through the point (19.7, 0.3).

  $y = 0.35x - 6.595$

- Write the equation of the line that is one-third of the way from $y = {}^{-}5.2x + 43$ to $y = {}^{-}5.2x + 13$.

  $y = {}^{-}5.2x + 33$

- Write the equation of the line passing through the points (1, 500) and (7, 100). Is the point (5, 150) on the line? If it is, prove it. If it is not, find the residual for this point.

  $y = \frac{-200}{3}x + \frac{1700}{3}$. No, substitute the values for x and y and you get $\frac{700}{3} = 150$, which is not true. The residual at that point is $-83\frac{1}{3}$.

- Find the equation of the least-squares line for the data below.

Volts	5.00	7.50	10.00	12.50	15.00	17.50	20.00
Amps	2.35	3.53	4.69	5.87	7.15	8.23	9.40

  a. What is the sum of the squares of the residuals?

  b. What is the real-world meaning of the slope?

  c. Use the model (that is, the equation) to find the number of amps for a voltage of 27.50 volts.

  The equation of the least-squares line is $y = 0.4715714286x - 0.0060714286$.

  a. sum of the squares of the residuals = 38.92

  b. amps per volt **c. 12.96**

- On each graph below, sketch the best-fit line using the "by eye" criteria.

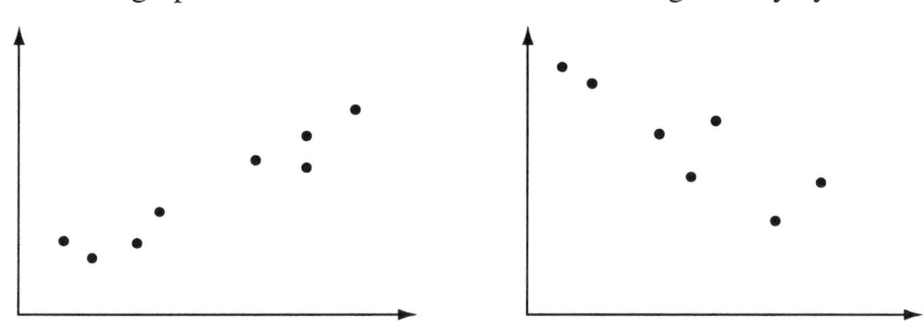

Answers will vary.

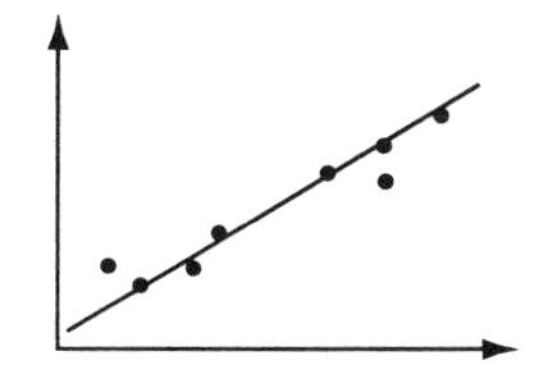

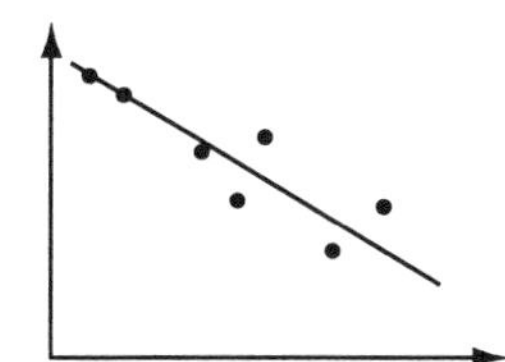

- Find the y-intercept of the line $y = 2.43(x - 17.4) - 8.11$.

  (0, -50.392)

- Find the equation of the line through the points (5.28, −2.9) and (3.11, 4.7).

  $y = {}^{-}3.5023x + 15.5922$

- The following data, showing U.S. coal production in millions of tons from 1973 to 1982, has a best-fit line of $y = 29x - 1529$ using a reference year of 1900.

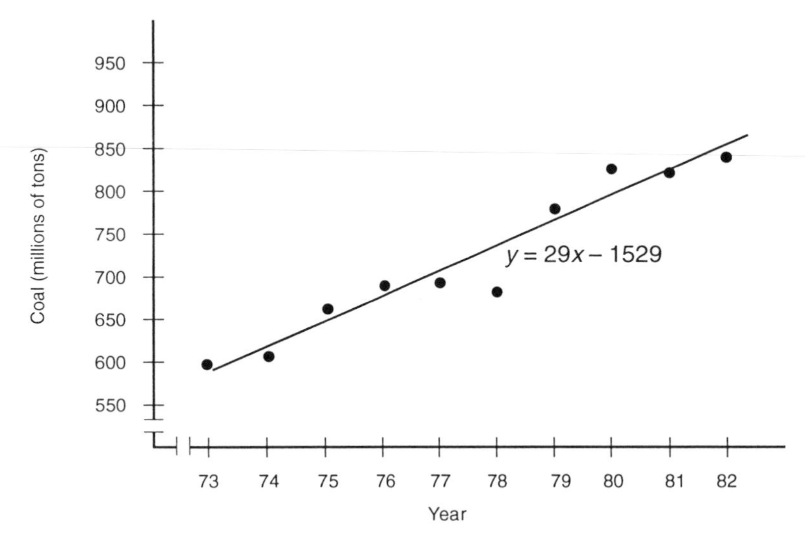

a. What is the real-world meaning of the slope?

b. What would you expect the coal production to be in 1984?

c. When would you expect the coal production to be 1000 million tons of coal?

a. Average number of millions of tons by which coal production increases per year

b. 907 million tons **c. In 1987**

- Suppose you wish to plot the relationship between the price of a pizza and its diameter. What is the independent variable? Justify your choice with at least one good reason.

Diameter is the independent variable.

Call a pizza place and find the prices and diameters for one variety of pizza (for example, cheese and pepperoni). Plot the data and find a best-fit line. Write a paragraph presenting this information. Be sure to discuss the slope and any intercepts. Make a conclusion after you have completed your study.

Answers will vary.

- Find the equation of the line shown at right.

$y = \frac{4}{3}x - 2$

- What is the slope of the line $4.7x + 3.2y = 12.9$?

$^{-}1.46875$

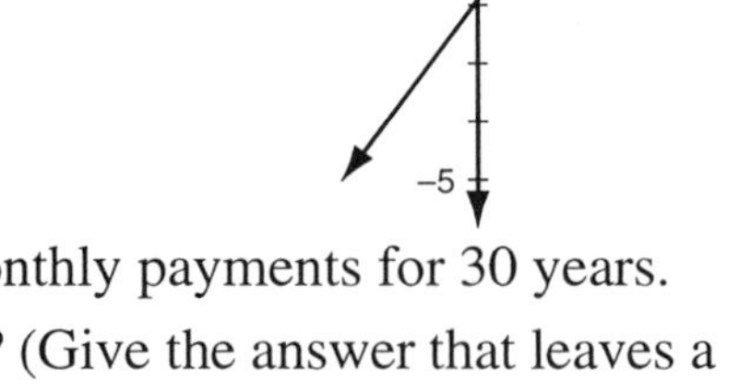

- Suppose your older sister is about to buy a condo and will have to borrow $50,000 on a 10.6% mortgage. She has two options: (1) make monthly payments for 20 years or (2) make monthly payments for 30 years.

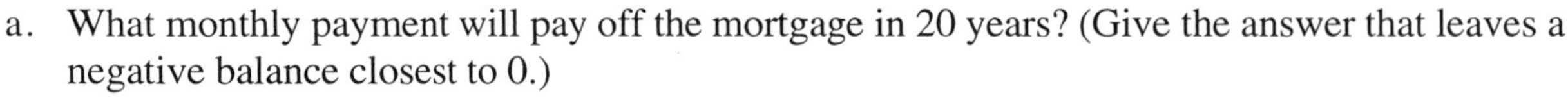

a. What monthly payment will pay off the mortgage in 20 years? (Give the answer that leaves a negative balance closest to 0.)

b. What monthly payment will pay off the mortgage in 30 years? (Give the answer that leaves a negative balance closest to 0.)

c. What is the difference between the mortgage payments in parts a and b?

d. What is the difference between the total cost of the loans in parts a and b?

e. What is your financial advice for her?

a. \$502.55 **b. \$461.11** **c. \$41.44 per month** **d. \$45,387.60**

e. If she can afford the extra \$41.44 each month, pay it. That extra money paid each month for 20 years totals to \$9,945.60, much less than the difference in the total cost of the loans.

• Consider the graph at the right.

a. Write the equation of this line in $y = mx + b$ form.

b. Name the slope.

c. Name the y-intercept.

d. Find the value of y when $x = {}^-1$.

e. Find the value of x when $y = 0$.

(−5.2, 3.18)
(1.4, −4.41)

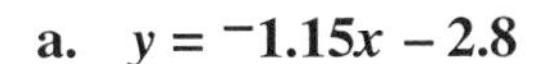

a. $y = {}^-1.15x - 2.8$ **b.** ${}^-1.15$

c. ${}^-2.8$ **d.** ${}^-1.65$

e. $\approx {}^-2.43478$

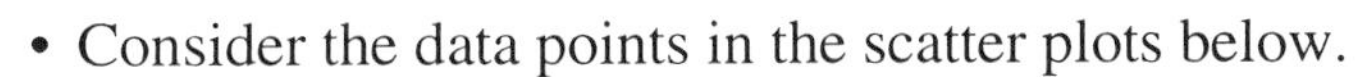

• Consider the data points in the scatter plots below.

a. Draw your best-fit line for each set of data pictured below.

b. Draw a circle around each group of points that you would use for the median-median procedure.

c. Draw an X to indicate the representative point for each of the groups in the median-median procedure.

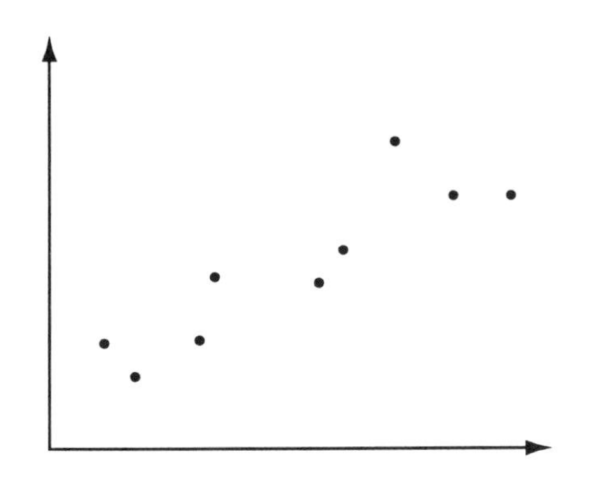

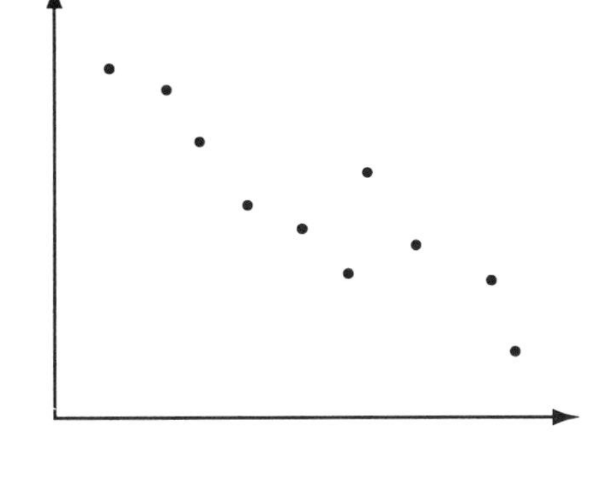

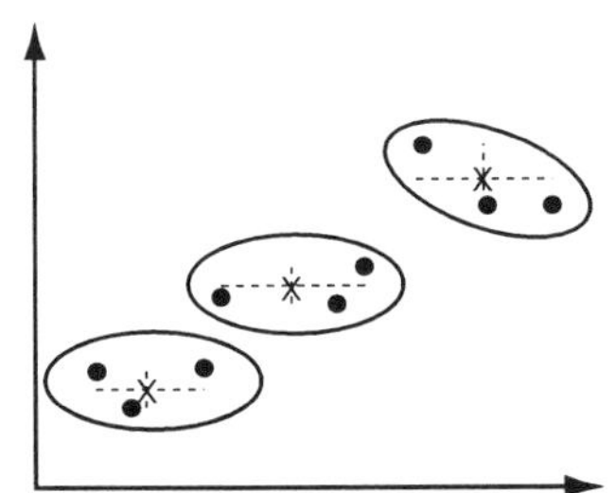

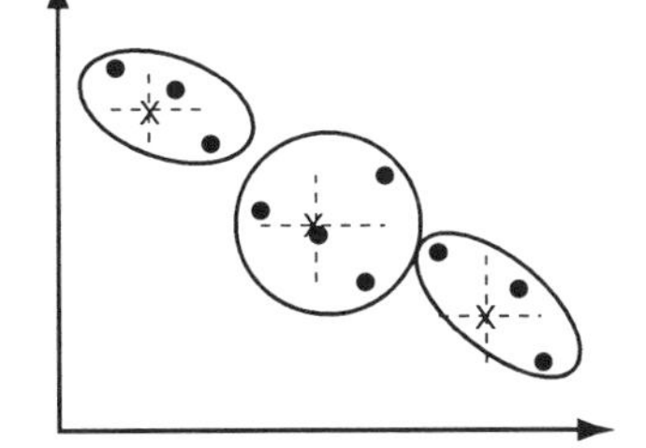

- Suppose these points are representative points for three groups in the median-median procedure.

  Find the equation for the median-median line.

  $y = \frac{32}{73}x + 9.258$

(17.7, 16.2)
(8, 14.4)
(3.1, 9.8)

- A boy measured the depth of the water in a bathtub at one-minute intervals after the faucet was turned on. His data are shown below.

Time (min)	Depth (cm)
1	3
2	6
3	7
4	7
5	8
6	12
7	13
8	18
9	18

Time (min)	Depth (cm)
10	19
11	25
12	23
13	27
14	31
15	31
16	36
17	35
18	37

a. Draw a scatter plot of the data and label the axes.

b. Draw a line of best fit by eye.

c. What is the equation of this line?

d. What is the real-world meaning of the slope?

e. Use the model to predict the height of water at 25 minutes.

f. Use the model to predict when the height is 60 centimeters.

g. Find the median x and median y of each of the three groups as if you were going to find the equation of the median-median line.

a.

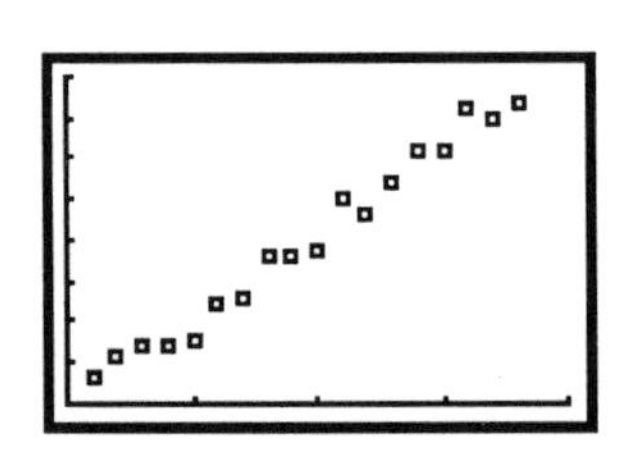

[0, 20, 5, 0, 40, 5]

b. Answers will vary. The graph shows the median-median line.

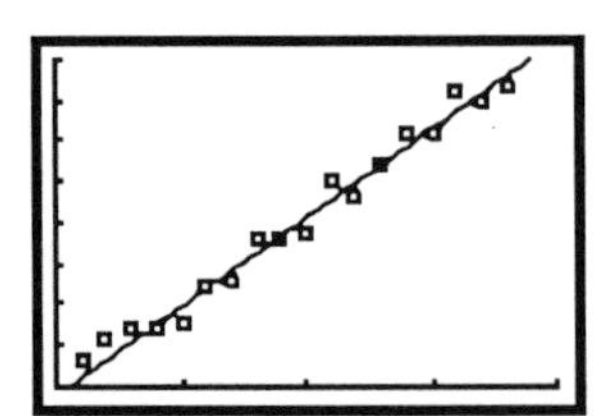

c. **Answers will vary. The equation of the median-median line is $y \approx 2.17x - 1.08$.**

d. **How much the depth is increasing per minute.**

e. **≈ 53.08 centimeters** f. **≈ 28.1 minute** g. **(3.5, 7), (9.5, 18.5), (15.5, 33)**

- How would you divide a set of 31 elements into three groups for the median-median line procedure?

  10–11–10

- You are looking at a set of data. The top line ($y = 10.4x + 121.3$) contains the representative points of the first and third groups.

  The lower line ($y = 10.4(x - 3.4) + 130$) is the parallel line through the middle representative point.

  a. What is the equation of the median-median line?

  b. Sketch a graph of the median-median line.

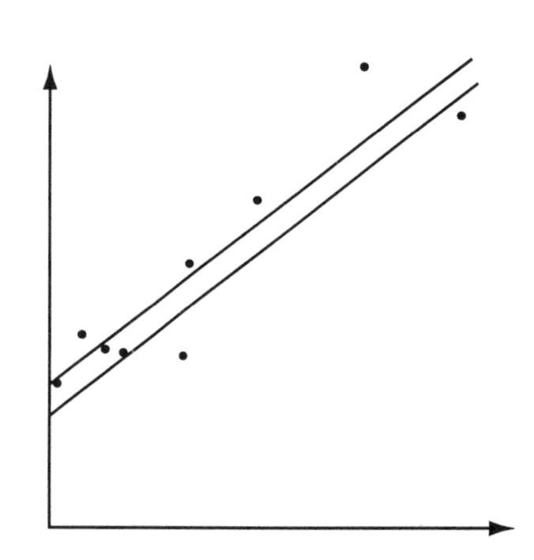

The equation of the median-median line is $y = 10.4x + 112.41$

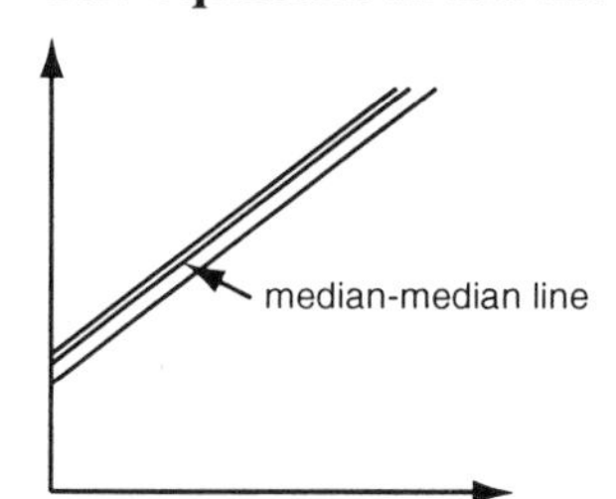

- For each graph below, draw your best-fit line and draw the segments that represent the errors involved between the line and the actual data points.

a.

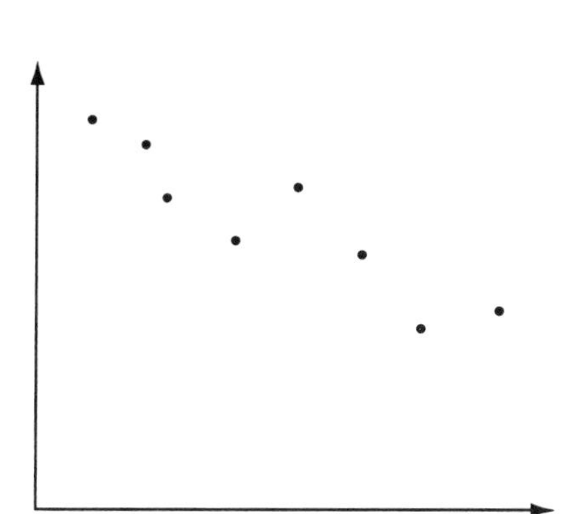

b.

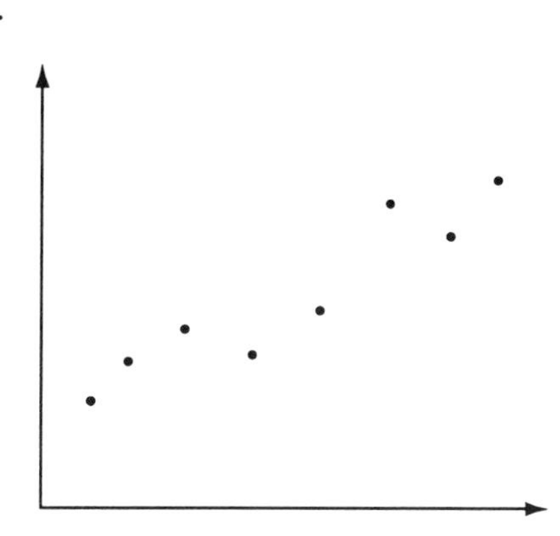

a.

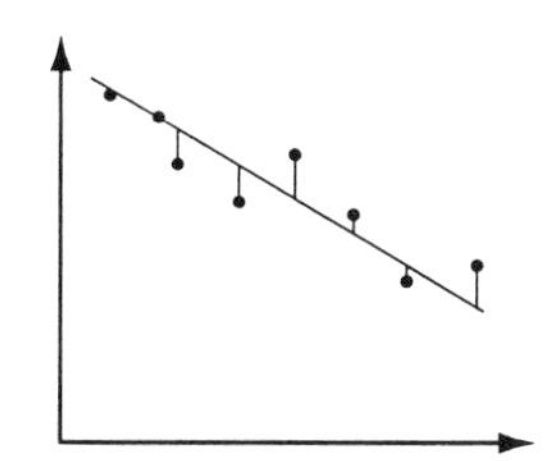

b.

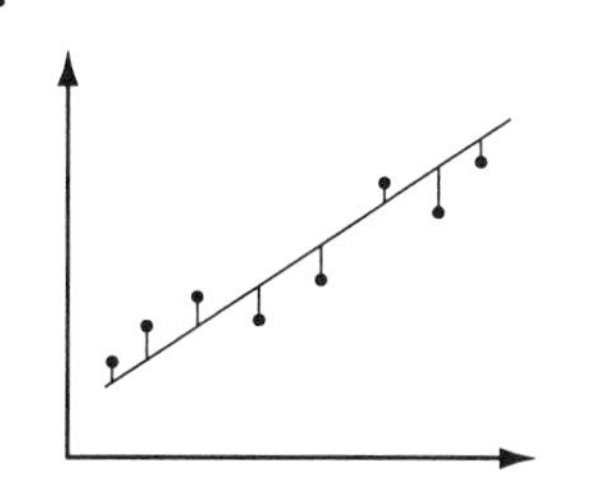

- Consider the graph at the right.
  a. Write the equation of the line through the two points.
  b. Find the residual for the point that doesn't lie on the line.

  a. $y = {}^{-}1.6x + 4.7$ **b. 0.82**

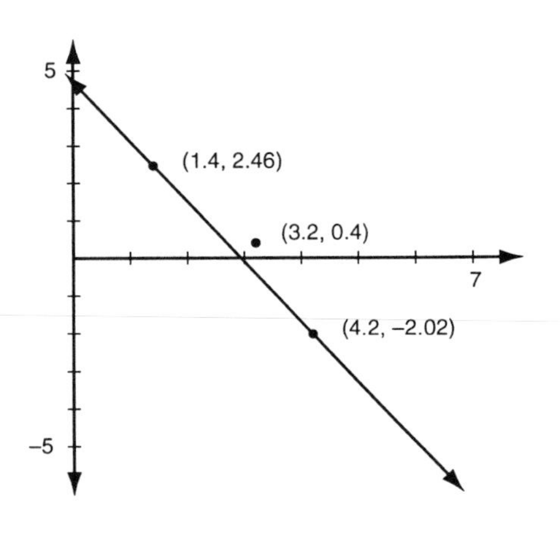

- When given a set of data, how do you determine which variable will be represented by the *x*-value and which will be represented by the *y*-value? Explain your answer completely.

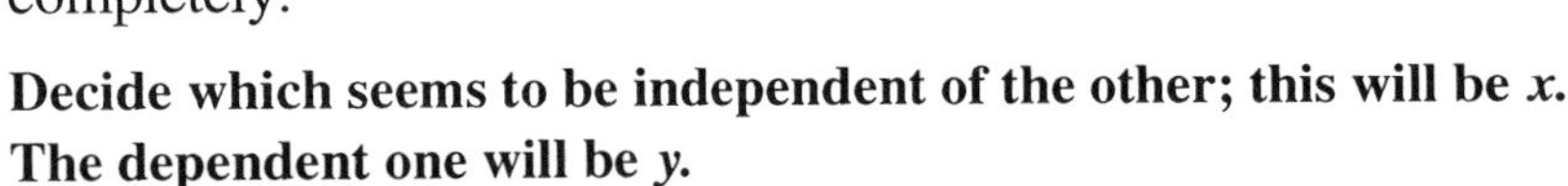

Decide which seems to be independent of the other; this will be *x*. The dependent one will be *y*.

- How do you determine if a line is the best fit for a set of data? Be specific.

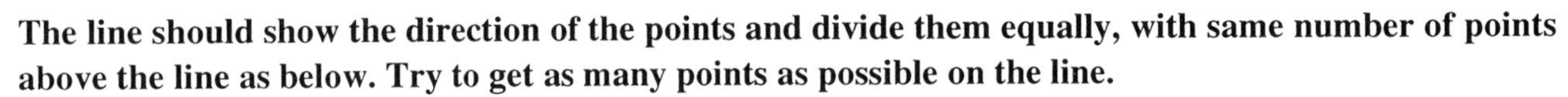

The line should show the direction of the points and divide them equally, with same number of points above the line as below. Try to get as many points as possible on the line.

- The data below represents the reaction time of a group of ten people who were given different dosages of a drug. Determine the three points you would use to find the median-median line. (Do not find the equation, just the points.)

Dosage (mg)	Reaction time (sec)
85	0.5
89	0.6
90	0.2
95	1.2
95	1.6
103	0.6
107	1.0
110	1.8
111	1.0
115	1.5

(89, 0.5), (99, 1.0), (111, 1.5)

- Consider a set of data collected on the weight, in pounds, of a loaded suitcase and the volume, in cubic inches, of that suitcase.
  a. Which variable will be represented by the *x*-value and which will be represented by the *y*-value? Justify your answer.
  b. What are the units of the slope? Explain how you know that these are the correct units.
  c. Where would you expect the *y*-intercept to be? Why?

  a. *x* is volume, *y* is weight since weight depends on volume.

  b. Pounds per cubic inch

  c. At (0, 0) because 0 volume would weigh 0 pounds.

- Consider the set of data graphed at right.
  a. Give at least three arguments that support the line drawn to be a good model for the data.
  b. Give at least two suggestions as to how you could improve the model.

  a. Answers will vary. It does show direction.

  b. Answers will vary. Move the line down because there are too many points below the line.

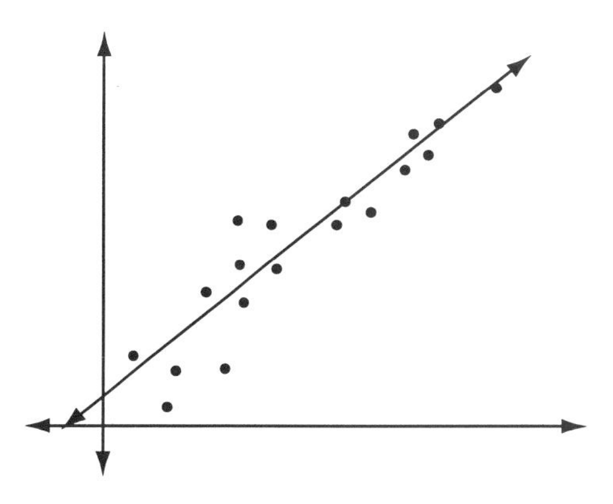

Group Problems

The following problem was submitted by Sal Quezada and Bob Drake, Los Angeles Unified School District.

- *Modeling Exponential Growth*

  Field biologist Mayra Verduzco wishes to introduce a red fox population into a wild animal refuge. She has collected a total of ten red foxes. She needs to predict how many foxes there will be in 40 years. She also wants to know in what year (if ever) there will be 400 foxes if she releases them in 1994. You will help her solve these problems by doing the following: Start with 10 dice. Each die represents a fox and each throw represents one year. A roll of a 3 or a 6 represents the birth of a baby fox, so each time one of these numbers comes up, add a die to the population. If a 1 comes up, a death has occurred, so remove one die from the population. Hence, you are modeling a situation in which the birth rate is twice the death rate. (Can you explain that?) Continue the above process until the population reaches or exceeds 300 foxes.

  Record the data in a chart similar to the one below.

Trial number (year)	Number of births	Number of deaths	Number of dice
0	none	none	10
1			
2			
3			
. . .			

  a. Enter the data into your graphing calculator and make a scatter plot. Be careful to set your range according to the data. Find the regression equation that best fits the data.
  b. Using the equation as your mathematical model, what do you predict the fox population to be after 40 years? Justify the reasonableness of your response.

  a. and b. Answers will vary.

Chapter 5: Functions

Journal Questions

- In Chapter 5, you learned about certain families of functions and their graphs. What do you think is the point of Chapter 5? If you have a graphing calculator, do you need to study the topics and ideas of this chapter? Be clear and justify your response.

  Answers will vary.

- Find three problems in the chapter that you feel are representative of the chapter. Write out the problem and the solution. For each problem, explain why you feel it is representative of the chapter. Please use complete, coherent sentences.

  Answers will vary.

- So far this year you have considered six different levels of understanding: knowledge, comprehension/understanding, application, analysis, synthesis, and appreciation/evaluation.

  Add any new ideas and concepts from this chapter to the list you started in the last chapter. Fill in your topics in the table at the right, and rate your level of understanding. Be prepared to support your rating by explaining or demonstrating that you are at each level.

Topic	knowledge	comprehension/ understanding	application	analysis	synthesis	appreciation/ evaluation

  Answers will vary.

- What ideas or topics were introduced in this chapter that you feel you do not quite understand yet or for which you do not see the purpose? Give examples.

  Answers will vary.

- Find a problem that you cannot solve. Write out the problem and as much of the solution as you can. Then, clearly explain what it is that is keeping you from solving the problem. Be as specific and clear as you can.

  Answers will vary.

- What graphing calculator skills have you mastered during this chapter? Explain thoroughly and use examples. What graphing calculator skills have you not yet mastered? Provide an example for which you need a calculator skill that you have not yet mastered.

  Answers will vary.

- As you get deeper and deeper into the mathematics of this course, do you find that you are relying more or less on your group? Explain completely by citing examples. Is this a good thing or a bad thing? Explain.

  Answers will vary.

- Have you discovered any new advantages of working in groups in your mathematics class? New disadvantages? Explain these completely.

  Answers will vary.

Open-ended Problems

- You have studied several families of functions (parabolas, square roots, absolute value, semicircles) and transformations of these functions. Explain the similarities and differences of the families and their transformations.

  Answers will vary.

- Create your own problem that covers the material you have studied so far and that you think would make a good assessment question. Write out the complete solution to your problem and explain why you believe it to be a good problem. *Note:* Please make sure that it is a problem or question and not just an explanation or description.

  Answers will vary.

- Due to his recent bout with mononucleosis, your friend is a whole month behind in his course work in mathematics. Not only is he behind, but he also does not have a graphing calculator. He is becoming very frustrated trying to graph function after function by setting up tables, plugging in values, and plotting all the points. Help your friend by explaining, in great detail, how he can simplify his work when graphing an equation of the form $y = \pm(x + h)^2 + k$.

  Answers will vary, but should include that the exponent 2 indicates a parabola, h indicates the number of units to move the parabola right or left, the value of k tells us how far to move it up or down, and the $\pm$ tells us the direction the parabola opens (up or down).

- Remember your friend who is behind? Well, he has another problem. He is given the graph shown at right and told to sketch the graph of $f(x) - 4$ and $f(x + 5)$ on the same set of axes. He complains to you that is impossible because he does not know the equation for $f(x)$, so there is no way to get the graph. Explain to your friend, in detail, how to make sketches of $f(x) - 4$ and $f(x + 5)$. Then sketch both functions.

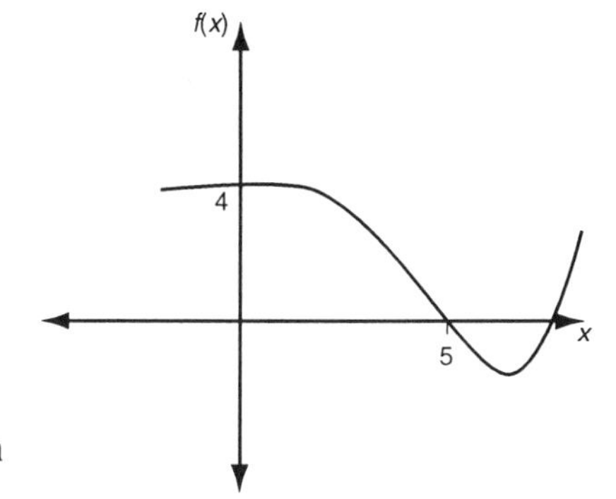

  Answers will vary, but should essentially say that the graph of $f(x) - 4$ is the original graph translated down 4 units, and the graph of $f(x + 5)$ is the original graph translated left 5 units.

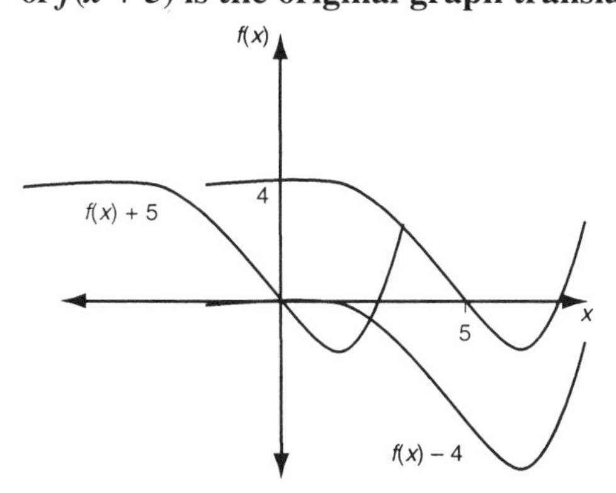

The next problem is adapted from the NCTM Addenda Series/Grades 9–12: Connecting Mathematics.

- You have looked at several families of functions in this chapter and studied how you can move a graph around by changing the equation. Now you will analyze some data, graph the data, then determine the family into which the graph fits. Once you have identified the family, write the equation representing the data.

  Consider what can happen if you roll two dice—a red die and a blue die—and add the number of spots on the pair of dice.

  a. What is the smallest sum you could possibly get?

  b. What is the largest sum you could possibly get?

  Fill in the table below showing the possible sums.

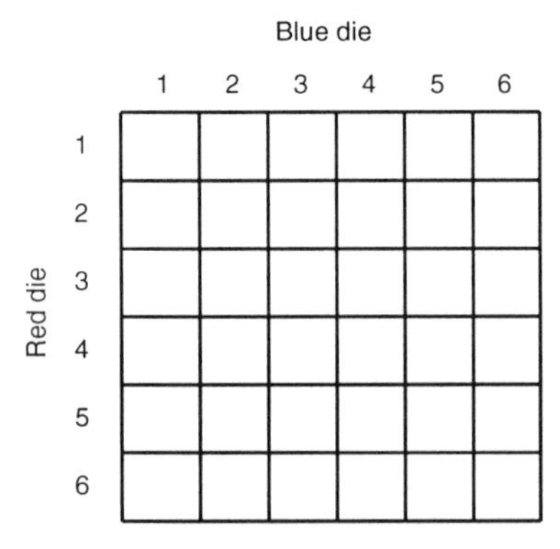

  A function is defined as follows: it is the relationship between the sum of the number of spots and the corresponding frequency of that sum. Thus, the sum of two (when a one shows up on both dice) has a frequency of one (it shows up only once in the table).

  c. What is the independent variable? The dependent variable? Graph the data on appropriately labeled axes.

  d. Into what function family does this data appear to belong? Justify your answer.

  e. Write an equation that models this data. Does the equation model the data perfectly? Explain.

  a. 2 **b. 12**

  c. Independent: the sum; dependent: frequency

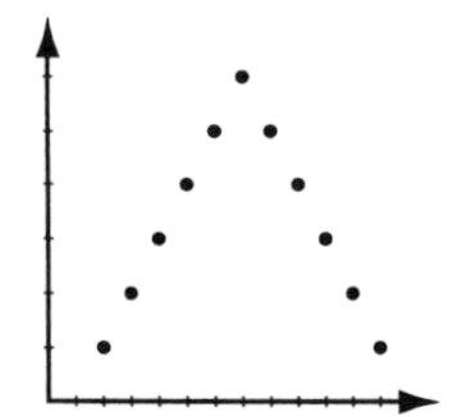

  d. Absolute value

  e. $y = {}^{-}|x - 7| + 6$ **for** $2 \le x \le 12$**. It doesn't fit perfectly unless you restrict the domain to integers within 2 and 12.**

- Recently, a scientist was collecting data as to how far she can see (in miles) on the earth's surface at different heights (in feet). She gathered these three data points when her ladder was toppled over by a thundering herd of turtles.

Height on ladder	1	10	25
Distance viewed	1.2	3.8	6

Unfortunately, she was too traumatized to continue her research. Using her data points, construct a graph with appropriately labeled axes. Give an argument as to which family of functions this data belongs. Come up with an equation to model this data. Is your equation perfect or does it have flaws? Explain.

$\mathbf{y = 1.2\sqrt{x}}$ **works fairly well.**

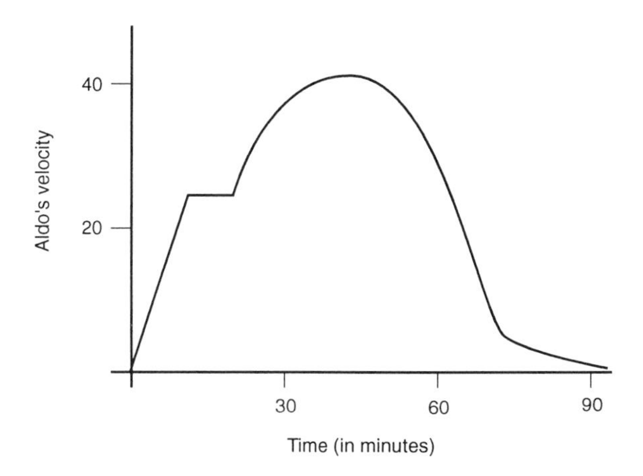

- Make up a story to fit the graph shown at right.

  Answers will vary.

Projects

In many of the projects of the last two chapters, we had students collect actual data. It might be appropriate, then, to pull that data, define appropriate independent and dependent variables, graph the data, determine the family to which the graph belongs, and try to write the equation modeling that data. The first project is asking students to do just this.

- For this project, you will need to come up with a relationship for which you can easily gather data; for instance, you might study the relationship between the time it takes a ball to reach the ground and the height from which it is dropped. Clearly state the relationship. Identify the independent variable and the dependent variable.

  a. Carefully collect the data.

  b. Graph the data. To what family does the graph appear to belong?

  c. Find an equation that models the data. Is the equation perfect? Use your equation to make a prediction. What are the flaws of your equation? Be clear.

  Answers will vary.

- Let an ice cube melt slowly at room temperature. Periodically, weigh the ice cube. Plot the weight versus the time. In what family does the graph of the data belong? Find an equation that models the data. How accurate is your equation? What are the flaws of the equation? Use your equation to make a prediction.

  Answers will vary.

Skill Questions: Appropriate for Quizzes or Tests

Any of Problems 4 through 20 in Problem Set 5.1 can be used to assess students' skills. Many of the problems in Problem Set 5.8 can be used as well.

- Solve the linear equation $5x + 9y = 45$ for y and determine the slope, y-intercept, and x-intercept.

  $\mathbf{y = \frac{^{-}5}{9}x + 5,\ m = \frac{^{-}5}{9}}$**, y-intercept is (0, 5), x-intercept (9, 0).**

- For each of the following, sketch the graph of the relationship. Label the axes clearly and appropriately.
  a. The time since a free throw has been released from the fouled player's hands, and the height of the basketball.
  b. The time since you put $100 in a savings account collecting simple interest, and the account balance.
  c. The temperature of coffee in a coffee cup as it sits on your desk over a period of time.
  d. The time since a baseball leaves the pitcher's hand, and the height of the baseball.
  e. The amount of writing on the blackboard during this class hour.

a.

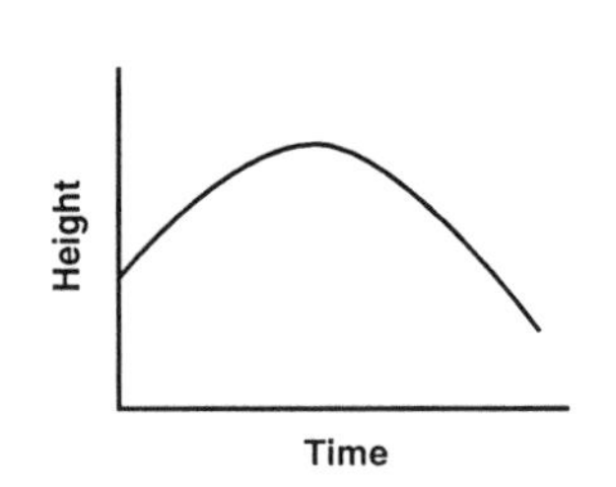

b.

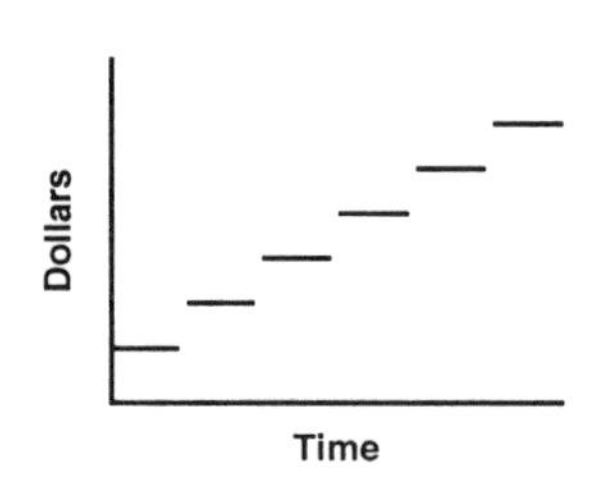

c.

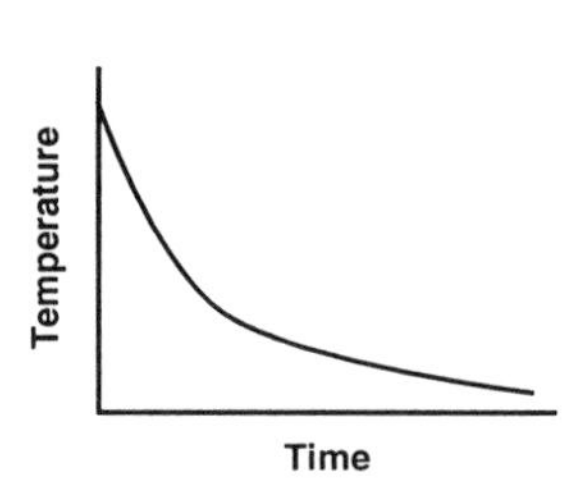

d.

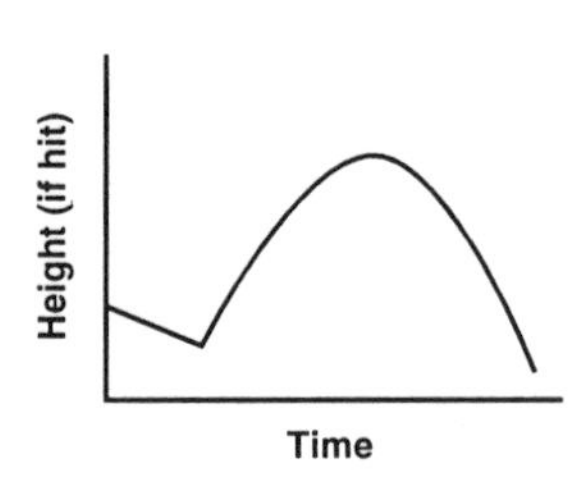

e.

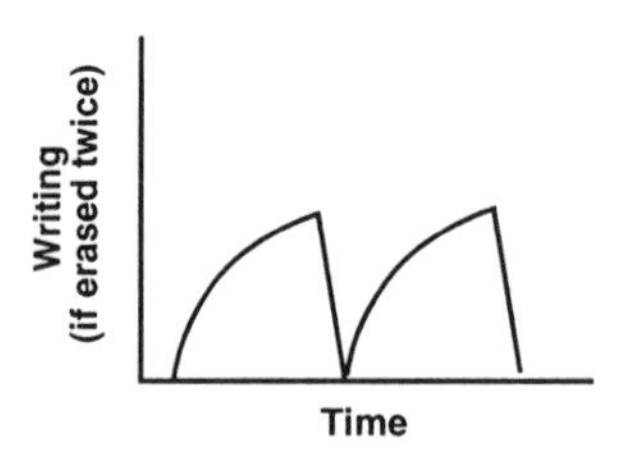

- Each graph at the right is a transformation of the function $y = |x|$. Determine the equation of each graph.

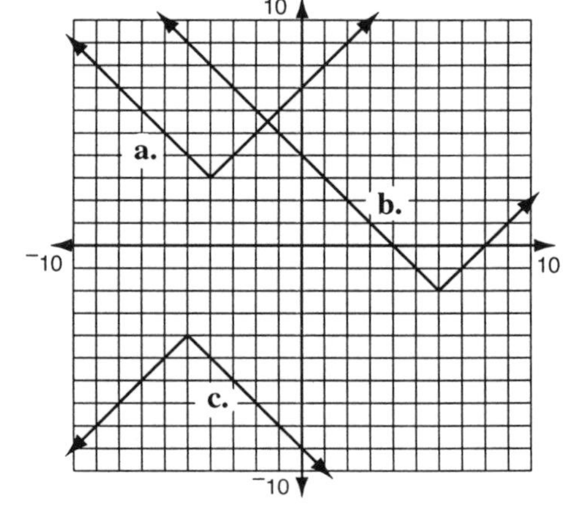

a. $y = |x + 4| + 3$ **b.** $y = |x - 6| - 2$

c. $y = ^{-}|x + 5| - 4$

- Consider the function $y = \sqrt{x}$.
  a. Make a sketch of this graph.
  b. What happens to the graph if x is replaced by $(x + 4)$?
  c. What happens to the graph if x is replaced by $(x - 4)$?
  d. What happens to the graph if y is replaced by $(y - 4)$?
  e. What happens to the graph if y is replaced by $(y + 4)$?

a.

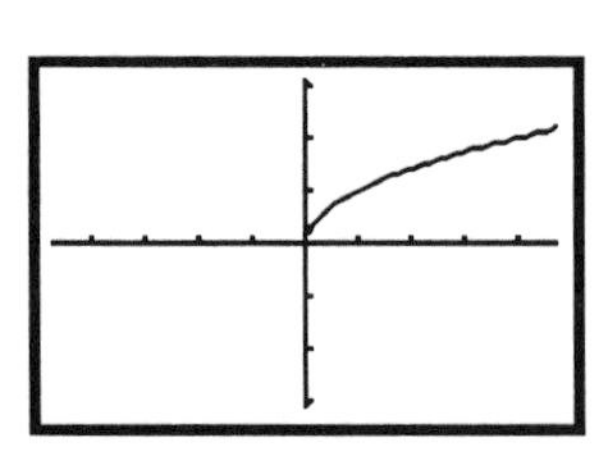

[⁻4.7, 4.7, 1, ⁻3.2, 3.2, 1]

b. moves left 4 units **c. moves right 4 units**

d. moves up 4 units **e. moves down 4 units**

- Describe as completely as possible what happens to the graph of $y = x^2$ if the equation is changed to $y = {}^{-}2(x + 5)^2 + 3$.

  Opens downward, skinnier, moves left 5 units and up 3 units.

- Find the equation of the line perpendicular to the graph of $y = \frac{3}{4}x - 2$ and passing through the point $(4, {}^{-}6)$.

  $\mathbf{y = \frac{-4}{3}x - \frac{2}{3}}$

- Each curve graphed at the right is a transformation of the graph of the unit semicircle $y = \sqrt{1 - x^2}$. Determine the equation of each graph. Check your answers with your calculator.

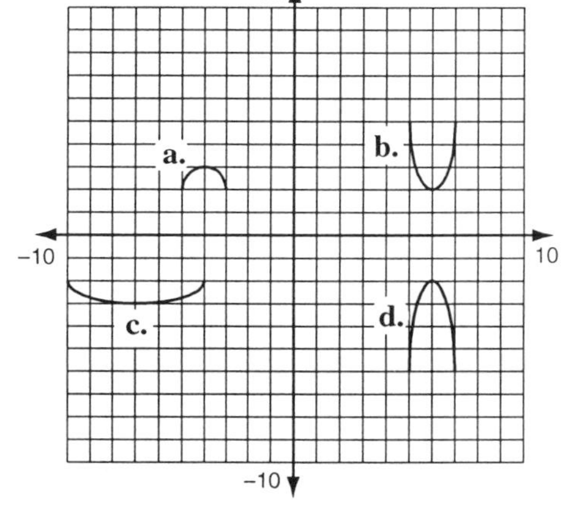

  a. 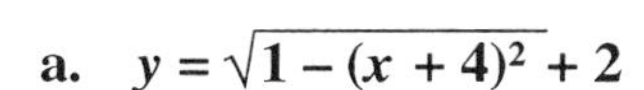 $\mathbf{y = \sqrt{1 - (x + 4)^2} + 2}$ **b.** $\mathbf{y = {}^{-}3\sqrt{1 - (x - 6)^2} + 5}$

  c. $\mathbf{y = -\sqrt{1 - \frac{(x + 7)^2}{9}} - 2}$ **d.** $\mathbf{y = 4\sqrt{1 - (x - 6)^2} - 6}$

- Graph each equation.
  a. $y = (x - 5)^2 + 7$
  b. $y = 3\sqrt{x + 2} - 1$
  c. $y = \left|\frac{x + 3}{2}\right| - 4$

a.

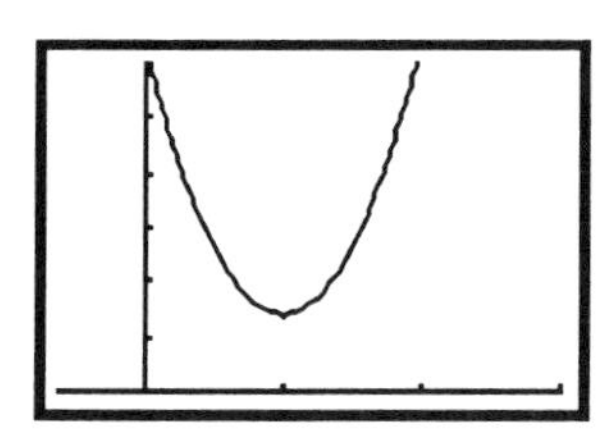

[⁻3, 15, 5, 0, 30, 5]

b.

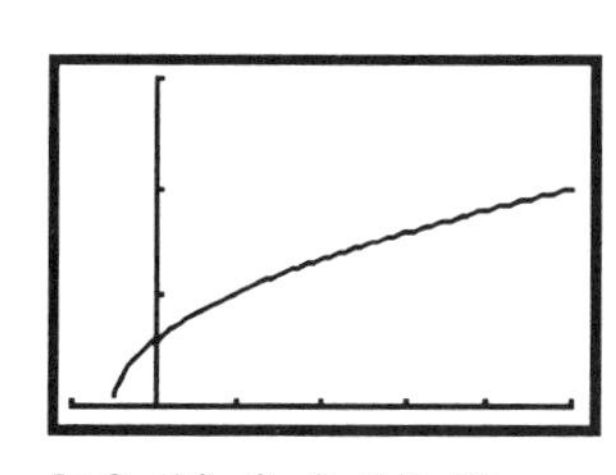

[⁻2, 10, 2, 0, 15, 5]

c.

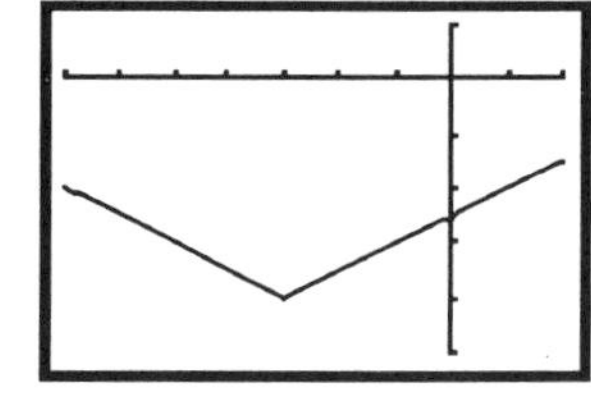

[⁻7, 2, 1, ⁻5, 1, 1]

- Write the equation that produces each graph shown at right. Use your calculator to check your equations.

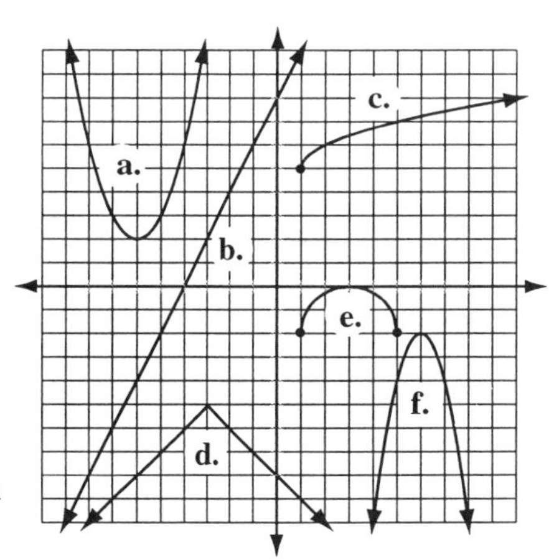

  a. $\mathbf{y = (x + 6)^2 + 2}$ **b.** $\mathbf{y = 2x + 8}$

  c. $\mathbf{y = \sqrt{x - 1} + 5}$ **d.** $\mathbf{y = {}^{-}|x + 3| - 5}$

  e. $\mathbf{y = \sqrt{4 - (x - 3)^2} - 2}$ **f.** $\mathbf{y = {}^{-}2(x - 6)^2 - 2}$

- Explain in your own words what happens to the graph of a function when x is replaced with $(x + h)$. Explain what happens when y is replaced with $(y + k)$.

  Answers will vary. Should be specific as to: $h > 0$ moves the graph left $|h|$ units, and $h < 0$ moves it right $|h|$ units; $k < 0$ moves the graph up $|k|$ units, and $k > 0$ moves it down $|k|$ units.

- Write the equation of the graph that is congruent to $y = {}^{-}2(x + 4)^2 - 6$ but is shifted four units left and three units down from this graph.

  $\mathbf{y = {}^{-}2(x + 8)^2 - 9}$

- If $f(x) = \sqrt{1 - x^2}$, graph $^{-}2 \cdot f(x) + 4$ and $f\left(\frac{x-2}{2}\right) - 2$.

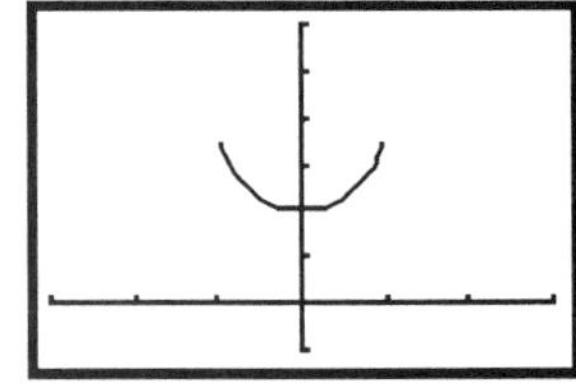

[⁻3, 3, 1, ⁻1, 6, 1]

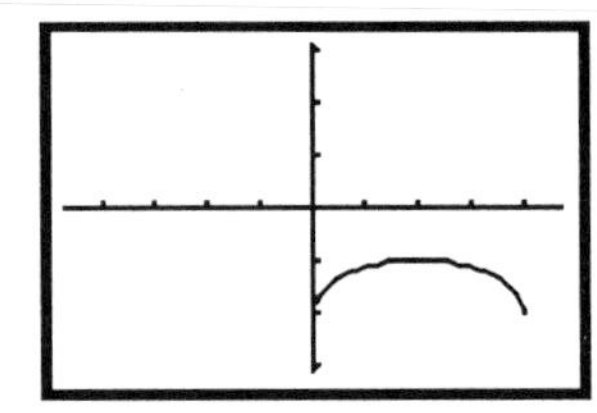

[⁻4.7, 4.7, 1, ⁻3.1, 3.1, 1

- The graph at the right is of a function simply known as $f(x)$. Sketch the graph of each function. 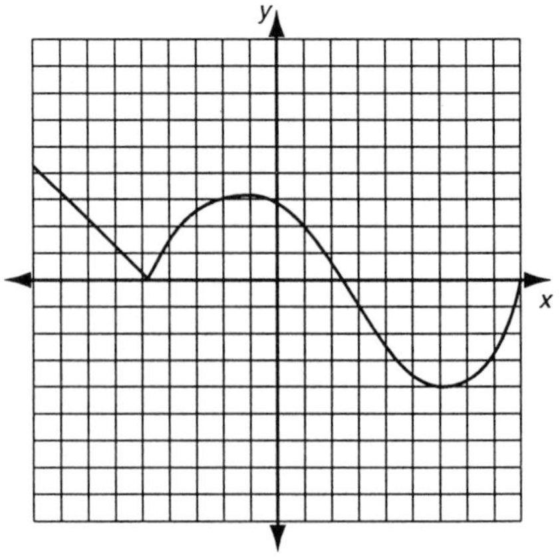
  - a. $f(x + 3) + 1$
  - b. $f({}^{-}x)$
  - c. $^{-}f(x) + 1$
  - d. $f(x) - 2$
  - e. $2f(x - 4) - 5$

  a. left 3, up 1 **b. reflected across the *y*-axis**

  c. reflected across the *x*-axis and up 1

  d. down 2 units

  e. right 4, down 5, and stretched vertically

- Rewrite without parentheses: $^{-}3(x + 2)^2 - 3$

  $\mathbf{{}^{-}3x^2 - 12x - 15}$

- Solve for *y*.
  - a. $(y + 1)^2 - 4 = x$
  - b. $\sqrt{y - 1} + 4 = x$

  a. $\mathbf{y = \pm\sqrt{x + 4} - 1}$ **b.** $\mathbf{y = (x - 4)^2 + 1,\ x \geq 4}$

- Suppose $f(x) = \frac{1}{x - 1}$, $g(x) = |2x - 3|$, and $h(x) = 2x^2 + 3x - 1$. Find each value or expression.
  - a. $f(g(3))$
  - b. $h(f({}^{-}4.6))$
  - c. $f(h(x))$

  a. 0.5 **b.** $\mathbf{\approx {}^{-}1.6790}$ **c.** $\mathbf{\frac{1}{2x^2 + 3x - 2}}$

- Suppose f is a linear function. What is the equation of $f(x)$ if $f(5) = 4$ and $f(3) = {}^{-}1$?

  $\mathbf{y = \frac{5}{2}x - \frac{17}{2}}$

- Graph these two functions on the same set of axes:

  $f(x) = 3x + 7$

  $g(x) = x^2 - 6$

  a. How many times do the two functions intersect?

  b. How many solutions does $3x + 7 = x^2 - 6$ have? Explain how you know.

  c. How many solutions does $\sqrt{x-3} + 2 = {}^{-}(x-4)^2 - 6$ have? Explain completely how you know.

  a. twice

  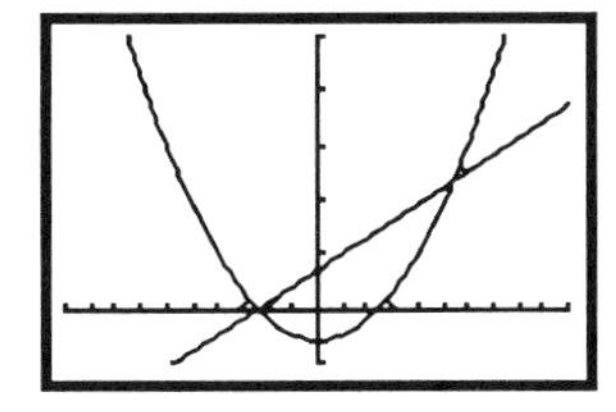

  [⁻10, 10, 1, ⁻10, 50, 10]

  b. Two, because the graphs of $y = 3x + 7$ and $y = x^2 - 6$ cross twice and each point of intersection is a solution to the equation.

  c. No solution; the graphs of the two functions do not intersect.

- Given $f(x) = \frac{-2}{3}x + 5$.

  a. What is the value of $f(6)$?

  b. What is the value of $f(0)$?

  c. If $f(x) = 0$, find x.

  d. If $f(x) = 1$, find x.

  e. Describe the location of the point $(2.4, f(2.4))$.

  a. 1 **b. 5** **c. 7.5** **d. 6**

  e. In the first quadrant, on the line $y = \frac{-2}{3}x + 5$. The coordinates of the point are (2.4, 3.4).

- a. Sketch the graph of $g(x) = \frac{-3}{5}x + 2$

  b. Write the equation of the line perpendicular to $g(x)$ at its y-intercept.

  c. Sketch the graph of this new equation.

  a. and c.

  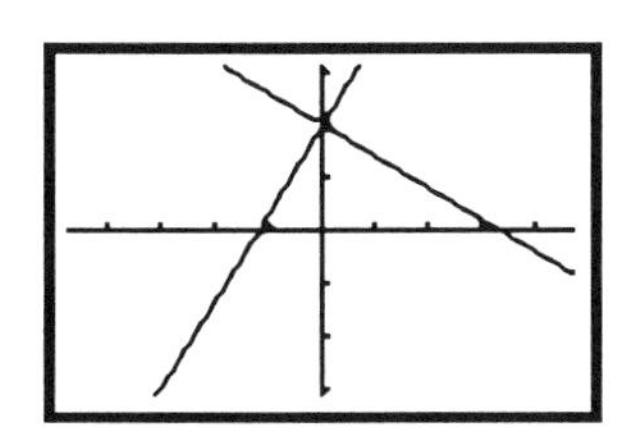

  [⁻4.7, 4.7, 1, ⁻3.1, 3.1, 1]

  b. $y = \frac{5}{3}x + 2$

- Describe the graph of $f(x+3)-2$ as related to the graph of some generic $f(x)$.

  Moved left 3 units and down 2 units from the graph of $f(x)$.

- Describe a situation that could produce the following graph. Give as much detail as possible.

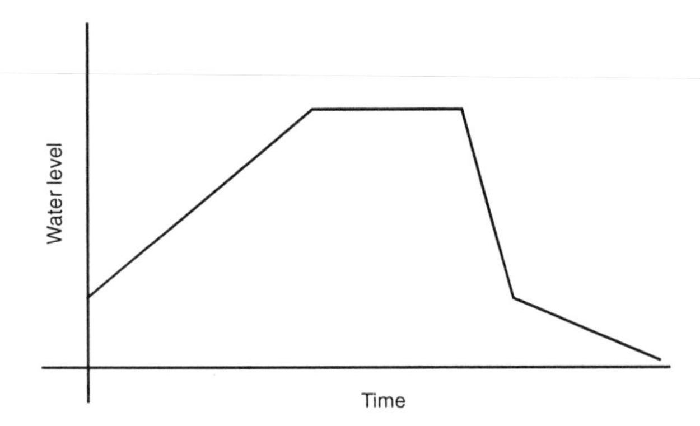

Answers will vary.

- Write an equation for each graph. (Each grid mark represents one unit.)

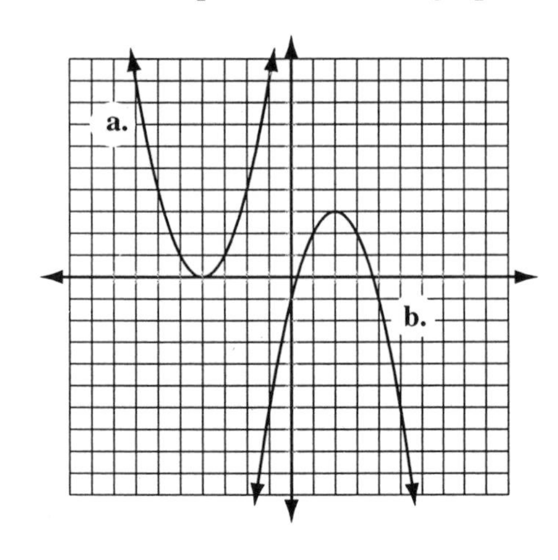

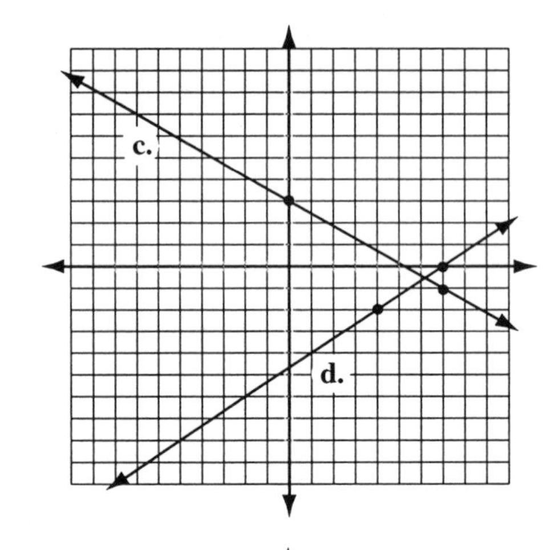

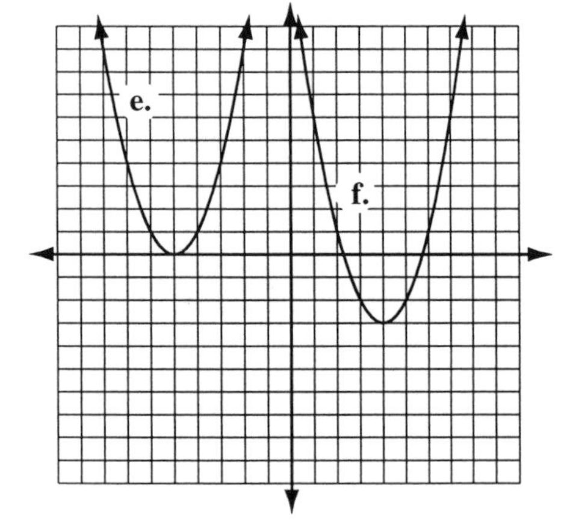

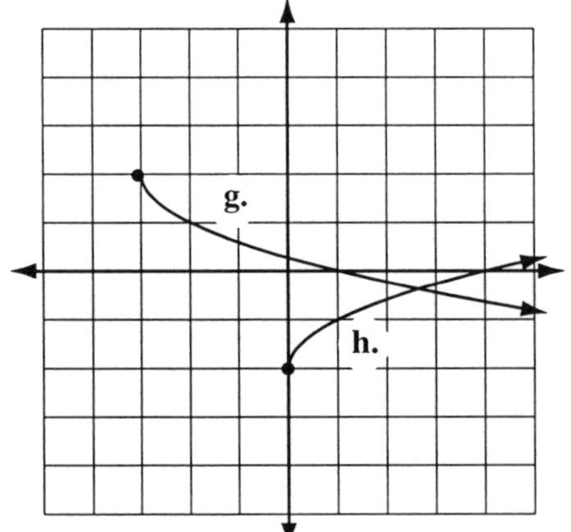

a. $y=(x+4)^2$ **b.** $y={}^{-}(x-2)^2+3$ **c.** $y=\frac{-4}{7}x+3$

d. $y=\frac{2}{3}x-\frac{14}{3}$ **e.** $y=(x+5)^2$ **f.** $y=(x-4)^2-3$

g. $y={}^{-}\sqrt{x+3}+2$ **h.** $y=\sqrt{x}-2$

- Graph the function, $y = \pm\sqrt{(x+2)} - 3$

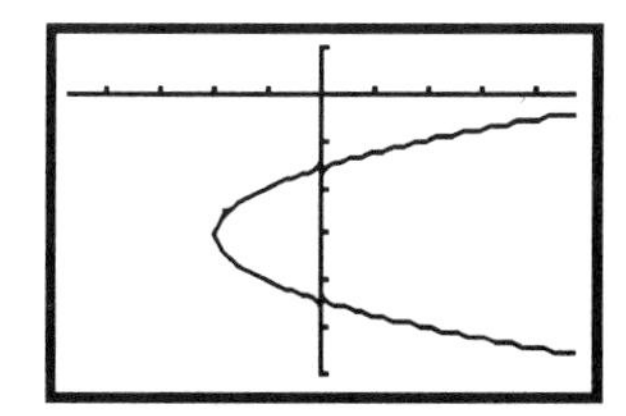

[⁻4.7, 4.7, 1, ⁻6, 1, 1]

- A cat and a dog are initially 3 feet apart. They slowly back away from and then begin to circle each other. Which of the following graphs (where time is on the x-axis, distance apart is on the y-axis) best depicts this situation? What is wrong with each of the other three graphs?

a. 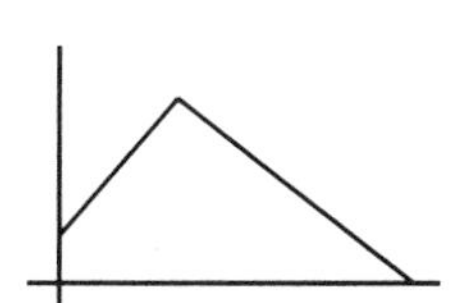
b. 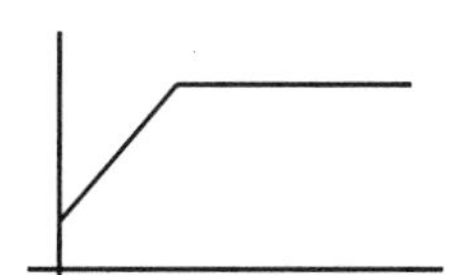
c. 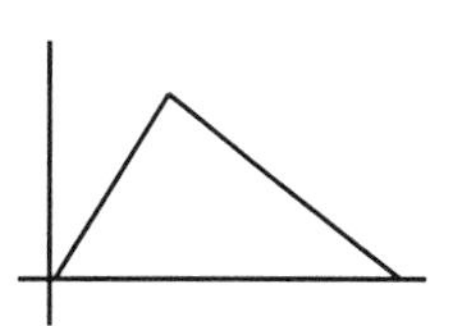
d. 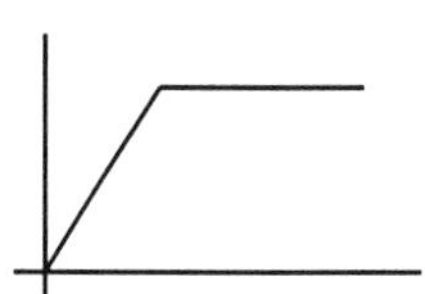

Graphs a and c are wrong because when the dog and cat are circling, they are a constant distance apart. Graph d is wrong because it depicts their starting positions as zero feet apart, whereas initially they are 3 feet apart.

- Give an interpretation, in words, of the following graph. Be specific and use complete sentences.

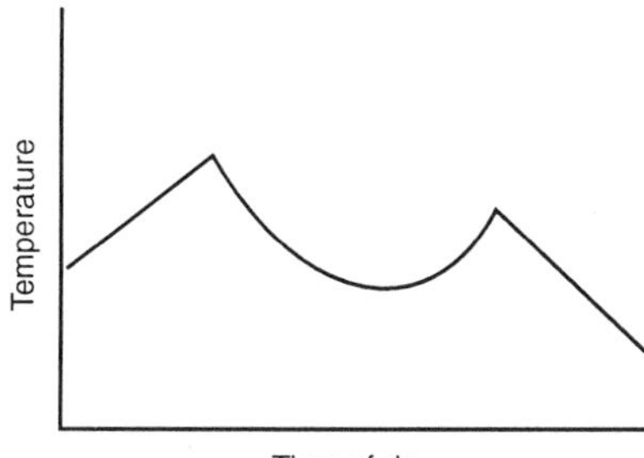

Answers will vary.

- Use function notation to write the equation for the graph that contains the points defined by the sequence $t(n) = \begin{cases} 5 & n = 1 \\ t(n-1) + 3 & n > 1 \end{cases}$

$\mathbf{f(x) = 3x + 2}$ **for** $\mathbf{x \geq 1}$

- Name the vertex of the parabola $f(x) = (x - 0.5)^2 - 0.25$.

(0.5, ⁻0.25)

- Consider the graph of $f(x)$ pictured at right.
  a. What is $f(3)$?
  b. What is x such that $f(x) = 3$?
  c. Is f a function? Explain.
  d. What is the domain of f?
  e. What is the range of f?

a. **2**   **b.** $x = {}^-3, \approx {}^-0.5, \approx 2$

c. **Yes**   **d.** ${}^-6 \le x \le 5$

e. ${}^-2 \le y \le 4$

- Use the figure to the right to perform the following steps.
  a. Write the equation of graph Y1.
  b. Write the equation of graph Y2.
  c. Shade the values of x on the x-axis where Y1 ≥ Y2.
  d. What values of x make Y1 ≥ Y2?

a. $Y1 = 2\,|x + 3| - 1$ **b.** $Y2 = 3$

c. $x \le 1$ **and** $x \ge 5$ **d.** **Same as part c**

- The graph below on the left shows the relationship between the depth of snow on the dome of the state capitol during a recent storm and the amount of time it had been snowing. The graph below on the right shows the relationship between the depth of the snow on the dome and the weight of this snow.

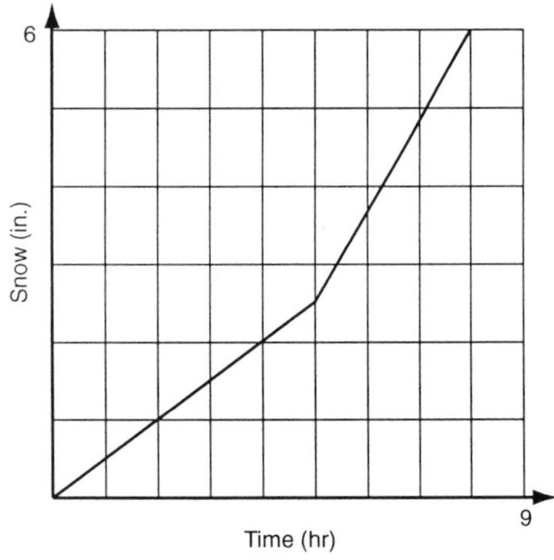

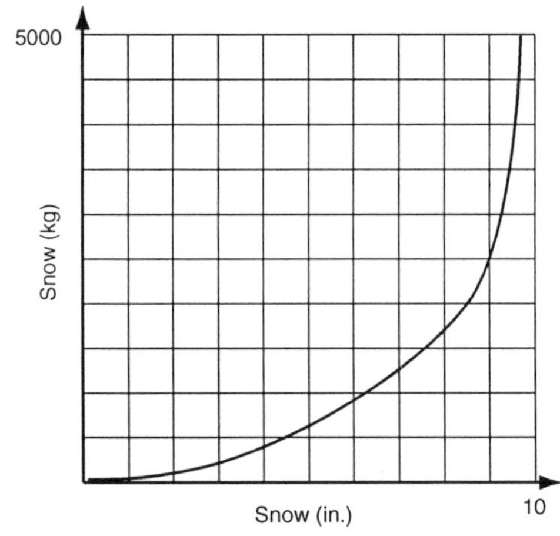

  a. What happened to cause the bend in the line of the left graph?
  b. After 5 hours, how deep was the snow on the dome?
  c. After 5 hours, how much did the snow on the dome weigh?
  d. How long did it take before the snow was 6 inches deep?
  e. How long did it take before the snow weighed one metric ton? (1 metric ton = 2000 kilograms)

a. **It started snowing harder.**   **b.** **2.5 inches**

c. **≈ 200 kg**   **d.** **8 hours**   **e.** **≈ 8.5 hours**

Group Problems

- You climb to the top of a 500-foot building to do an experiment. You are going to throw an object off the top and collect data to write an equation relating the time and distance the book has fallen.

  a. What do the dependent and independent variables represent? Which is which?

  b. Make a reasonable sketch of the graph of this relationship. What type of curve would best represent this relationship? Why?

  c. After one second, the book has fallen 16 feet. After three seconds, it has fallen 144 feet. After four seconds, it has fallen 256 feet. Use this information to write an equation representing this situation.

  d. Using this equation, when will the book hit the ground?

  a. Dependent: distance fallen; independent: time

  b. parabola **c.** $y = 16x^2$ **d.** $\approx$ **5.6 seconds**

- Suppose that your family is going to buy a new heat pump. One brand costs $2200 and $60 a month to operate. A more expensive brand costs $3300, but it is more efficient and costs only $45 a month to operate.

  Let x = number of months since you purchased the unit, $f(x)$ = total number of dollars spent in x months if you buy the cheaper unit, $g(x)$ = total number of dollars spent in x months if you buy the more expensive unit.

  a. Copy and complete the table below.

  b. Write a formula for $f(x)$ and $g(x)$.

  c. Find $f(100)$ and $g(100)$. What do these tell you about the relative costs of the two units?

  d. What is the "break-even" point—that is, when would the total costs be the same? Use this to advise your family as to which unit they should buy and why.

x months	**cost $f(x)$**	**cost $g(x)$**
0	2200	3300
1	2260	3345
2		
3		
4		
5		

  a. $f(x)$**: 2200, 2260, 2320, 2380, 2440, 2500,**
  $g(x)$**: 3300, 3345, 3390, 3435, 3480, 3525**

  b. $f(x) = 60x + 2200$; $g(x) = 45x + 3300$

  c. $f(100) = 8200$, $g(100) = 7800$. **Answers will vary, but students should mention that ultimately the $3,300 unit is cheaper.**

  d. At 73.3 months, more than 6 years. Answers will vary.

Chapter 6: Parametric Equations and Trigonometry

Journal Questions

- In Chapter 6, you are introduced to parametric equations and trigonometric functions. What do you think is the point of Chapter 6? Be clear and justify your response.

  Answers will vary.

- Why would somebody want to know about parametric equations? Be clear. Use complete sentences.

  Answers will vary.

- Find three problems in the chapter that you feel are representative of the chapter. Write out the problem and the solution. For each problem, explain why you feel it is representative of the chapter. Please use complete, coherent sentences.

- So far this year, we asked you to consider six different levels of understanding: knowledge, comprehension/understanding, application, analysis, synthesis, and appreciation/evaluation.

  Add any new ideas and concepts from this chapter to the list you started previously. Fill in your topics in the table at the right, and rate your level of understanding. Be prepared to support your rating by explaining or demonstrating that you are at each level.

  Answers will vary.

Topic	knowledge	comprehension/ understanding	application	analysis	synthesis	appreciation/ evaluation

- What graphing calculator skills have you mastered during this chapter? Explain thoroughly and use examples. What graphing calculator skills have you not yet mastered? Provide an example for which you need a calculator skill that you have not yet mastered.

  Answers will vary.

- What ideas or topics were introduced in this chapter that you feel you do not quite understand yet or for which you do not see the purpose? Give examples.

  Answers will vary.

- Find a problem that you cannot solve. Write out the problem and as much of the solution as you can. Then, clearly explain what it is that is keeping you from solving the problem. Be as specific and clear as you can.

  Answers will vary.

- If you had to choose a favorite problem from this unit, what would it be? Why?

  Answers will vary.

- Think back to the beginning of the school year, when you were first asked to work in groups. How did you feel about group work then? Are your feelings still the same, or have you changed your opinion? Is there something that you realize now that you wish you had been told back then? What role did you play in your group? (That is, were you a leader? Did you take charge? Keep your group on task? and so on.) Explain completely.

  Answers will vary.

Open-ended Problems

- You have studied parametric equations in several different contexts. Explain the advantages and disadvantages of using parametric equations. Include examples if appropriate.

  Answers will vary.

- Create your own problem that covers the material you have studied so far and that you think would make a good assessment question. Write out the complete solution to your problem, and explain why you believe it to be a good problem. *Note:* Please make sure that it is a problem or question and not just an explanation or description.

  Answers will vary.

- For the following problem, please follow this format.
  i. State the problem.
  ii. What do you already know that would help you solve this problem? Who (in your group) knows it and how does he or she know it?
  iii. What information do you need to assume? Why are you assuming it?
  iv. Record all your steps in solving the problem.
  v. State your answer clearly and completely.
  vi. How good is your answer? Remember: "A chain is only as strong as its weakest link!" What are your most unreliable approximations and weakest assumptions?

  A fly is flying around your classroom for the entire class period, never landing. If its path could be tracked and stretched out in a straight line, how *long* would its path be?

  Answers will vary. Hopefully, students will estimate a velocity for the fly and then multiply by the time it spends flying to get a distance.

Projects

Part 2c of Investigation 6.4.1, Drawing Polygons, could be a project. Ask students to continue to experiment until they can come up with a rule (or more likely, rules) to explain what is happening under all circumstances. Their work should be thorough enough so that if they are given a situation ("$x = 3 \cos t$, $y = 3 \sin t$, Tstep of 150°"), they should be able to describe the result *without* graphing first.

For the next project, have students put their calculators into radian mode, and change the t-interval to $0 \le t \le 2\pi$.

- Consider the parametric equations $x = \cos t$ and $y = \sin nt$ for $0 \le t \le 2\pi$. (Be sure your calculator is in radian mode.)
  a. Explore the cases when $n = 1, 2, 3, 4, \ldots$ (n is any natural number). Describe what happens and make a conjecture that will hold for any natural number n. *Note:* You may need to experiment with the Tstep, Xmin, Xmax, Ymin, and Ymax initially.

b. Now let $n = 0.5, 1.5, 2.5, 3.5, 4.5, \ldots$ and increase the Tmax so that the parametric plot completes a whole cycle. Describe what happens and make a conjecture that will hold for any such case with n of this form.

c. Try several different rational numbers for n. (A rational number is any number of the form p/q where p and q are both integers and $q \neq 0$.) Be sure Tmax is large enough! Describe what happens and try to make a conjecture that will hold for any such case with n of this form.

d. Whenever you write a decimal number, it is equivalent to some rational number. Thus, every single number displayed on your calculator is a rational number. Amazingly enough, however, most real numbers are not rational, but *irrational.* The number π is irrational and any rational multiple of π (like 3π) is also irrational. See what happens when you allow n to be an irrational number. Describe what happens and make a conjecture that will hold for any such case with n irrational. Can you explain your discovery? *Hint:* Tmax will have to be fairly large.

Your project will be graded on the following criteria:

i. Were you careful to consider each case completely?
ii. Are your descriptions clear enough for someone not working on this project to understand them? Sample plots should be included with labels and captions, clearly cited in the explanations.
iii. Are your conjectures written as complete sentences with correct spelling and grammar?
iv. Are your conjectures reasonable given the supporting work?
v. Bonus points may be awarded to any group that ventures beyond these questions to consider extensions to this exploration.

Answers will vary, as students will notice different things. For example, changing n through the natural numbers adds loops to a chain, with $n = 1$ being a one-looped chain. With $n = 0.5$, 1.5, and so on, you still see "loops" but the pattern is no longer symmetric. However, it does overlap.

Skill Questions: Appropriate for Quizzes or Tests

- Write parametric equations for each description below. Sketch each graph and verify your results with your grapher.

a. An ellipse with center $(-3, 4)$, horizontal radius 5, and vertical radius 3.

b. A line that makes an angle of 47° with the x-axis and contains the point $(4, 7)$.

c. A circle with center at $(-2, 7)$ and radius 4.

d. A line that makes an angle of 75° with the x-axis and passes through the point $(3, 7)$.

e. A line that makes an angle of 135° with the x-axis and contains the point $(5, -3)$.

a. $x = 5 \cos t - 3, y = 3 \sin t + 4$

b. $x = t \cos 47° + 4, y = t \sin 47° + 7$

c. $x = 4 \cos t - 2, y = 4 \sin t + 7$

d. $x = t \cos 75° + 3, y = t \sin 75° + 7$

e. $x = t \cos 135° + 5, y = t \sin 135° - 3$

- Solve for the missing parts of each right triangle.

a.

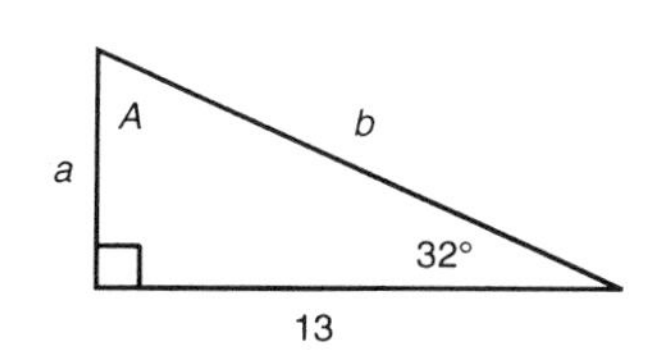

b.

a. $A = 58°, b \approx 15.329, a \approx 8.123$ **b.** $B \approx 81.585°, A \approx 8.415°, b \approx 40.559$

- Rewrite each equation as a parametric equation with parameter t. Verify that your equation is correct by graphing it on your calculator.

a. $y = x^2 - 4x + 3$

b. $y = 3x^2 + 5$

Answers will vary.

a. $x = t, y = t^2 - 4t + 3$ **b.** $x = t, y = 3t^2 + 5$

- Rewrite each pair of parametric equations as one equation in x and y. Verify that your equation is correct by graphing it on your calculator.

a. $x = 3t + 1, y = t + 3$

b. $x = 3t + 2, y = 4t - 6$

c. $x = t^2, y = t + 2$

d. $x = 4 \cos t, y = 4 \sin t$

a. $x - 3y = {}^-8$ **b.** $y = \frac{4}{3}x - \frac{26}{3}$

c. $y = \pm\sqrt{x} + 2$ **d.** $x^2 + y^2 = 16$

- Consider the parametric equations $x = t - 1$ and $y = \sqrt{4 - t^2}$ for ${}^-2 \le t \le 2$.

a. Find the point that corresponds to $t = {}^-1$.

b. Find the value of y when $x = {}^-1$.

c. Sketch the graph and show the direction of movement.

d. Eliminate the parameter and solve for y.

a. $({}^-2, \sqrt{3})$ **b.** $y = 2$

c. **d.** $y = \sqrt{4 - (x + 1)^2}$

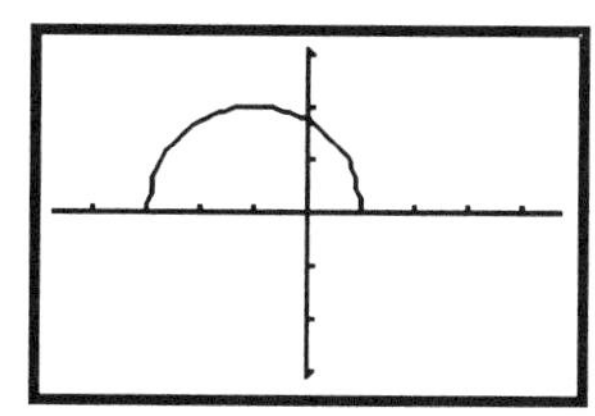

[⁻2, 2, .1, ⁻4.7, 4.7, 1, ⁻3.1, 3.1, 1]

- Write the parametric equation that will create each transformation on $x = 2t - 3, y = t + 2$.

a. Reflection across the y-axis.

b. Slide the curve 3 units right and 1 unit down.

a. $x = {}^{-}2t + 3,\ y = t + 2$ **b.** $x = 2t,\ y = t + 1$

- A ball is rolled off the end of a table with a horizontal velocity of 9 feet per second. The table is 3.5 feet high. When and where does the ball hit the ground?

Using the equation $y = {}^{-}16t^2 + 3.5$, the ball lands ≈ 4.21 feet away at ≈ 0.47 seconds.

- A bowling ball is rolled off a 10-foot-high wall with a velocity of 22 feet per second. When and where does the ball hit the ground?

Using the equation $y = {}^{-}16t^2 + 10$, the ball lands ≈ 17.39 feet away at 0.79 seconds.

- Todd Rosewell is expected on the other side of Beagul River in 30 minutes. He can row his boat 4 miles per hour in still water. The river is 2 miles wide and the current is running at 1.5 miles per hour. The boat launch is directly across from the spot at which he wishes to land. Therefore, he must head upstream from his destination so that the current will push him back, and he will land at his destination. At what angle must he head (measured from the riverbank), what will his effective speed be, and will he make it to his destination in time? Explain.

He must head upstream at an angle of approximately 67.98° from the riverbank. His effective speed is about 3.71 miles per hour, and it takes him about 32.5 minutes to get to his destination, so he will not make it in time.

- A plane is scheduled to land at its destination 1000 miles due west of its place of departure. It is traveling 200 mi/hr in a 24 mi/hr wind blowing from the north. What heading should the pilot set so that he arrives at this destination? How long will it take?

Head ≈ 276.89° (≈ 6.89° north of west) for ≈ 5.04 hours.

- A ship is traveling at 24 miles per hour at a heading of 50° on a trip of 480 miles.
  a. Make a sketch showing the path of the ship.
  b. How long will the trip take?
  c. How many miles east and north had the ship traveled when it reached its destination?

a.

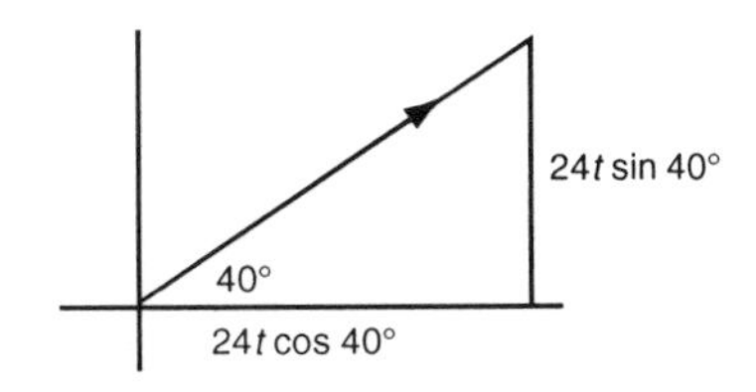

b. **20 hours** **c.** **east ≈ 367.70 miles, north ≈ 308.54 miles**

- A plane takes off from Phoenix, Arizona, heading 500 miles due west to Los Angeles, California. The plane flies at 200 mi/hr and there is a 50 mi/hr wind blowing from the north.
  a. Where is the plane after it has traveled 500 miles west?
  b. How far did the plane actually travel?
  c. How fast did the plane actually fly?
  d. At what angle did the plane fly?

a. **It is actually south of where it should be.**

b. **≈ 515.4 miles**

c. **≈ 206.2 mph**

d. **≈ 14.04° south of west (heading 255.96°).**

- A plane is headed from Albuquerque to Los Angeles, which is 900 miles due west. The plane flies at 300 mi/hr. On this trip, the pilot encounters a 35 mi/hr wind blowing toward a heading of 150°. At what heading should the pilot fly in order to land in Los Angeles?

  a. Make separate diagrams for the plane and the wind. Find the angle their paths make with the x-axis.

  b. Write equations for the horizontal and vertical components of both the wind and the plane.

  c. Write combined equations for x and y, and graph them.

  d. What is the instrument heading?

  a. **The wind makes an angle of 60° with the x-axis.**

  b. **wind: $x = 35t \cos 60°, y = {}^-35t \sin 60°$; plane: $x = 300t \cos 180°, y = 300t \sin 180°$**

  c. **$x = 35t \cos 60° + 300t \cos 180°; y = {}^-35t \sin 60° + 300t \sin 180°$**

  d. **≈ 275.579°**

- A ball is rolled off the end of a table with a horizontal velocity of 2.5 feet per second. The table is 4 feet high.

  a. How far from the table does the ball hit the floor? Give your answer to the nearest hundredth of a foot.

  b. How long does it take for the ball to hit the ground? Give your answer to the nearest hundredth of a second.

  c. If the ball rebounds to 85% of its previous height, how far will the ball travel (up and down) before it comes to rest?

  a. **1.25 feet** b. **0.50 seconds** c. **≈ 49.3 feet**

- Explain how to draw an ellipse with center at (−4, 5), horizontal radius of 4, and a vertical radius of 7 on your graphing calculator in parametric mode. Be clear and use complete sentences.

  Answers will vary. $x = 4 \cos t - 4, y = 7 \sin t + 5$

- What parametric equations could you use to graph a line that makes a 78° angle with the x-axis? Is this answer unique? (That is, are they the only equations that work, or are there others?) Explain completely.

  Not unique, $x = t \cos 78° + a$ and $y = t \sin 78° + b$ for any a and b will work.

- a. Write parametric equations for a circle with radius 4 and centered at the origin. (Include window values for Tmin, Tmax, Tstep.)

  b. Write a nonparametric equation for the same circle as in part a.

  a. **Tmin: 0; Tmax: 360; Tstep: 5; $x = 4 \cos t, y = 4 \sin t$**

  b. **$x^2 + y^2 = 16$**

• Write parametric equations that will graph each square shape below. Be sure to include window values for Tmin, Tmax, and Tstep. (Each grid mark represents one unit.)

a.

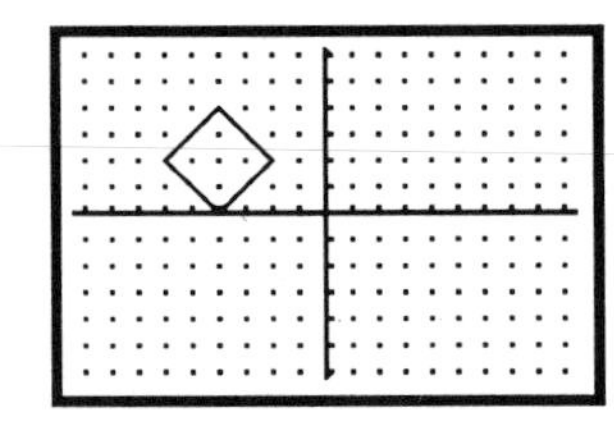

b.

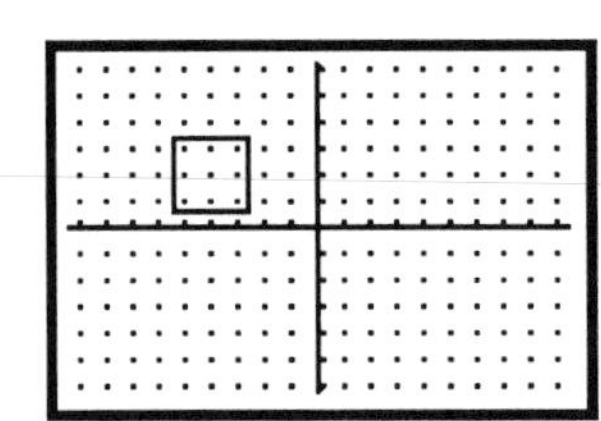

a. **Tmin: 0; Tmax: 360; Tstep: 90; $x = 2 \cos t - 4, y = 2 \sin t + 2$**

b. **Tmin: 45; Tmax: 415; Tstep: 90; $x = 2 \cos t - 4, y = 2 \sin t + 2$.**

• Find each length or measure.

a. The length of segment AB in the hexagon

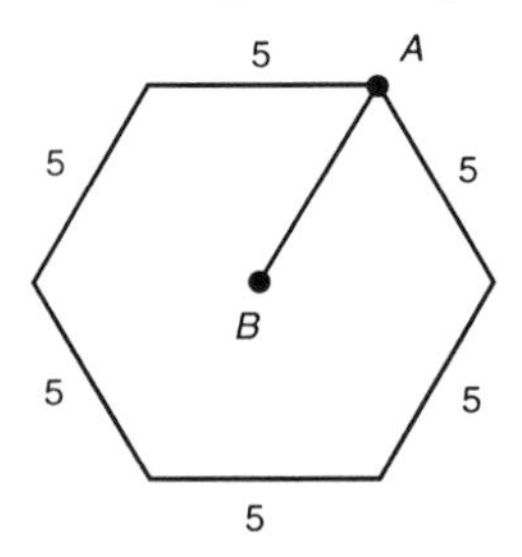

b. The measure of angle R in the triangle below

c. The measure of segment SR in the triangle below

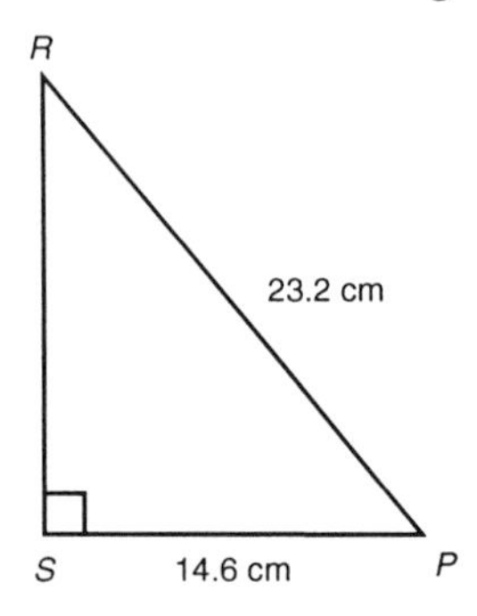

a. **5** **b.** **$\approx 39°$** **c.** **≈ 18.03**

• A graph is described by the equations $x = t - 3$ and $y = t^2 - 1$.

a. Write the equations that will slide the graph up 3 units and left 2 units.

b. Write the equations that will reflect the graph over the y-axis.

c. Write the equations that will rotate the graph 180° clockwise around the origin.

d. Eliminate the parameter from the equations and solve for y.

a. **$x = t - 5, y = t^2 + 2$** **b.** **$x = {}^{-}t + 3, y = t^2 - 1$**

c. **$x = {}^{-}t + 3, y = {}^{-}t^2 + 1$** **d.** **$y = (x + 3)^2 - 1$**

- A golf ball rolls off the edge of a 3-foot-high table at a speed of 8.4 feet per second. An ant is sitting directly in front of the table 3.5 feet away.
  a. Draw a graph of this situation and label the window used.
  b. Write the parametric equations for the ball.
  c. Does the ball hit the ant? If not, by how much does it miss?
  d. If the ant were sitting in a 4-inch-diameter puddle of ketchup, would the ball land in the ketchup?

  a. One possibility: [0, 1, 0.005, $^-1$, 5, 1, $^-1$, 4, 1]

  b. $x = 8.4t$, $y = {}^-16t^2 + 3$

  c. Close, but no. The ball overshoots by $\approx$ 0.137 feet (about 1.65 inches). It lands 3.637 feet from the edge of the table.

  d. Depends on where in the puddle the ant is. Since the ball hits $\approx$ 1.65 inches away from the ant, it is possible.

- Willy Ketchum, the police officer, is chasing a crook. The scoundrel has managed to jump a partially open drawbridge in his car. Willy is going to attempt to do the same thing. His car leaves the drawbridge at a 12° angle at a speed of 63 miles per hour. The other edge of the drawbridge is 100 feet away and at the same height. Does Willy make it to the other side or does he wind up in the River Floze? Record the equations you used to model this situation. (1 mile = 5280 feet, 1 hour = 3600 seconds)

  He barely makes it; $x = 92.4t \cos 12°$, $y = 92.4t \sin 12° - 16t^2$. The car returns to the level of the bridge after 108.52 feet.

- T. Uhpp, the golf pro, hits a ball off the first tee at an angle of 18° with the horizontal and a velocity of 240 feet per second. The hole is 350 yards away. Assuming there is no wind and the ball goes straight down the fairway, how close to the hole does the ball land? Record the equations you used to model this situation.

  $x = 240t \cos 18°$, $y = 240t \sin 18° - 16t^2$. The ball lands 1058.01 feet from the tee, or 8 feet past the hole.

- Complete the table of values for the parametric equations given by $x = 5t - 8$, $y = 4 - t$.

t	−6	−4	−2	0	2	4	6
x							
y							

  a. Use the table values to graph the points determined by the equations below.

$$x = 5t - 8$$
$$y = 4 - t$$
$$-6 \le t \le 6.$$

  b. Eliminate the parameter t and solve the resulting equation for y.

  a. x-values: $^-38$, $^-28$, $^-18$, $^-8$, 2, 12, 22; y-values: 10, 8, 6, 4, 2, 0, $^-2$

  b. $x + 5y = 12$ **or** $y = {}^-\frac{1}{5}x + \frac{12}{5}$

- A graph is described by the equations $x = t + 2$ and $y = t^2 - 1$.
  a. Write parametric equations that reflect the graph over the x-axis.
  b. Write parametric equations that reflect the graph over the y-axis.

c. Write parametric equations that slide the graph up 3 units.

d. Write parametric equations that slide the graph up 3 units and left 2 units.

a. $x = t + 2, y = {}^{-}t^2 + 1$ **b.** $x = {}^{-}t - 2, y = t^2 - 1$

c. $x = t + 2, y = t^2 + 2$ **d.** $x = t, y = t^2 + 2$

- Find each measure to the nearest hundredth.

a. side a b. side b and angle A c. angle B

10.81
34°
a

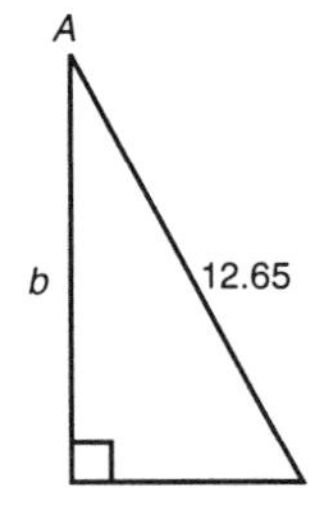

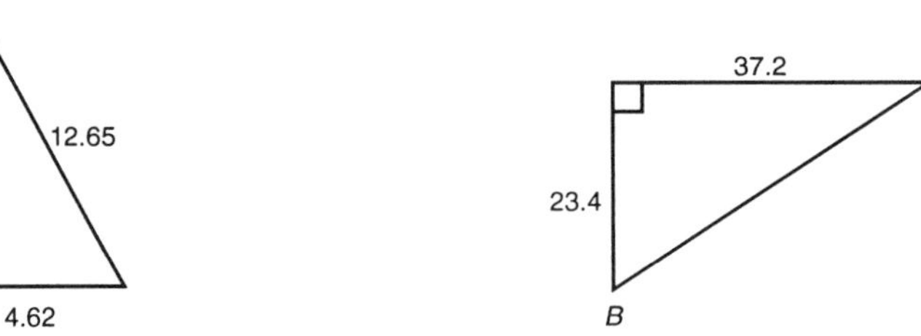

a. **side $a \approx 8.96$** **b.** **side $b \approx 11.78$, angle $A \approx 21.42°$**

c. **angle $B \approx 57.83°$**

- A DNR officer shoots a tranquilizer dart at an elk that is 200 feet away from him. The dart leaves his gun at 540 feet per second from a height of 5.75 feet and parallel to the ground.

a. Draw a graph of this situation and label the window used.

b. Write the parametric equations for the dart.

c. Does the dart hit the elk? If so, at what height? If not, by how much does it miss?

a.

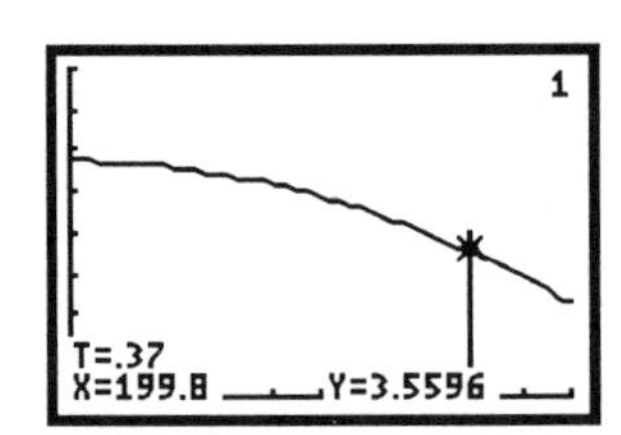

T	X_{1T}	Y_{1T}
[illegible]	199.8	3.5596
.371	200.34	3.5477
.372	200.88	3.5359
.373	201.42	3.5239
.374	201.96	3.512
.375	202.5	3.5
.376	203.04	3.488

T=.37

[0, 4, 0.01, 0, 250, 25, 0, 8, 1]

b. $x = 540t, y = {}^{-}16t^2 + 5.75$

c. **Yes, at a height of 3.56 feet.**

- Suppose Homer Uhn hits a ball at a height of 3.5 feet above the ground at a velocity of 160 feet per second and an angle of 17° with the horizontal. The fence is 420 feet away and 9 feet high.

a. Write equations to model the path of the ball and sketch a graph.

b. How many seconds does it take for the ball to get to the fence?

c. How high is the ball when it gets to the fence?

d. How high does the ball get?

e. Did Homer hit a home run?

a. $x = 160t \cos(17°)$, $y = 160t \sin(17°) - 16t^2 + 3.5$

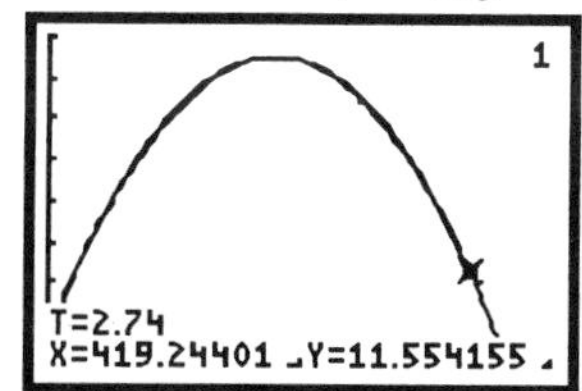

[0, 3, .01, 0, 500, 25, 0, 40, 5]

b. $\approx$ **2.74 seconds** **c.** $\approx$ **11.35 feet** **d.** $\approx$ **37.7 feet**

e. **yes**

- A small boat is crossing a 3-mile-wide river. The boat can move at 6 mi/hr and the river current is 2 mi/hr.
  - a. How far upstream must the boat be aimed so that it ends up straight across the river?
  - b. At what angle should the boat head?
  - c. How long does the boat take to get across?
  - d. Write the equations you would use to solve this problem.

a. $\approx$ **1.06 miles** **b.** $\approx$ **19.47° upstream** **c.** $\approx$ **31.82 minutes**

d. **boat:** $x = 6t \cos A, y = 6t \sin A$; **current:** $x = {}^{-}2t$; **combined equations:** $x = 6t \cos A - 2t, y = 6t \sin A$

Group Problems

- A wildlife biologist sees a deer standing 400 feet away. The gun is loaded with tranquilizer darts. The dart leaves her gun traveling at 650 feet per second. The biologist is holding the gun level at a height of 5.5 feet above the ground. Does the dart hit the deer or does it fall short? How far does the dart go? Record the equations and all pertinent information you used to model this motion.

$x = 650t, y = {}^{-}16t^2 + 5.5$. **The dart falls short, for it travels only** $\approx$ **381 feet.**

- A major league pitcher's fast ball leaves his hand with a initial speed of 150 feet per second and an initial height of 7 feet. Assume there is no wind resistance. (You will need to find out how far it is from the pitcher's mound to home plate.)
  - a. When will the ball cross home plate?
  - b. At what speed will it cross the plate?
  - c. Is it a strike? Justify your answer.
  - d. If the batter, catcher, and umpire all miss the ball, where will it first touch the ground?

a. **in** $\approx$ **0.4 seconds**

b. **With no wind resistance, its horizontal speed is 150 feet per second.**

c. **When the ball crosses the plate it is** $\approx$ **4.4 feet high. Sounds like the right height for a strike.**

d. $\approx$ **99.2 feet from the pitcher**

- To model the fast ball with wind resistance, one could use the parametric equations:

$$x = \frac{1000 \ln (0.45t + 1)}{3}$$

$$y = 7 - 16t^2$$

a. When does this ball cross home plate? Does it take longer than without wind resistance? If so, how much longer?

b. At what speed does it cross home plate?

c. At what height does it cross home plate?

d. If everyone misses the ball, where will it touch the ground?

a. The ball crosses home plate after almost 0.44 seconds, so it takes slightly longer when there is wind resistance.

b. about 136 feet per second

c. about 3.9 feet

d. The ball travels about 86.68 feet, which is more than 26 feet past home plate.

The next problem can be used to assess if students truly understand what the graph of the parametric equation represents. The solutions are provided following each pair. If you think your students will need the help, do part a together first and show them the solution.

- As you have been studying parametric equations, you have learned to recognize certain types of equations. For instance, you now know that equations of the form

$$x = x_0 + at,\ y = y_0 + bt$$

will produce a line when graphed. But suppose rather than looking at the two equations, $x(t)$ and $y(t)$ as above, you looked at their graphs. From these graphs, you should still be able to determine what the resulting parametric plot y versus x will look like. Below are five pairs of graphs showing x versus t and y versus t. Sketch the graph of y versus x.

a.

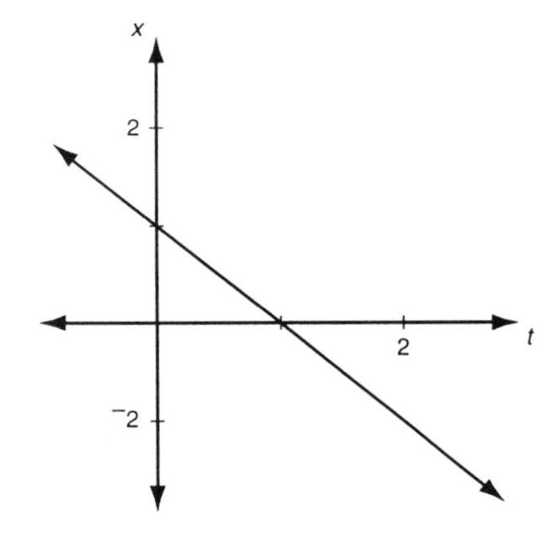

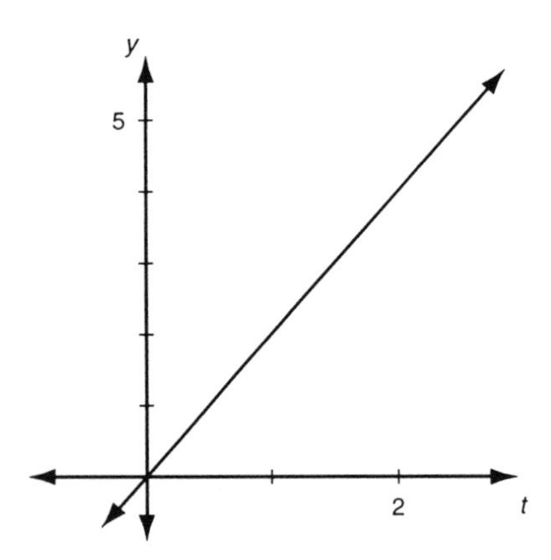

b.

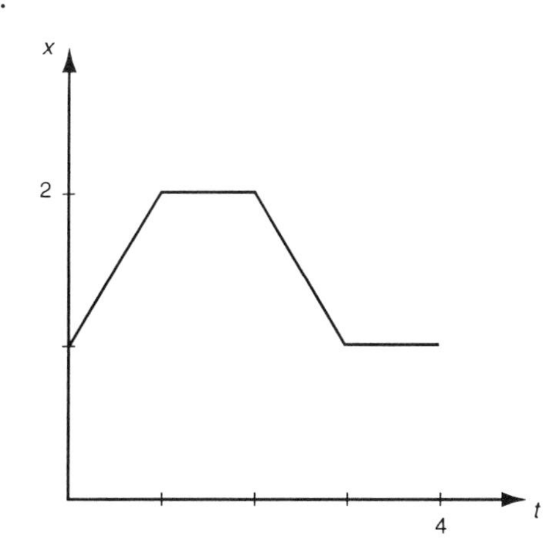

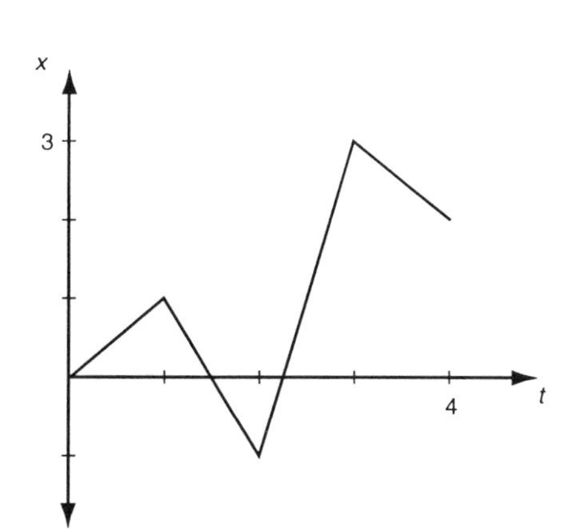

c.

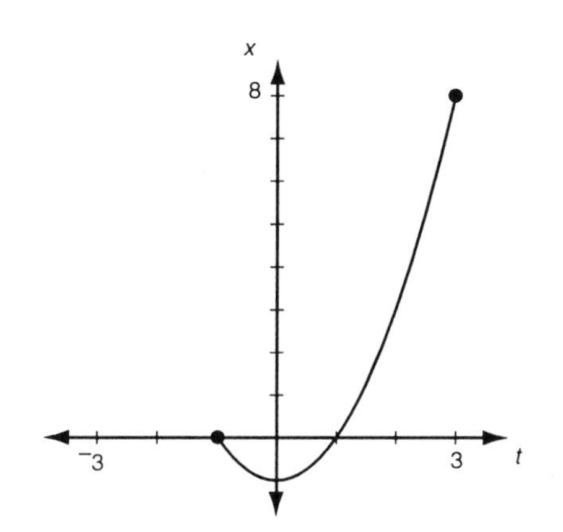

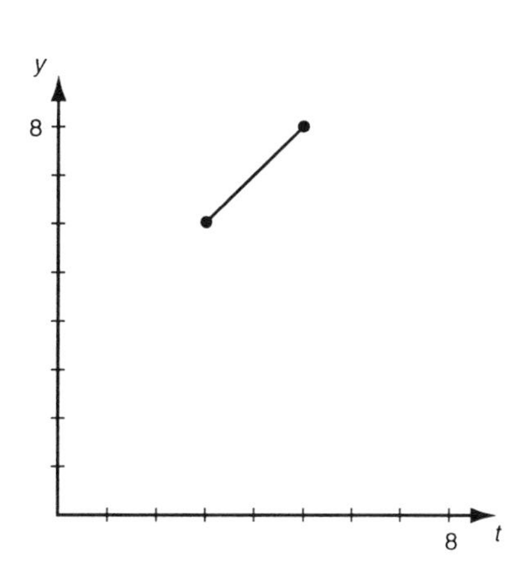

a. $x = {}^{-}t + 1,\ y = 2t$

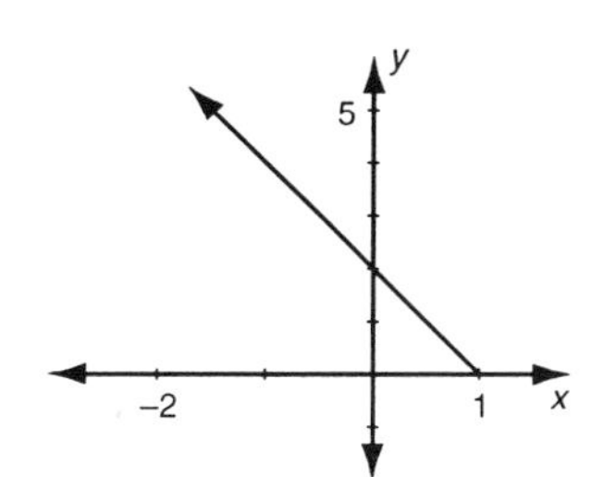

b.

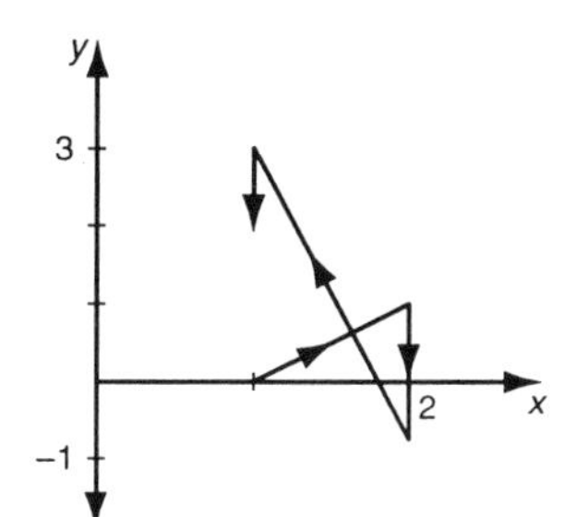

c.

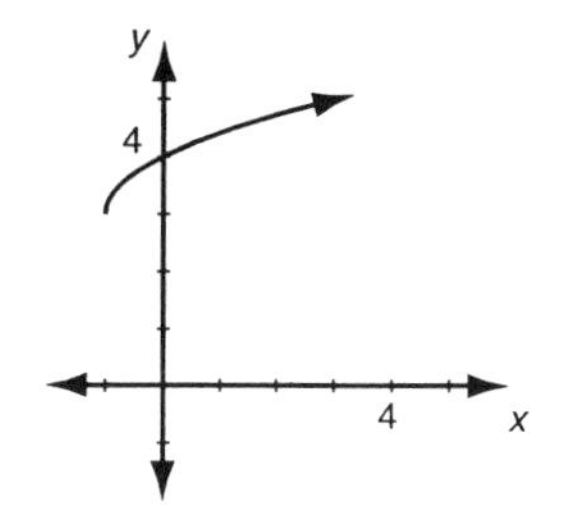

Chapter 7: Exponential and Logarithmic Functions

Journal Questions

- In Chapter 7, you are introduced to logarithms. Explain in your own words the usefulness of logarithms; consider both graphical and algebraic perspectives. Be clear and justify your response.

  Answers will vary.

- Explain fractional exponents in your own words. Give an example of their use.

  Answers will vary.

- Explain what a logarithm is in your own words. Give the mathematical definition.

  Answers will vary.

- List the properties of logarithms and give an example of how you would use each property.

  $\log (ab) = \log a + \log b$, $\log (a/b) = \log a - \log b$, $\log a^b = b \log a$

- What is the general logarithmic equation, and when would you use it?

  Answers will vary. General log equation: $y = \log_b x$, which would be used as the inverse of $y = b^x$.

- What graphing calculator skills have you mastered during this chapter? Explain thoroughly and use examples. What graphing calculator skills have you not yet mastered? Provide an example for which you need a calculator skill that you have not yet mastered.

  Answers will vary.

- Find three problems in the chapter that you feel are representative of the chapter. Write out the problem and the solution. For each problem, explain why you feel it is representative of the chapter. Please use complete, coherent sentences.

  Answers will vary.

- What ideas or topics were introduced in this chapter that you feel you do not quite understand yet or for which you do not see the purpose? Give examples.

  Answers will vary.

- Find a problem that you cannot solve. Write out the problem and as much of the solution as you can. Then, clearly explain what it is that is keeping you from solving the problem. Be as specific and clear as you can.

  Answers will vary.

- If you had to choose a favorite problem from this unit, what would it be? Why?

  Answers will vary.

Open-ended Problems

- List as many methods as you can to solve the equation $4^x = 15$, explaining your methods completely. Which method do you prefer? Why? Justify your preference.

Answers will vary. You could use the graphs of $y = 4^x$ and $y = 15$, or you could use logs.

- Rewrite the expression $125^{2/3}$ in as many different ways as you can.

  Answers will vary. $(\sqrt[3]{125})^2 = 5^2 = 25$

- Explain how you would solve each equation:

  a. $x^4 = 300$

  b. $4^x = \frac{1}{64}$

  c. $4^x = 300$

  d. $x = 300^4$

  a. Take the fourth root of each side.

  b. Use logs or rewrite as $4^x = 4^{-3}$.

  c. Use logs.

  d. Use a calculator.

- Create your own problem that covers the material you have studied so far and that you think would make a good assessment question. Write out the complete solution to your problem and explain why you believe it to be a good problem. *Note:* Please make sure that it is a problem or question and not just an explanation or description.

  Answers will vary.

- Manu has been stumped on a mathematics problem for some time now, and he has decided to come to you for some help.

  "See," Manu says. "I know I can figure out 125^3 even though my calculator is broken because I know that

  $$125^3 = 125 \bullet 125 \bullet 125$$

  and although it would take me a while to calculate it, I know that I can. But how in the world can I *calculate* 125^0? If I write down 125 *zero* times, there's nothing to do! Help!"

  Help Manu by telling him what 125^0 equals and why it equals that. Manu is pretty skeptical, so be convincing.

  Answers will vary as to the explanation (it does equal one). You could consider something similar to $\frac{125^3}{125^3} = 1$, but also by the 2nd law of exponents, this fraction equals $125^{3-3} = 125^0$.

- On your graphing calculator, graph these two functions simultaneously.

  $$y = 2^x$$
  $$y = \left(\frac{1}{2}\right)^x$$

  The middle portion of the graph looks somewhat like a parabola. Is it? Justify your answer completely.

  It is not a parabola. The easiest way to see it is to consider the table of values for the middle portion, or to see that there is a cusp at (0, 1).

- One day while working on your algebra assignment with your other group members, you find that you need to find an equation to represent a pattern. The other group members come up with their answers before you have a chance to work on it. Their three answers are

$$y = 2^{(^{-}x)},\ y = \frac{1}{2^x} \text{ and } y = 0.5^x.$$

Quickly, the heated discussion begins, each claiming ownership of the correct answer. Finally they turn to you to solve the mystery. What do you think? Explain.

All are equivalent.

- Your friend is still very confused about rewriting exponential equations as logarithmic equations and vice versa. Help her out by writing an explanation.

Answers will vary.

- Graph each equation below on the same set of axes.

$$y = x^2$$
$$y = 2^x$$

a. How are the two graphs related? Explain.

b. Solve $x^2 = 2^x$ correct to two decimal places.

a. Answers will vary. Both are ≥ 0.

b. ⁻0.77 and 2

- You might have noticed that your calculator has a button labeled "ln" and one labeled "eˣ." What do these have in common with what you have been studying? Explain.

Answers will vary. Students should be able to discover that $y = \ln x$ and $y = e^x$ are inverses of each other.

- Seung cannot get his calculator to work! Every time he tries to evaluate 0^{-5}, the calculator tells him "error"! Help Seung out, and give him some helpful advice.

The expression 0^{-5} is undefined because $\frac{1}{0}$ is undefined.

- The graph of $f(x)$ at the right is made up of pieces of two different exponential curves.

a. Is $f(x)$ increasing or decreasing on the interval $0 \le x \le p$? Justify your answer.

b. Is $f(x)$ increasing or decreasing on the interval $p < x \le q$? Justify your answer.

c. Come up with a real-world situation for which this graph could be a reasonable model. Explain your answer.

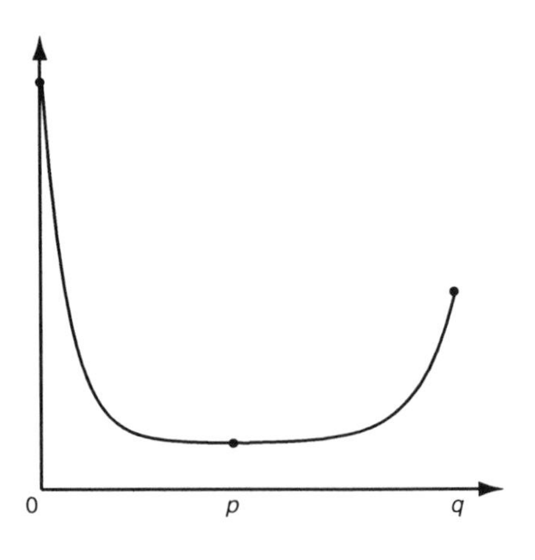

a. Decreasing

b. Increasing

c. Answers will vary.

- For the following problems, please follow this format.

i. State the problem.

ii. What do you already know that would help you solve this problem? Who (in your group) knows it and how does he or she know it?

iii. What information do you need to assume? Why are you assuming it?

iv. Record all your steps in solving the problem.

v. State your answer clearly and completely.

vi. How good is your answer? Remember: "A chain is only as strong as its weakest link!" What are your most unreliable approximations and weakest assumptions?

1. When will the world's population reach one trillion?

   Answers will vary.

2. When will our country's debt reach one quadrillion dollars?

   Answers will vary.

3. One hundred bacteria are in a petri dish. Every hour, the bacteria population doubles. How much space will the bacteria take up in 24 hours?

   Answers will vary.

Projects

- Manhattan Island (New York City) is considered to be the financial, commercial, and cultural center of the United States with a population of approximately 1.5 million. But in 1626, Peter Minuit of the Dutch West Indies Company bought the island from the Manhattan Indians for $24 worth of trinkets.

  a. If that money had been invested at the "going interest rate" at that time (you will have to research that!), what would be the value of the $24 in 1995? Show all work.

  b. What is the current value of Manhattan Island? (What are your references?)

  c. Was it a fair deal? Explain and justify your answer completely.

  Answers will vary.

- Write a program to print a table giving the value of a $2500 investment compounded quarterly, at 4.5%, 5%, 5.5%, 6%, 6.5%, and 7% annual interest rates.

  Answers will vary.

- By visiting several banks in your town, write a report, including any appropriate tables, equations, and diagrams, describing and analyzing the types of accounts that are available. Be sure to include all important information about the accounts (that is, minimum balance, fees, penalties, and so on). If you had $1000 to invest, which type of account would you choose? Why? Show how your $1000 would grow in the account of your choice.

  Answers will vary.

- The graphs below show the same line. However, the spacing between the grid lines is decreased in successive views. For each of the four graphs, count the total number of squares that contain some portion of the line, no matter how small. Record this information.

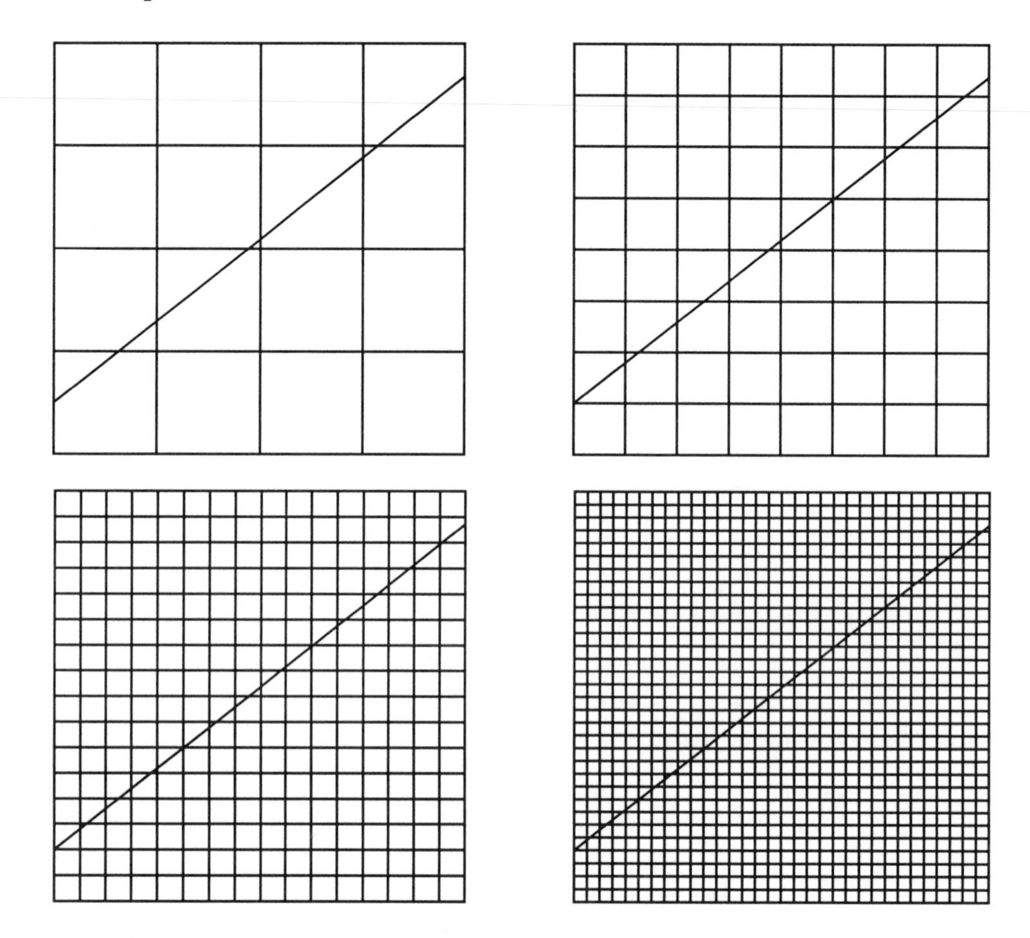

The second set of graphs show the same circle. In these graphs, count any square that contains part of the circumference of the circle, and also count any square that contains any point inside the circle. (It may be easier to count those squares that do not contain any part of the circumference or the interior of the circle, and then subtract this number from the total number of squares.) Record this information.

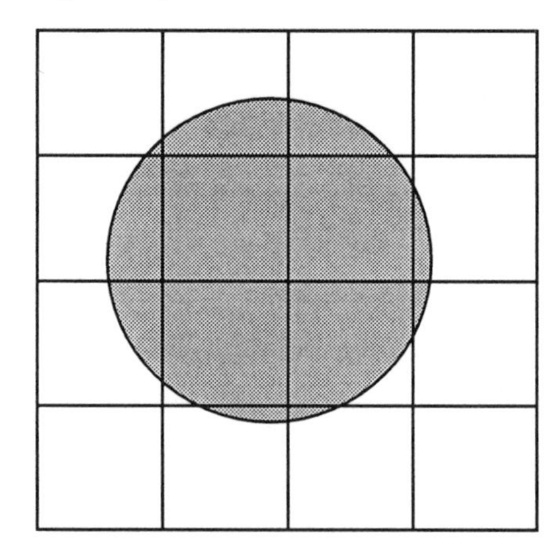

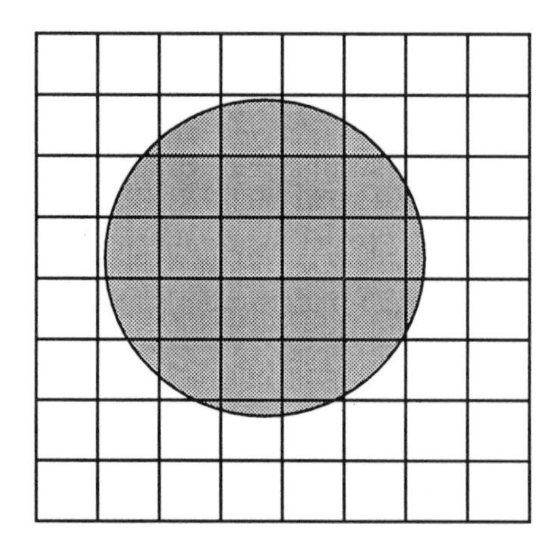

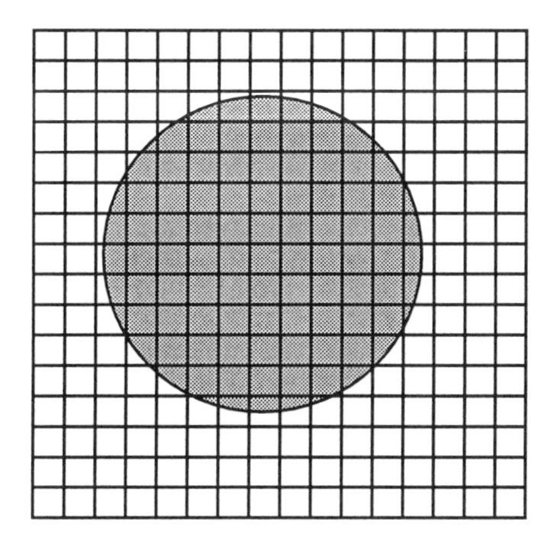

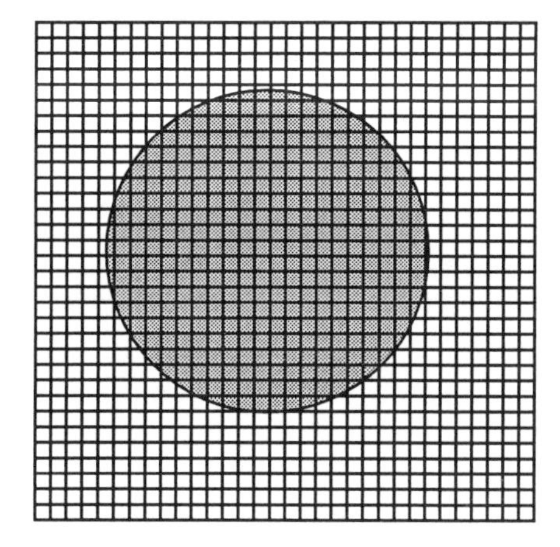

Finally, in the last set of graphs, count the squares that contain any part of the border of the state of Michigan. Record this information.

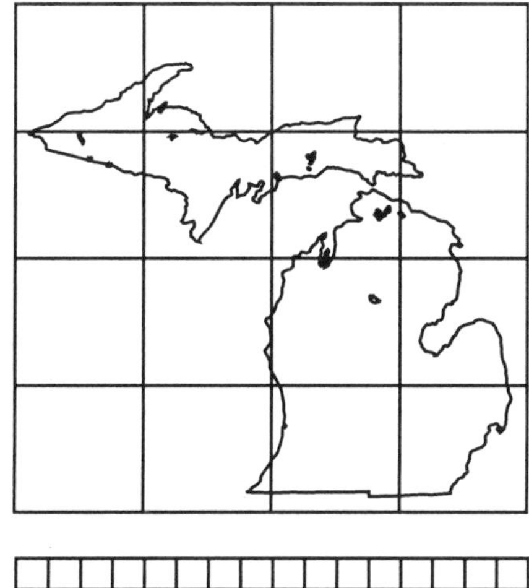

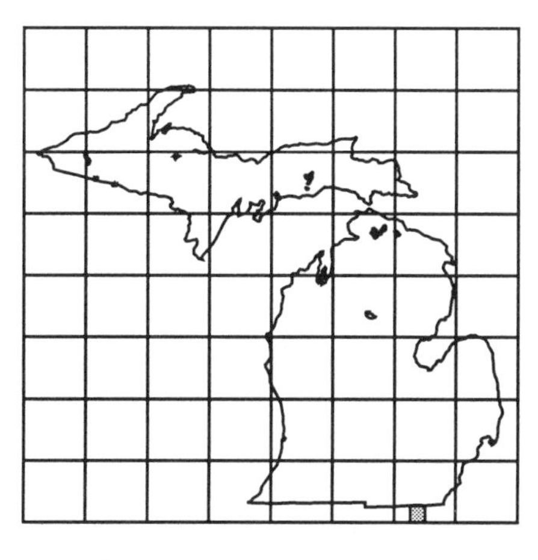

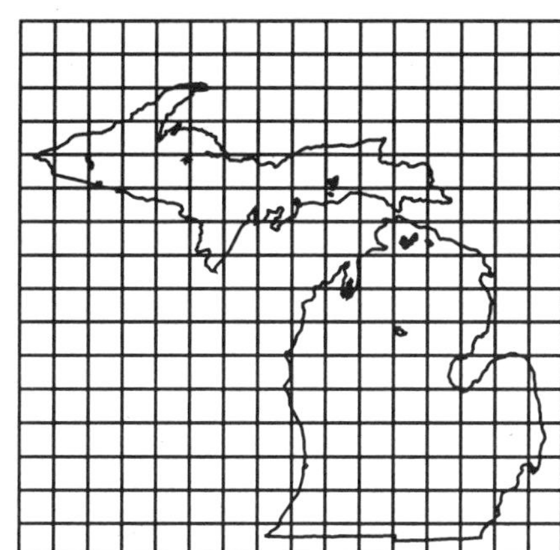

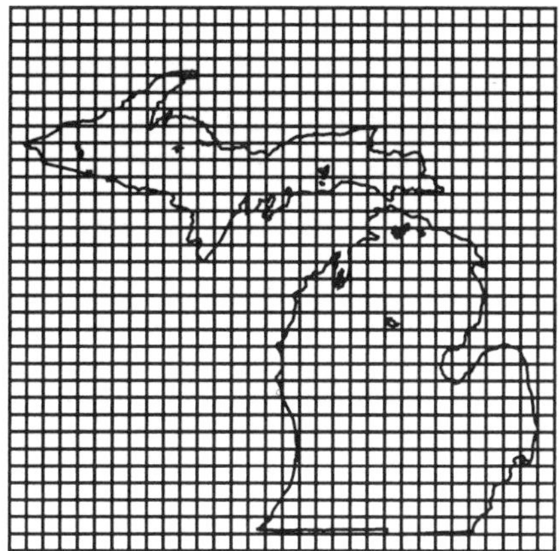

Put all of the information into a table like the one shown here. Find a power function for each set of data paired with the grid size. The power of x is called the dimension of the graph. It's not surprising that the dimension of a line or the circumference of a circle is one, because these are one-dimensional objects. And likewise the

Grid	Line	Circumference of circle	Area of circle	Michigan
4				
8				
16				
32				

dimension of a circle's area should be two. But why is the state of Michigan neither one-dimensional nor two-dimensional, but somewhere in between? Noninteger dimension values between one and two indicate the roughness or jaggedness of a boundary. A very crooked boundary, such as the seacoast of Maine, has a higher dimension than a smoother boundary, such as the west coast of Michigan. Fractal dimensions calculated for brain waves and other biological signals are being investigated as tools in medical diagnosis. Fractal dimensions of rock fractures are used to analyze the likelihood of groundwater contamination from underground storage of waste. Other applications of this concept are appearing in almost every area of science.

Select one of these two options to complete this project.

1. Find a map of your state or region. Choose a boundary of a natural feature such as a river. Overlay a series of grids on a copy of the map and calculate the fractal dimension of this feature.
2. Prepare a report of a developing application of fractal dimensions in some field of science.

Grid	Line	Circumference of circle	Area of circle	Michigan
4	7	12	13	11
8	14	20	33	28
16	27	40	109	68
32	55	76	397	143

When counting the squares, it is often easier to count the ones not to be included rather than the ones to be included. The numbers shown in this table are not necessarily the only correct ones as there are many squares where you have to interpret if the line goes through or misses. When doing the regression for the area of the circle, the exponent is not 2 as predicted by the text. However, if you were able to count on a finer mesh and ignore the first data point, you would find the exponent much closer to 2. Graphing the log of the grid vs. log of the area data will show that the data approaches a line. If you sketch this line by hand and then calculate a slope for it, you will find that it is 2. However, using a finer mesh on the map of Michigan will never resolve this to an integer exponent. Doing a log-log plot of any of the sets of data will linearize them.

The dimension found in this project is technically called the "box dimension" since that is the technique used to measure it. It is one way to estimate the fractal dimension of a border.

When choosing a feature to use for the later portion of the project, try to use a map with as much detail as possible. You may want to prepare grids on transparencies for students to use as overlays in counting. Rivers or coastlines are good choices to find fractal dimensions. Alternatively, you can use boundaries between countries which have been determined by following mountain ranges and other natural features.

For the second optional part, students can find information in many recent periodicals. Searching for "fractal dimension" as a key word should yield several sources.

Skill Questions: Appropriate for Quizzes or Tests

- For what values of x is x^{-5} a negative number? Justify your answer completely.

  $x < 0$

- Recently, while working on some mathematics homework, Amal and Chao got into a little argument! During the dispute, a part of their assignment was destroyed. All that remained of one particular problem is shown below.

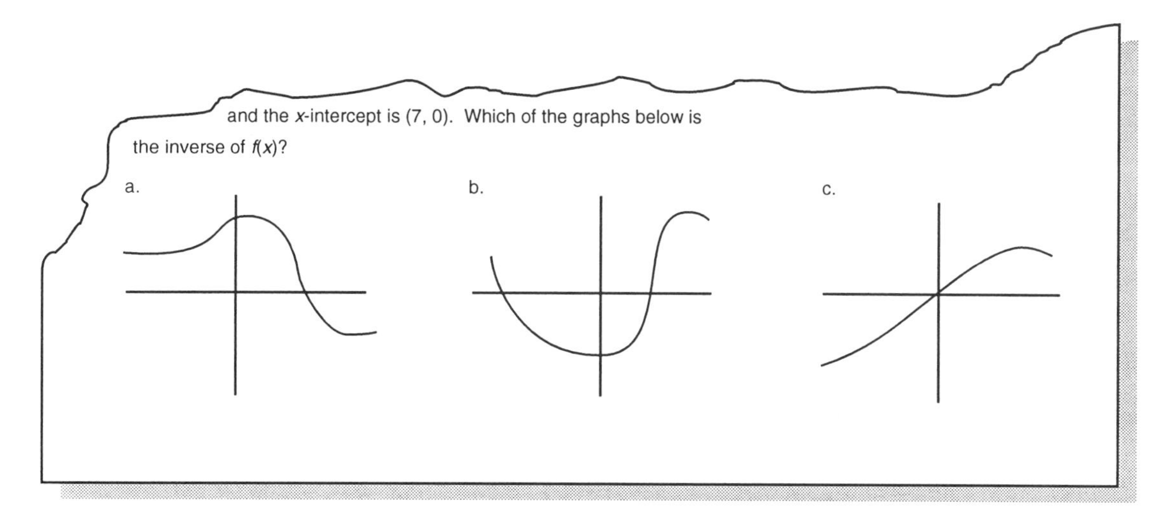

and the x-intercept is (7, 0). Which of the graphs below is
the inverse of f(x)?
a.
b.
c.

Amal was furious. "Way to go, Chao! Now there is no way to get this problem correct! We don't even know what $f(x)$ is."

"Wait a minute!" Chao quickly responded. "I'm pretty sure we can solve this anyway."

Amal shook his head. "No way, man. You're crazy."

Who is correct? Explain completely why and what the other person might be forgetting.

Chao. If $f(x)$ has an x-intercept of (7, 0), the inverse has a y-intercept of (0, 7). Graph a must be the graph of the inverse of $f(x)$.

- All you know about a function $f(x)$ is that it is an exponential function and that it is increasing for all values of x.

   a. State everything you know about the graph of $f(x)$. Be specific and justify your statements.

   b. State everything you know about the graph of $f(x) + a$. Be specific and justify your statements.

   a. Answer should include a description or picture giving the general shape of the graph, stating that it has a horizontal asymptote, one y-intercept, and 0 or 1 x-intercept.

   b. Include everything from the answer to part a including the following information as well: if the y-intercept of $f(x)$ is $(0, c)$, the y-intercept of $f(x) + a$ is $(0, c + a)$; if the horizontal asymptote of $f(x)$ is $y = b$, the horizontal asymptote of $f(x) + a$ is $y = b + a$.

- Dick and Sam love to gamble but, unfortunately, neither is very lucky. Each has his own "technique" for betting. Dick always bets one-half of all his money at each play. Sam bets only one-fourth of his current total on each play. They decide to see whose method is better. They each took $10,000 to the casino and sat down at separate tables. They both lost every bet they made and had to quit betting after each of them had less than $1.00 left. How many bets did each person place? Show all work. Whose method is better? Justify your response.

Dick makes 14 bets, Sam makes 33 bets. Most will say Sam's method is better because he can play longer.

- Give an example of an equation that would require the use of logarithms to solve. Solve it.

  Answers will vary.

- In 1993, the population of Mesa, Arizona, was 263,000. Assuming the population grows at 3.2% per year, write an explicit equation to model the growth. Call the equation $f(x)$. Find $f(10)$. What is the real-world meaning of $f(10)$? What would the population be after 6 years and 4 months?

  $f(x) = 263{,}000(1.032)^x$; $f(10) \approx 360{,}037$, which is the estimate for the population in 10 years if the growth rate remains the same. $f\left(6\frac{1}{3}\right) \approx 321{,}066$

- Rewrite each expression in a simpler way.

  a. $\log_3 (3^4)$ b. $10^{\log 17}$

  a. 4 **b. 17**

- Convert each expression to exponential form.

  a. $\sqrt{x}$ b. $\sqrt[3]{x^7}$

  c. $\left(\sqrt[3]{16}\right)^2$ d. $\log_{12} 144 = 2$

  e. $\log_5 \left(\frac{1}{25}\right) = -2$ f. $\left(\sqrt[3]{17}\right)^2$

  a. $x^{1/2}$ **b. $x^{7/3}$**

  c. $16^{2/3}$ **d. $12^2 = 144$**

  e. $5^{-2} = \frac{1}{25}$ **f. $17^{2/3}$**

- Convert each expression to radical form.

  a. $x^{1/3}$ b. $t^{2.5}$ c. $s^{6/4}$

  a. $\sqrt[3]{x}$ **b. $\sqrt{t^5}$** **c. $\sqrt[4]{s^6} = \sqrt{s^3}$**

- What does an exponent of 2/3 mean? What does an exponent of -3 mean?

  Explanations will vary. The first is the "cube root of the base squared." The second means "one over the base cubed."

- Solve for x. Show all work.

  a. $4^x = \frac{1}{64}$ b. $\log_x 49 = 2$ c. $\log_8 x = 3$

  d. $81^{3/2} = x$ e. $8 \bullet 13^x = 8$ f. $\log_6 216 = x$

  g. $\log_6 217 = x$ h. $9x^{1/4} = 76$ i. $7^x = 92$

  j. $7 \bullet 3^x + 39 = 298$ k. $\log x + \log 3 = \log 16$ l. $\log_3 x = 2.8$

  m. $47 + 12(4.2)^x = 75$ n. $10 = 100 - \frac{(x-15)^2}{4}$ o. $x = \log 316.8$

  p. $\log x = 3.168$

a. $^{-}3$	b. 7	c. 512
d. 729	e. 0	f. 3
g. $x \approx 3.003$	h. ≈ 5084.9	i. ≈ 2.32
j. ≈ 3.29	k. $\frac{16}{3}$	l. ≈ 21.67
m. ≈ 0.59	n. $15 \pm 6\sqrt{10} \approx 33.97$ or $^{-}3.97$	o. ≈ 2.5
p. ≈ 1472.3		

- Graph each function. Then state the domain, range, and inverse of each.

  a. $f(x) = \log x$ b. $f(x) = \log |x|$ c. $f(x) = |\log x|$

a. **D: $x > 0$; R: all reals; $y = 10^x$**

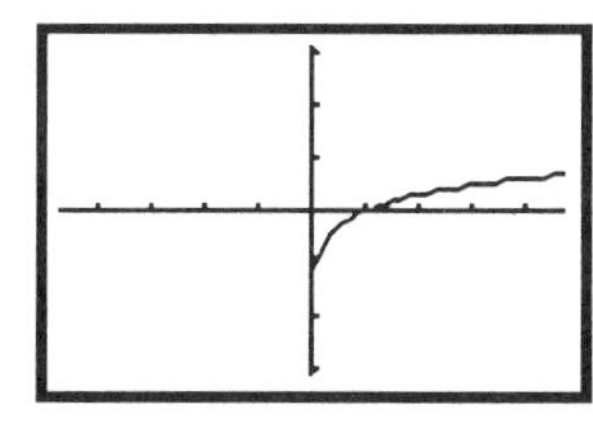

[⁻4.7, 4.7, 1, ⁻3.1, 3.1, 1]

b. **D: $x \neq 0$; R: all reals; $y = 10^x$ and $y = {}^{-}10^x$**

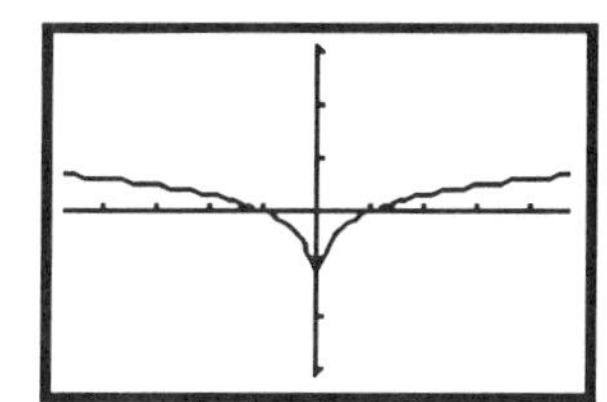

[⁻4.7, 4.7, 1, ⁻3.1, 3.1, 1]

c. **D: $x > 0$; R: $y \geq 0$; $y = 10^x$ for $x \geq 0$ and $y = 10^{-x}$ for $x > 0$**

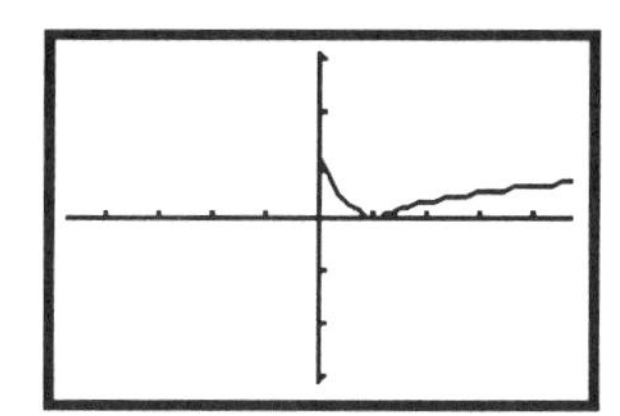

[⁻4.7, 4.7, 1, ⁻3.1, 3.1, 1]

- If $f(x) = 3x^2 + 7$, find $f^{-1}(x)$ and graph both the function and its inverse.

$y = \pm\sqrt{\frac{x-7}{3}}$,

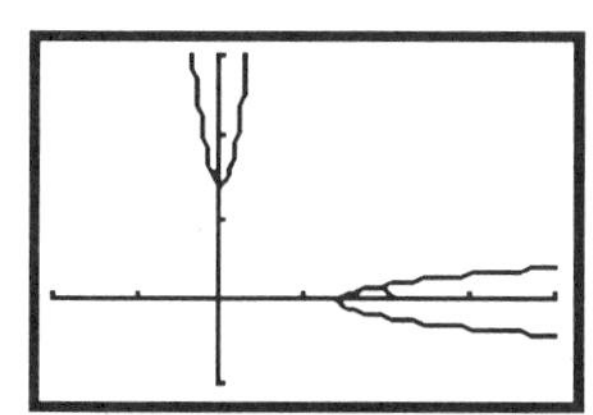

[⁻10, 20, 5, ⁻5, 15, 5]

- If $x = t + 7$ and $y = t^2 - 3$, find the inverse and graph both the function and its inverse.

  $x = t^2 - 3, y = t + 7,$

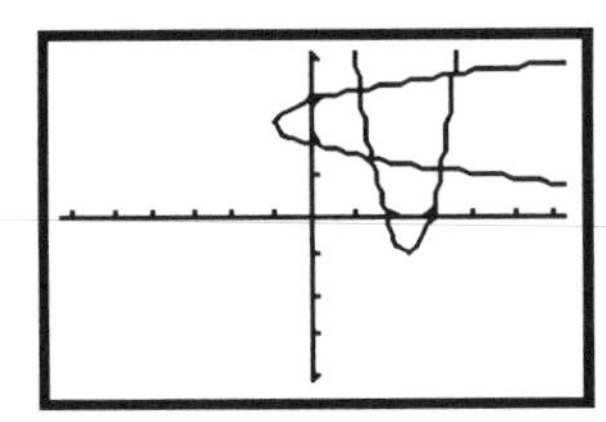

  [⁻10, 10, 1, ⁻18.8, 18.8, 3, ⁻12.4, 12.4, 3]

- If $y = 4^x$, find the inverse and graph both the function and its inverse.

  $y = \frac{\log x}{\log 4}$ or $y = \log_4 x,$

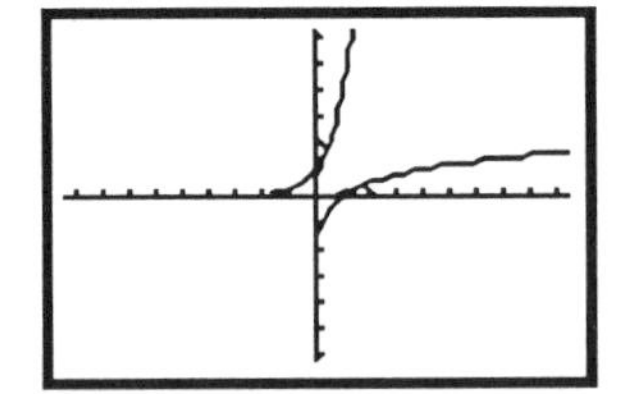

  [⁻9.4, 9.4, 1, ⁻6.2, 6.2, 1]

- Graph each pair of equations on the same set of axes. Describe how the two graphs in each pair relate to each other.

  a. $y = \log_2 x$
     $y = \log_2 (x + 3)$

  b. $y = 5^x$
     $y = 5^{5x}$

  a. The second graph is the first graph shifted to the left 3 units.

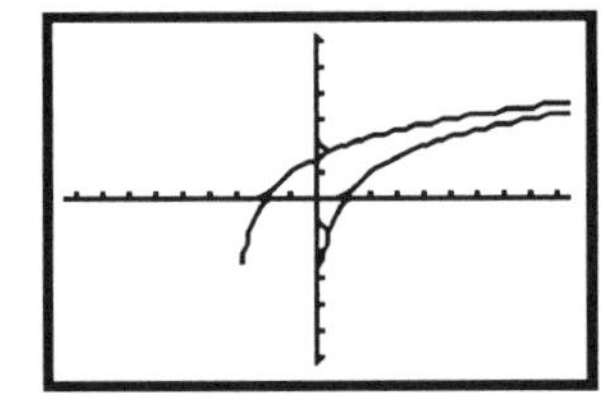

  [⁻9.4, 9.4, 1, ⁻6.2, 6.2, 1]

  b. The second graph is much steeper that the first graph.

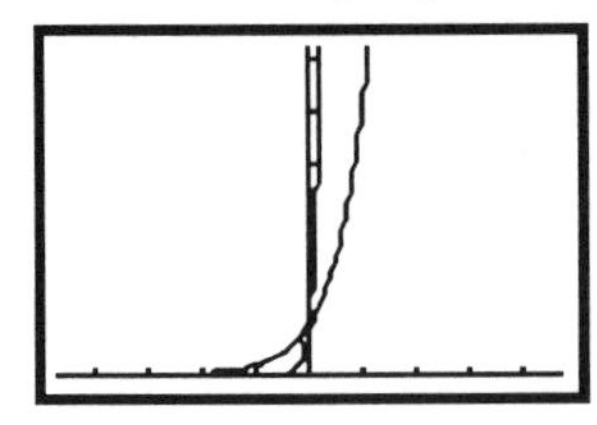

  [⁻4.7, 4.7, 1, 0, 6.2, 1]

- Find the value of x where $y = 2.43^x + 4.2$ crosses the line $y = 12.5$. (Find this answer to the nearest 0.001.)

  $x \approx 2.383$

- Is $y = 2.48(1.065)^x$ the same as $y = 2.6412^x$? Support your claim.

  No, the exponent is only operating on the 1.065, not the product of the two numbers.

- Is $\frac{\log a}{\log b}$ the same as $\log a - \log b$? Support your claim.

  No. Can be shown by substituting numbers for *a* and *b*.

- Once a certain medicine is in the bloodstream, its half-life is 16 hours. How much time (to the nearest 0.1 hours) passes before an initial 45 cc of the medicine has been reduced to 8 cc? Show all work.

  ≈ 39.9 hours

- If \$10,000 is invested at 5.5% compounded quarterly, how long will it take to double? Show all work.

  ≈ 12.7 years (≈ 50.756 quarters)

- If $f(x) = 7x - 3$

  a. Find $f^{-1}(x)$.

  b. Graph $f(x)$, $f^{-1}(x)$, and $f(f^{-1}(x))$ on the same set of axes. Clearly label each graph.

  a. $y = \frac{x+3}{7}$

  b.

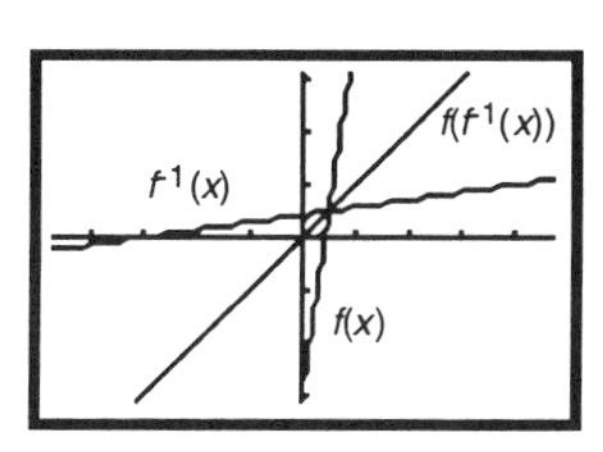

[⁻4.7, 4.7, 1, ⁻3.1, 3.1, 1]

- Consider the table of values shown below.

  The variables *x* and *y* are related exponentially.

  a. Find the exponential equation relating *x* and *y*.

  b. Use the equation to complete the two missing table values.

x	y
0	14.7
2	9.46
7.6	
	6.3

  a. $y = 14.7(0.802)^x$

  b. (7.6, 2.75) and (3.84, 6.3)

- Suppose a set of data points (x, y) is

  a. related exponentially. What points can you plot to linearize the data? Explain.

  b. related by a power function. What points can you plot to linearize the data? Explain.

  a. $(x, \log y)$ **b.** $(\log x, \log y)$

Year	Amount of debt (billions of dollars)
1976	620.4
1977	698.8
1978	771.5
1979	826.5
1980	907.7
1981	997.9
1982	1142.0
1983	1377.2
1984	1572.3
1985	1823.1
1986	2125.3
1987	2350.3
1988	2602.3
1989	2857.4
1990	3233.3
1991	3502.0

- The data in the table on the right represent the Public Debt of the United States in billions of dollars. Find the best model for this data. Carefully describe your process for finding this model.

  Answers will vary. The model should be an exponential function. Using the exponential regression on the calculator with 1900 as the reference year, you get $y \approx 0.058(1.129)^x$.

- Sketch (and label) a graph of $y = \log_3 x$ and its inverse. What is its inverse? Describe why these equations are inverses of each other.

  Inverse: $y = 3^x$; because $\log_3(3^x) = x$ and $3^{\log_3 x} = x$ where they are both defined.

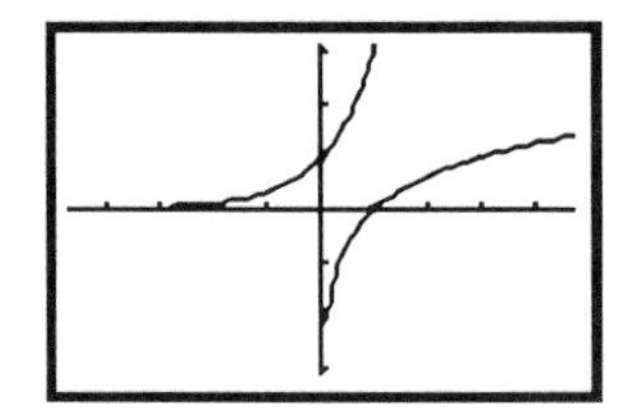

- You have purchased a $16,470 car that will depreciate in value 16% each year.
  a. What is the half-life? (How long until the car is worth one-half as much?)
  b. If you plan to trade in the car when it is worth $5000, how long will you have it?
  c. What will the car be worth in 5.5 years? (Show your work on all solutions. Graphic solutions are acceptable but won't receive quite as much credit.)

  a. $\approx$ **3.98 years** **b.** $\approx$ **6.84 years** **c.** $\approx$ **$6,312.91**

- Consider the equation $x^2 + 2y = 3$.
  a. Write this equation in function form as $f(x)$.
  b. What is its inverse, $f^{-1}(x)$?
  c. Find $f(f^{-1}(1.2))$.
  d. Sketch and label both the function and its inverse.

  a. $f(x) = -\frac{1}{2}x^2 + \frac{3}{2}$ **b.** $f^{-1}(x) = \pm\sqrt{3 - 2x}$ **c.** **1.2**

  d.

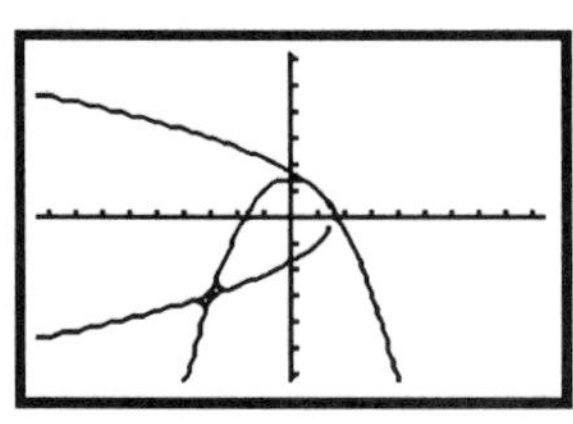

[⁻9.4, 9.4, 1, ⁻6.2, 6.2, 1]

- Give a detailed account of two different ways to solve each equation.
  a. $5x^5 + 18 = 1550$
  b. $347 = 12.1(1 + x)^{2.5}$

a. **Answers will vary. Graphing is acceptable. Otherwise, students should mention the "fifth root."**

b. **Answers will vary. Algebraically, solutions will need the 2/5 root.**

- Find the inverse of $x = t - 1$, $y = (t - 3)^2 + 2$.

  $\mathbf{x = (t - 3)^2 + 2,\ y = t - 1}$

- Given that $f(x) = 2.34x - 144$, find each of the following.

  a. $f^{-1}(x)$ b. $f(f^{-1}(14))$

  c. $f^{-1}(f(14))$ d. $f(f^{-1}(x))$ and $f^{-1}(f(x))$

  a. $f^{-1}(x) = \frac{x + 144}{2.34}$ **b. 14**

  c. 14 **d.** x **and** x

- Write a letter to your Uncle Bert and Aunt Ernie explaining how to evaluate each of these expressions. (Remember that they do not have a calculator of any kind!)

  a. $-36^{3/2}$ b. $8^{-2/3}$ c. $\left(\frac{4}{9}\right)^{-1/2}(16)^{1/4}$

  Explanations will vary. Make sure they are clear <u>and</u> correct.

  a. -216 **b.** $\frac{1}{4}$ **c. 3**

- You have purchased a $14,475 car that will depreciate in value 18% each year.

  a. What is the half-life? (How long until the car is worth one-half as much?)

  b. If you plan to trade in the car when it is worth $2000, how long will you have it?

  c. What will the car be worth in 5.5 years?

  a. ≈ 3.49 years **b. ≈ 9.97 years** **c. ≈ $4859.54**

- Two years ago I invested $900 in a company called "Tops to Bottoms" that specializes in recycling plastic bottle caps into seats for park benches. Today, two years later, the stock is worth $1347.

  a. What is the annual interest rate that I am earning?

  b. If this rate continues, what will the stock be worth in 3 more years (5 years from the purchase)?

  c. What is the doubling time for this investment based on these 2 years of growth?

  a. ≈ 22.34% **b. ≈ $2466.52** **c. ≈ 3.44 years**

- Beginning in January 1990, a forest of 470,000 trees has been harvested by removing 8% of the trees each year. (No new trees are planted.) The tree population can be modeled with the equation

$$f(x) = 470{,}000(1 - 0.08)^x.$$

  a. Find $f(5)$ and give the real-world meaning this answer.

  b. Find $f(3.333333)$ and give the real-world meaning of this answer.

  c. Find x such that $f(x) = 100{,}000$. What does this number mean?

  d. Find $f(0)$ and give the real-world meaning of this answer.

a. $\approx$ **309,768. This is approximately how many trees there were in this forest in 1995.**

b. $\approx$ **355,951. This is approximately how many trees there were in April 1993.**

c. $\approx$ **18.56. In $\approx$ 18.5 years there will be only 100,000 trees left if the rate continues.**

d. **470,000. This is the initial number of trees in 1990.**

- Find the value of each expression and explain in words how to find these answers. Give all answers in fraction form.

a. $64^{2/3}$ b. $-4^{5/2}$ c. $\left(\frac{3}{5}\right)^{-2} \cdot \left(\frac{3}{2}\right)^{-3}$

a. **16** b. **$^{-}$32** c. $\mathbf{\frac{200}{243}}$

- Classify the following equations as (a) true for **all** x, (b) true for **some** x, or (c) true for **no** x, and give evidence to support your claim.

a. $^{-}x^{1/2} = \sqrt{^{-}x}$ b. $x^{5/7} = (\sqrt[5]{x})^7$ c. $x^{5/4} = x\sqrt[4]{x}$

a. **b; $x = 0$** b. **b; $x = {}^{-}1, 0,$ or 1** c. **b; $x \geq 0$**

- Use a graph to solve $4 \cdot 3^x = 17$. Show evidence of how you obtained your answer.

$x \approx$ **1.32**

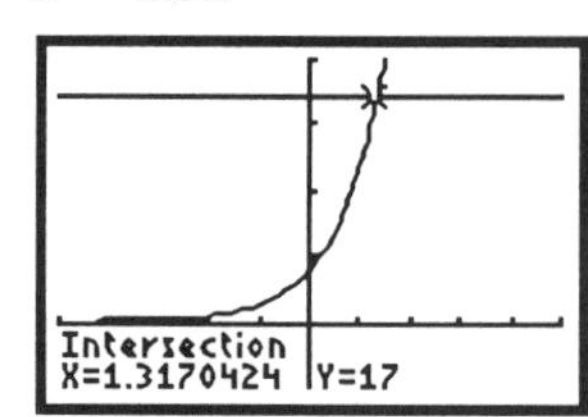

[$^{-}$5, 5, 1, $^{-}$5, 20, 5]

- A population of bugs is growing at a rate of 3.5% every hour. At this very instant there are 4300 bugs in this colony of bugs.
  a. Write an equation that will model this growth.
  b. Use your model to find the total population 2 days from now.

a. $\mathbf{y = 4300(1.035)^x}$ b. $\approx$ **22,418**

- Indicate whether each statement is true or false. Justify your answer.
  a. A negative number raised to a negative power is always positive.
  b. When a number larger than one is raised to a positive power that is less than one, it becomes larger.
  c. A positive number raised to the zero power is equal to zero.

a. **false** b. **false** c. **false**

- The patient was given 47 cc of an anesthetic. The drug loses effectiveness at a rate of 4% an hour. The patient will awake when only 12 cc of the drug is still effective. When will he wake up?

In $\approx$ 33.44 hours

- The volume of a sphere can be approximated by 4.1888 times the radius to the third power.
  a. Find the volume for a basketball with a radius of 4.5 inches.
  b. Find the radius of a ball that is filled with 47,000 cubic centimeters of water.
  c. Find the radius of a ball in inches that is equal to the square root of its volume in cubic inches.

a. $\approx$ **381.7 cubic inches** **b.** $\approx$ **22.39 centimeters** **c.** $r \approx$ **0.2387 inches**

- The cost of operating a water heater grows exponentially as the temperature of the water is raised from the temperature of the incoming water. The cost to own and operate a particular water heater is 5¢ a day when the water temperature is not changed. The cost is increased to 8¢ a day to raise the temperature of the water by 20°F.
  a. Using the information given find an equation representing this exponential model.
  b. Give a real-world meaning for the values you found in finding the equation.
  c. Use your model to predict the cost per day to raise the temperature of the water by 80°F. Show some work, please!
  d. If you decide that you can afford only $731.60 a year (20¢ a day), then by how many degrees can you raise the temperature of the water heater? Show some work, please!

a. $y = 5(1.024)^x$

b. **The number 5 represents the cost of no change in water temp (5¢); 1.024 represents the percent increase per degree of temperature change (2.4%).**

c. $\approx$ **33¢**

d. $\approx$ **58.45°**

- Use a graph to approximate the value of x for the equation $1.2^x = 2.9$. Sketch the graph and give the window values you used.

$x \approx$ **5.84**

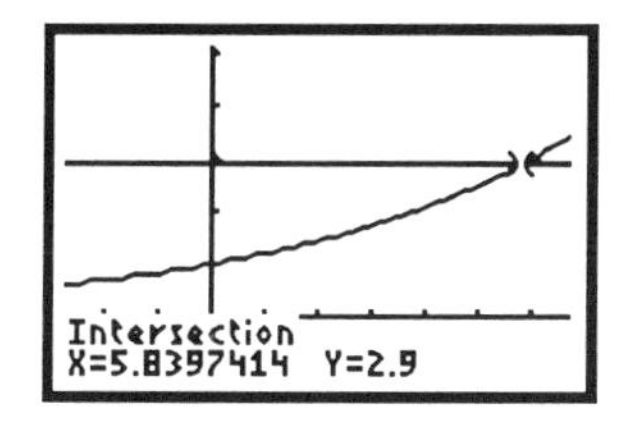

[⁻2.7, 6.7, 1, ⁻1.1, 5.1, 1]

- Give as much information as you can about the equation for each graph below. If you cannot give the exact equation, then at least give the type of function plotted. (Each grid mark represents 1 unit.)

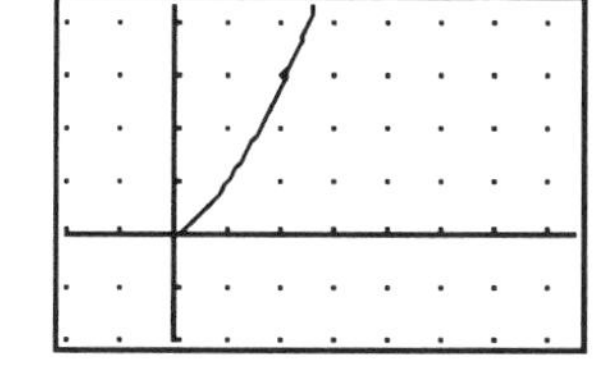

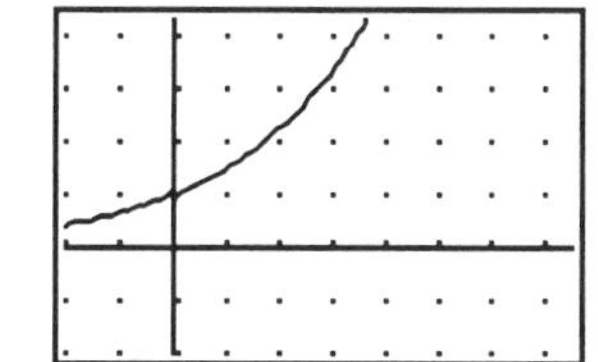

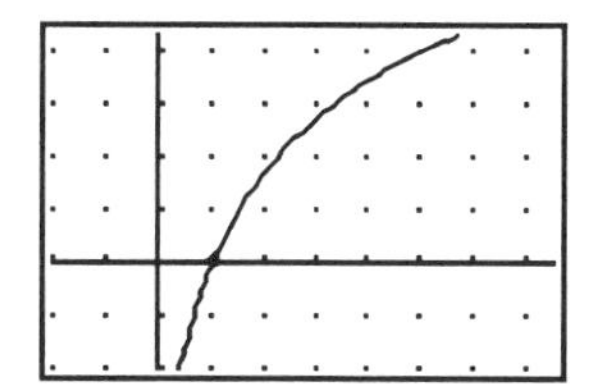

The first graph looks like a parabola; $y = 0.5x^2 + 0.5x$. **The second graph looks exponential:** $y = 1.5^x$. **The last graph looks logarithmic:** $y = \log_{1.5} x$.

- The bacterial culture showed an exponential growth. Initially there were 470 individual bacteria in the sample. After 30 minutes the number had grown to 2020. What can you expect after 2 hours and 15 minutes?

  ≈ 332,500 bacteria

Group Problems

- Recently you were contacted by a lawyer informing you that you are the *only* descendant to Bernard Bighound, a trader who died in 1689. On the first day of that year, he left $10 in an account earning 4% interest, compounded quarterly. His will left specific instructions that if, in 1995, he had any descendants living, these descendants could share the complete account if they could determine the exact balance on a specified day in 1997. Today is that day! For all this money, what is the exact account balance?

  Answers will vary depending on the date today, but it should be around $2,108,300 for a date in 1997.

- Suppose a country, with a population of more than 1.2 billion in 1993, allows parents to continue to have children until a live boy is born. After the first boy, they have no other children.

  a. Explain how you could simulate this situation. Be complete.

  b. Carry out this simulation at least 200 times.

  c. Use your simulation to answer these questions. Be sure to justify every answer.

     i. Will more boys or more girls be born in this country?
     ii. What is the average number of children per family in this country?
     iii. Will the population of this country increase, decrease, or stay the same?
     iv. What percentage of families will have only one child? Two children? Three children? Four or more?
     v. What percentage of the people in this country will have no brothers or sisters?
     vi. Will all of the groups in this class get the same results to this question? Explain.

Number of children	Frequency
1	
2	
3	
4	
5	
6	
7	
8	
9	
10	

  a.–c. Answers will vary. One possible way to simulate this is to flip a coin until heads comes up, then stop.

Chapter 8: Topics in Discrete Mathematics

Journal Questions

- In Chapter 8 you explored topics in discrete mathematics. In your friend's mathematics class, they are not studying discrete mathematics, yet your friend is curious as to what it is. Explain to her what discrete mathematics is and give reasons for studying it.

  Answers will vary.

- If you were going to write the test for this chapter, what would you cover? Why?

  Answers will vary.

- Look up "discrete" in the dictionary. How does this definition agree (or disagree) with what you have studied in this chapter?

  Answers will vary.

- Give three examples of discrete mathematics. What makes these examples discrete? What makes the mathematics you have already studied *not* discrete? What do you call mathematics that is not discrete? Explain.

  Answers will vary.

- As you move closer and closer to the end of the year, think about how you felt about your mathematics class, your group, and your ability to learn. Compare how you feel now to how you felt at the start of the school year. Has your perspective changed? Explain.

  Answers will vary.

- What graphing calculator skills have you mastered during this chapter? Explain thoroughly and use examples. What graphing calculator skills have you not yet mastered? Provide an example for which you need a calculator skill that you have not yet mastered.

  Answers will vary.

- Find three problems in the chapter that you feel are representative of the chapter. Write out the problem and the solution. For each problem, explain why you feel it is representative of the chapter. Please use complete, coherent sentences.

  Answers will vary.

- What ideas or topics were introduced in this chapter that you feel you do not quite understand yet or for which you do not see the purpose? Give examples.

  Answers will vary.

- Find a problem that you cannot solve. Write out the problem and as much of the solution as you can. Then, clearly explain what it is that is keeping you from solving the problem. Be as specific and clear as you can.

  Answers will vary.

- If you had to choose a favorite problem from this unit, what would it be? Why?

  Answers will vary.

Open-ended Problems

- Describe a problem or situation in which random numbers are used.

  Answers will vary.

- Name two different ways to generate random numbers from 10 to 30.

  Answers will vary.

- Critique the following methods of generating random numbers from −6 to −1.

  a. Roll one die. Take zero minus the number that comes up.

  b. Call a random phone number and ask the person answering the phone to pick a number from the list −6, −5, −4, −3, −2, and −1.

  c. Draw a card from a shuffled deck, and for each card take the number on that card, with Jacks = 11, Queens = 12, Kings = 13, and Aces = 1. The random number is the number needed to add to the card value to get either zero if the value of the card is less than seven, or to get seven if the value of the card is seven or greater.

  d. On six 3×5 cards, write the numbers −6, −5, −4, −3, −2, and −1. Tape the cards to the wall. Throw darts at the cards to determine the number.

  e. Ask the next person you see how old he or she is. Take the age and divide by seven to get a remainder. (If the remainder is zero, wait and ask the next person.) Then take zero minus the remainder.

  a. Good. Gives all outcomes needed with equal probability.

  b. Would work but would be time-consuming!

  c. Not good. You won't always generate a number in the desired range. For instance, if a 7 is drawn, the random number would be 0.

  d. If the person is really throwing the darts at random, then it is a good method.

  e. Not very good if done in a classroom since most students would be roughly the same age. Could be a good method if done in a place where there are people of all ages.

- A game consists of flipping two different two-colored disks. The first disk is red on one side and blue on the other. The probability of red, P(R), is 0.35.
  The second disk is purple on one side and green on the other. With this disk, the probability of purple, P(P), is 0.55. The following table shows the prizes for the different outcomes.

Second disk outcome

First disk outcome	Purple	Green
Red	$1.00	$2.00
Blue	$0.50	$0.75

  a. What is the expected amount of winnings for this game?

  b. If a play consists of flipping each disk once, what would be a fair amount to charge for one play of this game? ("Fair" means that the player is equally likely to win as to lose.)

c. Suppose you were the person in charge of running this game, and thus you got to keep any of the players' losses. What would you charge for people to play this game? (Keep in mind that the player should *want* to play, with the hopes of winning.) Would you change any of the prize amounts? Explain.

a. $\approx$ **\$.91** **b.** $\approx$ **\$.91**

c. Answers will vary. You would make money in the long run if you charge more than \$.91 per double flip.

- Explain why each matrix arithmetic problem below cannot be done.

a. $\begin{bmatrix} 1 & ^-2 & 2 \\ 1 & ^-1 & ^-4 \end{bmatrix} + \begin{bmatrix} 4 & ^-5 & 6 \\ ^-7 & 8 & 9 \\ 1 & 10 & 2 \end{bmatrix}$

b. $\begin{bmatrix} 9 & 8 & 7 \\ 6 & 5 & 4 \\ 3 & 2 & 1 \end{bmatrix} - 8$

c. $\begin{bmatrix} 7 & 3 & 2 \\ 2 & 8 & 5 \end{bmatrix} \times \begin{bmatrix} ^-4 & 6 & ^-3 \\ ^-9 & 1 & ^-5 \end{bmatrix}$

a. Matrices are not the same dimensions.

b. Cannot subtract a "non-matrix" from a matrix.

c. Matrices can be multiplied only when the number of rows of the first equals the number of columns of the second: $(m \cdot n)(n \cdot p)$

- Create your own problem that covers the material you have studied so far and that you think would make a good assessment question. Write out the complete solution to your problem and explain why you believe it to be a good problem. *Note:* Please make sure that it is a problem or question and not just an explanation or description.

Answers will vary.

- For the following problem, please follow this format.
  - i. State the problem.
  - ii. What do you already know that would help you solve this problem? Who (in your group) knows it and how does he or she know it?
  - iii. What information do you need to assume? Why are you assuming it?
  - iv. Record all your steps in solving the problem.
  - v. State your answer clearly and completely.
  - vi. How good is your answer? Remember: "A chain is only as strong as its weakest link!" What are your most unreliable approximations and weakest assumptions?

What is the probability of any one person being selected for jury duty?

Answers will vary.

Projects

Both Problem 4 and Problem 5 in Problem Set 8.5 are long, and either could be used as a group project. You can use them to assess students' understanding of chromatic numbering as well as to assess students' abilities to work in groups. Depending on your situation, you might even ask students to approach the administration about designing the final exam schedule your school will use.

The following problem is based on an assignment submitted by Tim Trapp of Mountain View High School.

- *Secret Messages on the Calculator*

  At some time in your life, you may have tried to make up a secret code that only you, and maybe a few close friends, would know. Imagine sending encoded messages that look like nonsense to others, but to the people knowing the code they would make perfect sense. Encoding messages, or cryptography, actually has many uses in business and in the military. You might want to research some of these uses.

  Look at the simplest type of encoding. Assign a number to each letter of the alphabet as follows:

A	B	C	D	E	F	G	H	I
1	2	3	4	5	6	7	8	9
J	K	L	M	N	O	P	Q	R
10	11	12	13	14	15	16	17	18
S	T	U	V	W	X	Y	Z	SPACE
19	20	21	22	23	24	25	26	0

  Here is an encoded message:

  36, 53, −71, 58, 37, −56, 15, 52, −68, 17, 38, −52, 20, 66, −85, −2, 1, −1, 3, 57, −72, 20, 0, −4, 23, −2, −3

  a. Could this message have been encoded using the numbers above? Explain.

  To make it more difficult to decode the message, a matrix is used on the original code. First, each letter of the code was assigned a number using the assignment shown above. Then, an arbitrary 3×3 matrix [A] is created. Next, every three digits of the code are multiplied by [A] to arrive at the new numbers representing the message. For example, the first three letters of the message above are BAR. Using the number assignment above, rewrite BAR as 2, 1, 18. Here, [A] is

$$[A]=\begin{bmatrix} 1 & ^-2 & 2 \\ ^-1 & 1 & 3 \\ 1 & ^-1 & ^-4 \end{bmatrix}.$$

  Now multiply the two matrices:

$$\begin{bmatrix} 1 & ^-2 & 2 \\ ^-1 & 1 & 3 \\ 1 & ^-1 & ^-4 \end{bmatrix}\begin{bmatrix} 2 \\ 1 \\ 18 \end{bmatrix}=\begin{bmatrix} 36 \\ 53 \\ ^-71 \end{bmatrix}$$

This gives us the first three numbers of the encoded message. This is done with all the numbers from the original number assignment, each taken three at a time, creating an encoded message that cannot be quickly decoded.

So, how do you decode it? With mathematics of course! Think about what you did: You started with a 3×3 matrix, [A], multiplied by a 3×1 matrix, call it [X], to end up with your code matrix, [C]. Thus,

$$[A]\,[X] = [C].$$

You know [A] and [C]; you want to find [X]. This is just an algebra problem similar to solving $Ax = C$ for x! If

$$[A]\,[X] = [C],$$

then

$$[A]^{-1}[A]\,[X] = [A]^{-1}[C].$$

So

$$[X] = [A]^{-1}[C].$$

Now you just need to figure out what $[A]^{-1}$ (read "A inverse") is.

b. Here is $[A]^{-1}$ for your matrix A above. Ask your teacher if you should research how $[A]^{-1}$ is found or just proceed.

$$[A]^{-1} = \begin{bmatrix} ^-1 & ^-10 & ^-8 \\ ^-1 & ^-6 & ^-5 \\ 0 & ^-1 & ^-1 \end{bmatrix}$$

c. Using $[A]^{-1}$, decode the rest of the message above.

d. Decode this message:

−37, 12, −12, 51, 48, −68, 14, 1, −4, 48, 46, −65, 37, 8, −17, 25, −10, 7, 17, 4, −9, 50, 65, −88, −15, 35, −43, 4, 82, −103, 41, 48, −66

e. Code a message of your own (a minimum of 30 numbers, please!).
Show evidence that the message was received and decoded by someone in your group.

f. Find out where this process might be used in the real world. Give as many examples as you can, described in complete sentences.

g. Explain a method that would make the code more difficult to crack.

a. No, there are numbers listed that are greater than 26 and some that are negative.

b. Answers will vary.

c. Bart Simpson is a cool dude.

d. My mathematics class is coded with sugar.

e. Answers will vary.

f. Answers will vary. Used during World War II.

g. Answers will vary.

The project below is about the number of different pizzas available at a pizza restaurant. It could be changed to number of different ice cream choices available from an ice cream parlor.

- Take a trip to your local pizzeria and gather information on the different pizzas they offer. Be sure to find out about different sizes, different types of crusts, number of toppings allowed (is "extra cheese" an extra topping?), and so on. How many *different* pizzas are available at this pizzeria? Be sure to explain how you interpret "different." Should the pizzeria use what you have found as a marketing tool? Contact the owner and make suggestions.

  Answers will vary. They probably offer more than people think!

- As the social committee chairperson, you are in charge of ordering pizzas for the party. The conversation goes as follows:

  Patty: "I'd like pepperoni."

  Mark: "Mushrooms on mine, please."

  Helena: "I only eat pizza that has ham on it."

  Peter Allen: "I want pineapple, but not with pepperoni."

  Mark: "Pineapple, yuk! Not on my pizza!"

  Gert: "I have to have green peppers."

  Bryan: "I want black olives, but I'm allergic to mushrooms."

  Helena: "Keep those black things off my pizza."

  Sam: "Yea, same here."

  Gert: "I hate them, too."

  Olivia: "I would like onions on mine, but no pepperoni or pineapple."

  Sam: "What I really want is sausage, but not with any pineapple junk."

  Helena: "Don't put ham and sausage on the same pizza."

  Abby: "How about some anchovies? Hold the green peppers."

  Patty: "Keep those salty things off my pizza."

  Carl: "I love a pizza with crab."

  Patty, Peter Allen, Gert, Bryan, Sam, and Abby in chorus: "Yuk!!"

  Make a conflict matrix and a conflict graph that show the information and find the chromatic number of the graph. Explain how you made the matrix and graph. Give a real-world meaning of the chromatic number. Interpret your results in a real-world way. You will be graded on the neatness of your graph and the clarity of your explanation.

In this matrix an X means that the two toppings should not be on the same pizza. A blank square means that no one cares if these are together. In the diagram, vertices are connected to show the items that must be on different pizzas. These items must be a different color indicating a different pizza.

	P	M	H	PA	G	B	O	S	A	C
P				X			X		X	X
M				X		X				
H						X		X		
PA	X	X					X	X		X
G						X			X	X
B		X	X		X			X		X
O	X			X						
S			X	X		X				X
A	X				X					X
C	X			X	X	X		X	X	

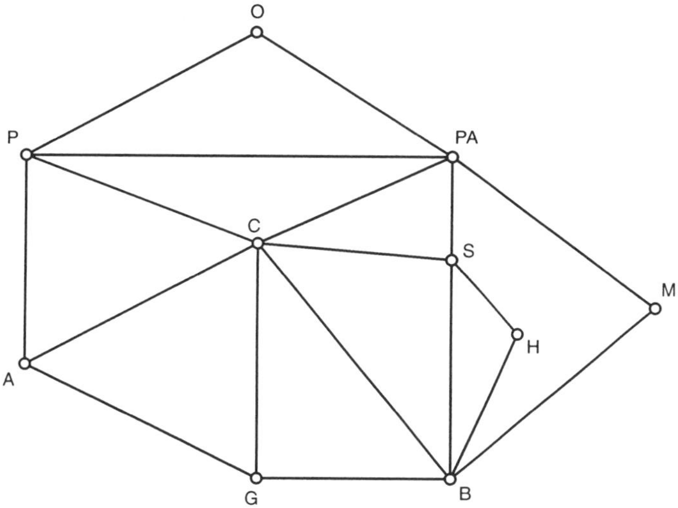

The chromatic number is three. This means that you only need to order three different pizzas and everyone will be happy. In the coloring here, pizza 1, or "green," would have pepperoni, green pepper, and sausage. The "blue" pizza would have pineapple, black olives, and anchovies. And the "red" pizza would have onions, mushrooms, ham, and crab. Many other three-pizza arrangements are possible.

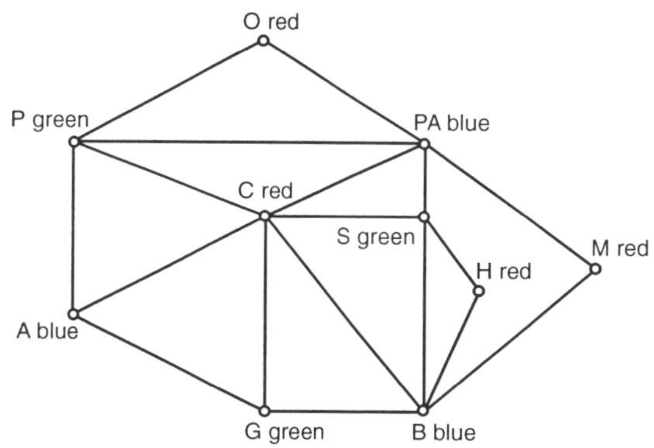

Skill Questions: Appropriate for Quizzes or Tests

- Write a calculator command to generate random numbers in each set named below.

a. $\{6, 7, 8, 9, \ldots, 14\}$ b. $\{-3, -2, -1, \ldots, 3\}$

c. $\{x\colon 0 < x < 5\}$ d. $\{-7, -6, -5, \ldots, -1\}$

e. $\{x\colon 0 < x < 2\}$

Answers could vary.

a. int 8 rand + 6

b. int 7 rand $^{-}3$

c. 6 rand

d. int 7 rand $^{-}7$

e. 3 rand

- Suppose you roll two fair octahedral (eight-sided) dice, with sides numbered one through eight.
  a. Draw a diagram that shows all possible outcomes.
  b. Indicate on your diagram all the possible outcomes for which the sum of the two dice is *less than* five.
  c. What is the probability that the sum is less than five?
  d. What is the probability that the sum equals five?
  e. What is the probability that the sum is *greater than or equal* to five?
  f. Would your answers to the previous problems be different if the dice were nine-sided? Explain.

a. The sums are shown here.

+	1	2	3	4	5	6	7	8
1	2	3	4	5	6	7	8	9
2	3	4	5	6	7	8	9	10
3	4	5	6	7	8	9	10	11
4	5	6	7	8	9	10	11	12
5	6	7	8	9	10	11	12	13
6	7	8	9	10	11	12	13	14
7	8	9	10	11	12	13	14	15
8	9	10	11	12	13	14	15	16

b. Sums less than 5 are shaded.

c. $\frac{6}{64} = 0.09375$ **d.** $\frac{4}{64} = 0.0625$ **e.** $\frac{58}{64} = 0.90625$ **f. Yes!**

- Symposium Pizza has the best pizza in the world, but the owners, although confident in the quality and taste of their pizza, are worried that they lose too many customers because their selection is not that large. They have eight different toppings and each customer is allowed to choose three different toppings. How many different pizzas is that? Explain to the owners whether or not their fears are justified.

Answers will vary. If each person must choose three (and no less), then there are $_8C_3 = 56$ different pizzas. If a customer can choose 0, 1, 2 or 3 toppings, then there are $_8C_0 + {}_8C_1 + {}_8C_2 + {}_8C_3 = 93$ different pizzas.

- A particular game is a two-step process, consisting of success or failure at each step. The tree diagram representing this game is shown at right.

  The point value of each different outcome is shown at the end of each branch.

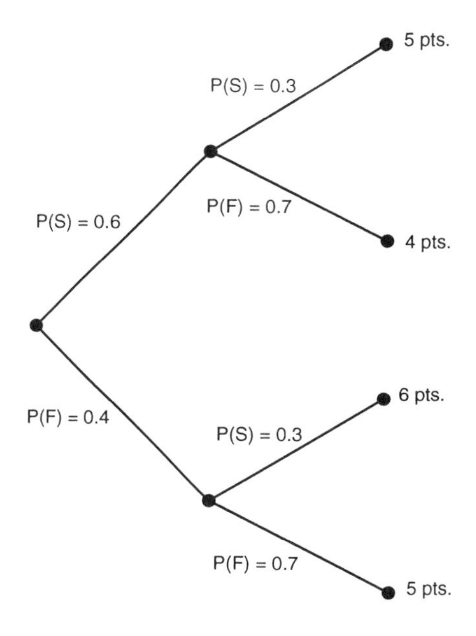

a. Describe a "game" that this tree diagram could represent. Be sure to explain the reasons for the probabilities and the points.

b. Find the expected value of this game.

a. Answers will vary. **b. 4.7 points**

- Draw a tree diagram of the following situation. A red chip, a green chip, and a blue chip are in a bag. One chip at a time is drawn from the bag, its color is recorded, and the chip is *not* placed back in the bag. This process is repeated until all chips have been removed from the bag.

  a. List all the possible outcomes.

  b. Find the probability of each outcome.

  a. RGB, RBG, GRB, GBR, BRG, BGR

  b. $\frac{1}{6}$ **each**

- There are six committees planning to meet at school next week, and there are some students on more than one committee. Is it possible for the six committee meetings to be scheduled so that the number of meeting times is kept to a minimum and no two committees that share a member will be scheduled to meet at the same time? Explain.

  Answers will vary. This is open-ended. Students need to consider different numbers of students on more than one committee.

- Ms. Goodteach has 15 desks for the 15 students in her class. She keeps them in one straight line. Also in her class she has one pair of identical twins, Aaron and Darren; not only do they look exactly alike, they also dress exactly alike. When making up her seating chart, Ms. Goodteach decides that she does not want Aaron and Darren sitting next to each other. How many ways can she assign Aaron and Darren to desks?

  182

- Complete the following matrix arithmetic problems.

  a. $\begin{bmatrix} 2 & 3 & 5 \\ 4 & 8 & 9 \end{bmatrix} + \begin{bmatrix} 6 & 4 & ^-5 \\ 3 & 4 & ^-6 \end{bmatrix}$ b. $\begin{bmatrix} 1 & 4 \\ 5 & 7 \\ 2 & 1 \end{bmatrix} \begin{bmatrix} ^-6 & ^-1 & 5 \\ 5 & 4 & 3 \end{bmatrix}$

  a. $\begin{bmatrix} \mathbf{8} & \mathbf{7} & \mathbf{0} \\ \mathbf{7} & \mathbf{12} & \mathbf{3} \end{bmatrix}$ **b.** $\begin{bmatrix} \mathbf{14} & \mathbf{15} & \mathbf{17} \\ \mathbf{5} & \mathbf{23} & \mathbf{46} \\ ^-\mathbf{7} & \mathbf{2} & \mathbf{13} \end{bmatrix}$

- There are six people in a room and each person must introduce himself to each person in the room. If person A introduces himself to person B and vice versa, that is considered to be one introduction.

  a. How many total introductions will there be?

  b. If you were to draw in every possible diagonal on a regular hexagon, and then counted the number of diagonals and the number of edges, how many segments would there be?

  b. Explain the similarities and differences between the last two problems.

  a. 15 introductions

  b. 15 counting the edges as well.

  c. Really the same problem: people are the vertices of the hexagon, and each introduction is represented by the unique diagonal or edge between any two vertices.

- A class of twelve students has four males and eight females. If two students are selected at random, what is the probability that they are both female? Explain how you arrived at your answer.

  $\mathbf{\frac{28}{66} \approx 0.42}$

- The Continental Divide runs from the northern border to the southern border of the United States. Rain falling to the east of this boundary will flow east, toward the Atlantic Ocean. Rain falling on the west side of this boundary will flow toward the Pacific Ocean. If a raindrop falls somewhere in Wyoming, what is the probability that it will head toward the Atlantic?

  $\mathbf{\frac{73{,}350}{96{,}250} \approx 0.76}$

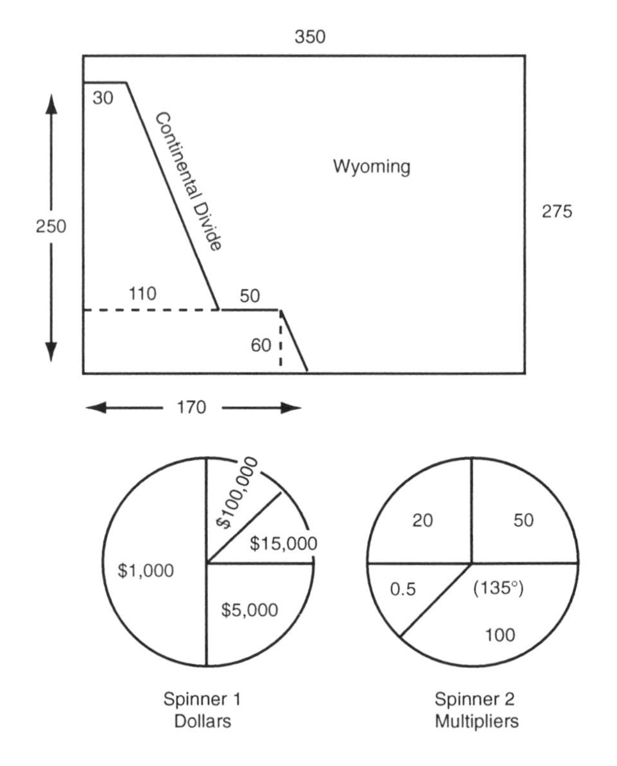

- California *Lotto* officials want to try out a new "big wheel" game. This new game actually consists of two big wheels (spinners).
  A contestant spins Spinner 1 and then, immediately after, spins Spinner 2 to determine the "multiplier." When both spinners have stopped turning, the dollar amount shown on Spinner 1 is multiplied by the "multiplier" on Spinner 2 and the contestant wins that much money.

  a. What is the most money a contestant can win? Explain.

  b. What is the least amount of money a contestant can win? Explain.

  c. Find the probability of winning the "most" amount of money. Show all work.

  d. Find the probability of winning the "least" amount of money. Show all work.

  e. If *Lotto* uses these spinners for many, many years, how much money could a contestant expect to win on an average game? Show all work.

a. **100 • 100,000 = $10,000,000** b. **$500 ($1,000 • 0.5)**

c. $\frac{3}{64} \approx 0.047$ d. $\frac{1}{16} = 0.0625$

e. **Expected value is ≈ $887,882.81**

- Frosty Fred's Ice Cream Parlor offers five different toppings. How many different possibilities of choosing three different toppings are there? Explain.

  $_5C_3 = 10$

- By accident Claud Klutz cut his wallet in half. The wallet contained a one, a five, and a ten dollar bill. If all of the "half bills" are placed in a bag and two are drawn at random, what is the expected value of two half bills? Explain. *Note:* A half bill is worthless unless its mate is selected.

  $\approx \$1.07 \left(\frac{16}{15}\right)$

- The freshman class at Cotati Tech are put into three dormitories: Picasso, Hemingway, and Mozart. The students are permitted to switch from one dorm to another, but only on the first Sunday of each month. The following is a graph of the movements between dorms last year. Note that Mozart is an all-female dorm, Hemingway is an all-male dorm, and Picasso is co-ed. (The percentage of students who do *not* move is *not* shown on the diagram.)

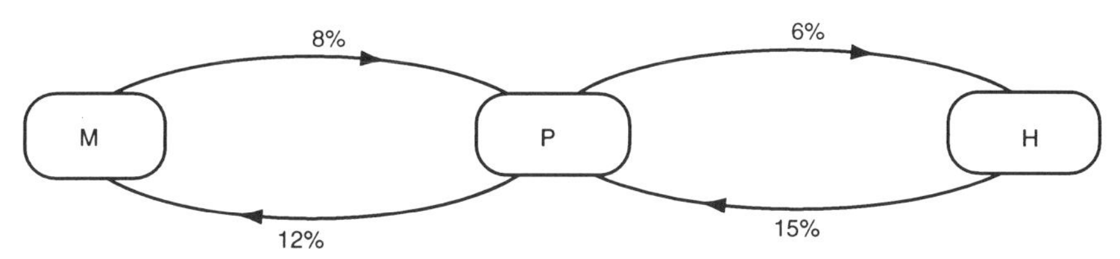

a. Create a transition matrix of this movement.

b. In September there were 80 students in Mozart, 60 students in Picasso, and 70 students in Hemingway. What were the populations of the dorms in October? In November? In May?

c. All this shifting may cause a problem of too many staff in some places and not enough in others. With what student distribution in the dorms should the school start the year to avoid having a staffing problem next year? Justify your response.

a. $$\begin{bmatrix} 0.92 & 0.08 & 0 \\ 0.12 & 0.82 & 0.06 \\ 0 & 0.15 & 0.85 \end{bmatrix}$$

b. **October: ≈ 81 in Mozart, ≈ 66 in Picasso, and ≈ 63 in Hemingway; November: ≈ 82 in Mozart, ≈ 70 in Picasso, and ≈ 58 in Hemingway; May: ≈ 94 in Mozart, ≈ 76 in Picasso, and ≈ 40 in Hemingway**

c. **Answers will vary. A population of approximately 109 in Mozart, 72 in Picasso, and 29 in Hemingway would remain stable. Whether that is possible depends on the number of men and the number of women enrolled in the school. It also depends on the capacity of the dorms, particularly Mozart.**

- Camila is told to prepare for her studio class a piece that is less than 10 minutes in length. Roberto (who is not as good yet) is asked to prepare something that is less than 5 minutes long. If class is to be over in 11 minutes and both of them still have to perform, what is the probability that they will run over the 11 minutes remaining? Explain.

$\frac{8}{50} \approx 0.16$

- Label each of the following statements about random numbers either true or false. Explain your answer.
  a. A random number generator should give an equal dispersion throughout its range.
  b. A random number generator should never give the same number twice in a row.
  c. The computer (calculator) is better at generating random integers than drawing numbered balls out of a velvet bag.
  d. Using a good random number generator, the experimental probability will approach the theoretical probability.

a. true **b. false** **c. false** **d. true**

- Suppose two numbers, x and y, are selected at random to hit this square.
  a. Shade the points (x, y) where $x + y < 80$.
  b. What is the theoretical probability that $x + y < 80$?

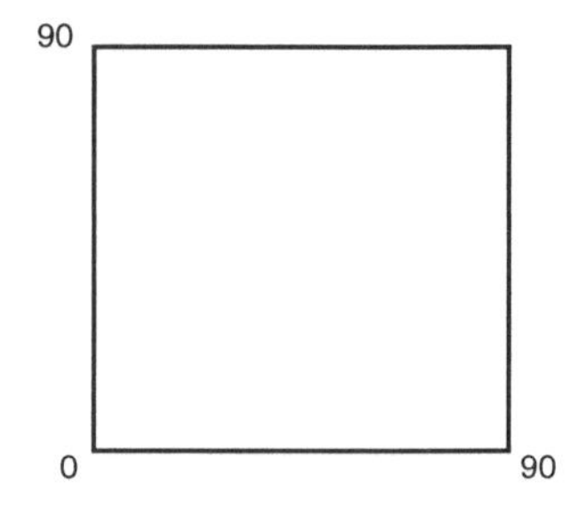

a.

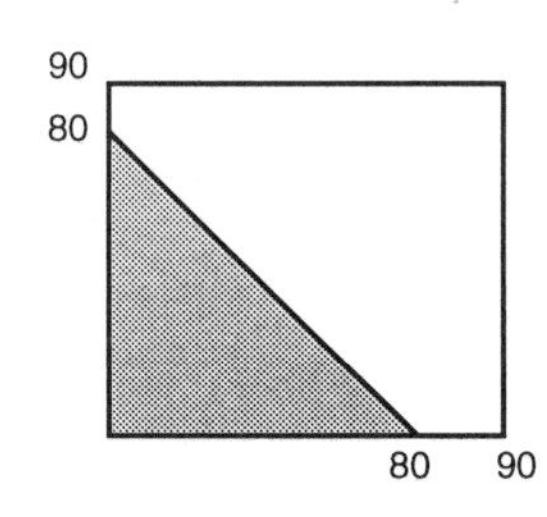

b. $\frac{32}{81} \approx 0.395$

- Driving northbound on Eugene Ormandy Avenue, a maintenance truck drops a gallon of red paint that spreads into a 20-foot-diameter circle. Later, on the same stretch of 200 feet of road, another truck drops a gallon of yellow paint that also spreads into a 20-foot-diameter circle.
  a. If the first truck dropped the can at the 30-foot mark, then the paint would spread from what point to what point?
  b. What is the meaning of the point at (30, 150) on the diagram.
  c. Indicate on the graph the region that represents where the two paint circles would overlap?
  d. Find the area of this region.
  e. What is the probability that the circles of paint will overlap?

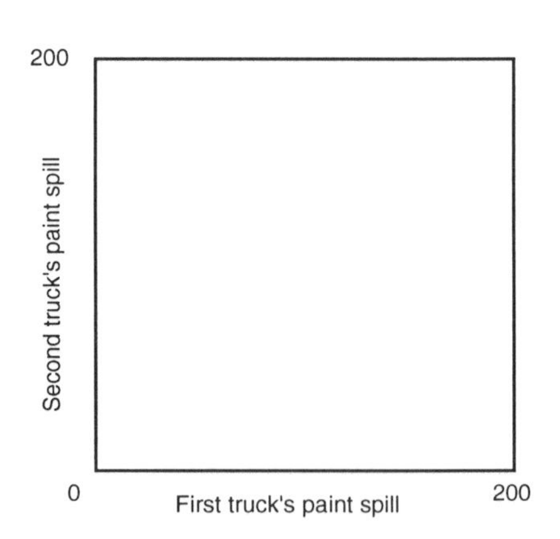

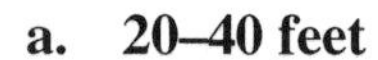

a. 20–40 feet

b. The first truck's paint spilled at 30 feet while the second truck's paint spilled at 150 feet.

c.

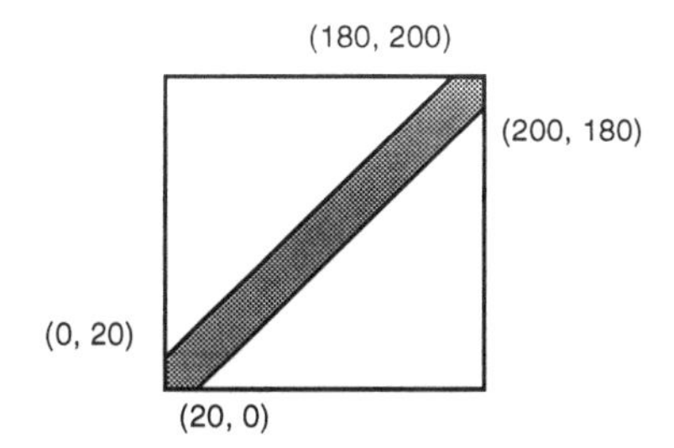

d. **7600 ft²**

e. $\mathbf{\frac{19}{100}}$

- One thousand points are randomly plotted in the rectangular region at right. Suppose that 263 of the points land in the shaded region of the rectangle. What is your best approximation of the area of the shaded region? Explain completely how and why you arrived at your answer.

  $\mathbf{\frac{263}{1000}(11.3)(7.4) \approx 22}$

- Your friend has created what he thinks is the best dart board possible. The dart board is in the shape of a regular hexagon and is divided into six regions. To each region he has assigned a point value from one to six. Your friend feels that this dart board is perfect for those people who are sure to hit the board, but not sure where on the board the dart will land.

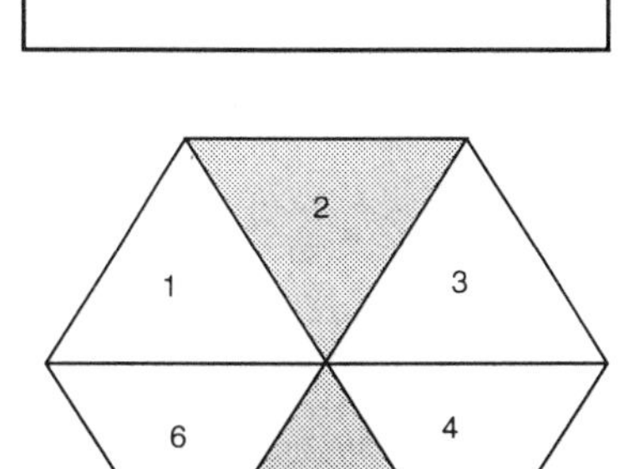

  a. Given this situation, what is the expected value of this dart board?

  b. Would you consider this dart board to be "fair" or "perfect"? Explain.

  a. **3.5**

  b. **Answers will vary. All scores are equally likely.**

- As you and a friend pass through the cafeteria line, you notice that all the good desserts are rapidly disappearing. When you finally reach the desserts, there are only four left: one chocolate pudding, one vanilla pudding, one strawberry Jell-O bowl, and one lime Jell-O bowl. Both you and your friend take one of the four remaining servings of dessert.

  a. Draw a tree graph representing all possible combinations that the two of you could choose.

  b. If one of the four desserts is poisoned and you took your dessert first, then what is the probability that you took the poisoned dessert?

  c. If your friend took her dessert second, what is the probability she took the poisoned dessert?

  d. If your friend does *not* have the poisoned dessert, what is the probability that you have it?

a. 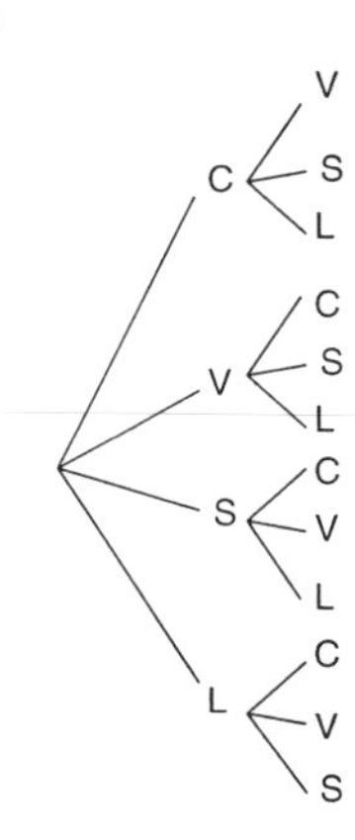

b. $\frac{1}{4}$ c. $\frac{1}{4}$ d. $\frac{1}{3}$

- How many ways can you list the five vowels, A, E, I, O, U?

5! = 120

- The table lists the distribution of students in Mr. and Mrs. K's algebra classes.

	10th grade	11th grade	12th grade	Total
Mrs. K.	7	7	1	
Mr. K.	2	12	2	
Total				

a. Complete the table by filling in any blank spaces.

b. Suppose both classes are meeting in the gym to play basketball. One student is selected at random to keep score. What is the probability that the score-keeper will be a sophomore?

c. The juniors decide to protest and they all sit down in the bleachers. One of them is selected at random to state the reason for the protest. What is the probability that the junior selected is in Mrs. K's class?

d. What is the probability that someone who is in Mr. K's class is a senior?

a.

	10th grade	11th grade	12th grade	Total
Mrs. K.	7	7	1	**15**
Mr. K.	2	12	2	**16**
Total	**9**	**19**	**3**	**31**

b. $\frac{9}{31}$ **c.** $\frac{7}{19}$ **d.** $\frac{2}{16}$

- Each year in your town, 72% of the people who have a profession in the fine arts continue to work in that profession. However, 28% of these people start a new career outside of the arts. Meanwhile, 94% of those who work outside of the arts continue to do so, and 6% switch to a career in the arts.

a. Draw a transition graph representing this situation.

b. Create a transition matrix representing this information.

c. Currently there are 1495 people who have a career in the arts and 1265 people who work outside of the arts. Write a matrix which displays this information.

d. Find the number of people with each type of career after 1 year; after 2 years; after 3 years.

a.

0.28
0.72 FA NC 0.94
0.06

b. $\begin{bmatrix} \mathbf{0.72} & \mathbf{0.28} \\ \mathbf{0.06} & \mathbf{0.94} \end{bmatrix}$

c. $\begin{bmatrix} \mathbf{1495} & \mathbf{1265} \end{bmatrix}$

d. $[\approx \mathbf{1152} \quad \approx \mathbf{1608}]$; $[\approx \mathbf{926} \quad \approx \mathbf{1834}]$; $[\approx \mathbf{777} \quad \approx \mathbf{1983}]$

- Ms. Smythe asks six students to to line up in front of the class.
  a. How many ways can these six students—Alonzo, Bahari, Carmel, Dai, Efia, and Frida—stand in a row for the line-up?
  b. What is the probability that Alonzo and Dai will stand next to each other if they line up randomly?
  c. How many different committees of four can be chosen from this same group of people?
  d. How many of these committees will contain Dai?
  e. A committee of four is selected at random. What is the probability that both Alonzo and Dai are on this committee?

a. $\mathbf{6! = 720}$ **b.** $\frac{1}{3}$ **c. 15**

d. $\frac{2}{3}$ **of the committees, or 10** **e.** $\frac{2}{5}$

- Your teacher is about to give you a true-or-false quiz with five questions on it, and you did not study at all. As a matter of fact, you don't even know what the quiz is going to cover. Consequently, you will have to guess at every answer.
  a. Draw a tree graph representing all possible answers for the five true-or-false questions on the quiz. How many different possibilities are there?
  b. If the correct answers were T, T, F, F, T, what is the probability that you will get them all correct?
  c. If all you knew is that the quiz contained three Trues and two Falses, how many possibilities are there?
  d. Knowing there are three Trues and two Falses, what is the probability you will get them all correct?
  e. If you knew that the answers to the first two questions on the quiz were True, how many possibilities are there having three Trues and two Falses?
  f. Knowing only that there are three True and two False answers and that the first two questions on the quiz are True, what is the probability you would get them all correct?

a. Branches double five times, once for each question. There are 32 possibilities.

b. $\frac{1}{32}$ **c. 10** **d.** $\frac{1}{10}$ **e. 3** **f.** $\frac{1}{3}$

- The debate continues! Should the toilet paper unroll over the top or from underneath? Every year 92% of those who mount their toilet paper so that it comes off over the top of the roll continue to do so. However, 8% of these persons switch and mount their toilet paper so that it comes off underneath the roll. Meanwhile, 87% of those who mount their toilet paper so that it comes off underneath the roll continue to do so, and 13% switch to mount it so that the paper comes off over the top of the roll.

  a. Draw a transition graph representing this situation.

  b. Create a transition matrix representing this information.

  c. Currently 135 million persons mount the paper so it comes off over the roll and 105 million mount it so it comes off underneath the roll. Write a matrix that displays this information.

  d. Find the number of persons with each paper mounting style after 1 year; after 2 years; after 3 years.

a.

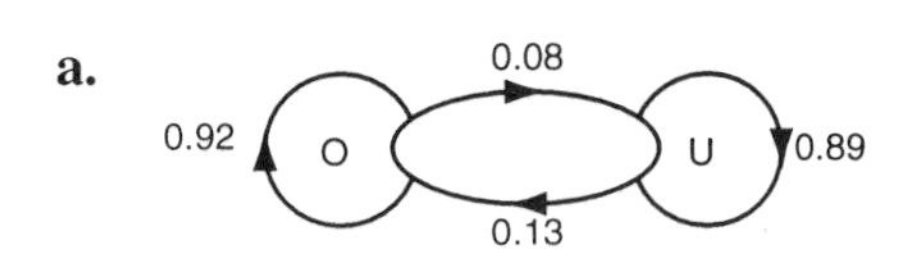

b. $\begin{bmatrix} \mathbf{0.92} & \mathbf{0.08} \\ \mathbf{0.13} & \mathbf{0.87} \end{bmatrix}$

c. $[\mathbf{135{,}000{,}000} \quad \mathbf{105{,}000{,}000}]$

d. $[\mathbf{137{,}850{,}000} \quad \mathbf{102{,}150{,}000}]$;
$[\mathbf{140{,}101{,}500} \quad \mathbf{99{,}898{,}500}]$;
$[\mathbf{141{,}880{,}185} \quad \mathbf{98{,}119{,}815}]$

- Can you guess what I'm thinking? If you think you can, perhaps you have ESP, extrasensory perception. This is not a sense like sight or smell, but a "sixth sense." The most common forms of ESP are telepathy (communicating without using the normal five senses), clairvoyance (the power to see objects or events not perceived by the normal five senses), and precognition (knowledge of future events).

  To test for ESP, parapsychologists perform different tests on people who believe they possess ESP. The most common test consists of the person believing to have ESP, the candidate, guessing what is on the back side of a card. Usually, the "deck" of cards contains 100 cards in random order. One side is completely blank and not transparent in any way. The other side has one of five patterns on it. There are equal numbers of each type of card in the deck.

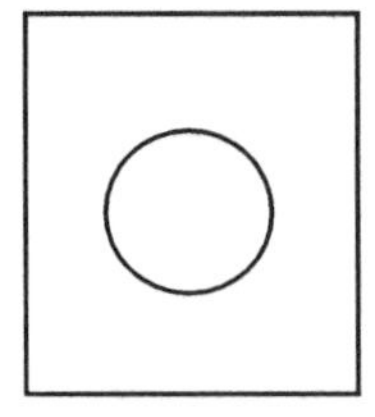 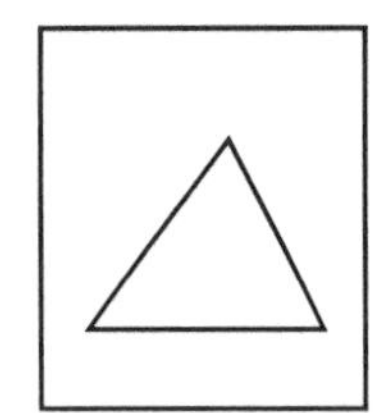 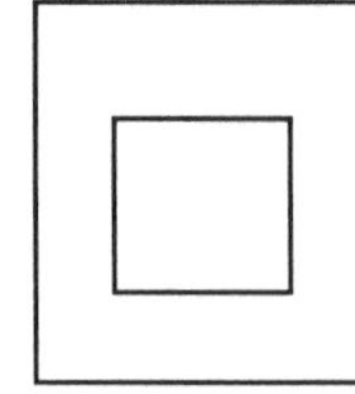 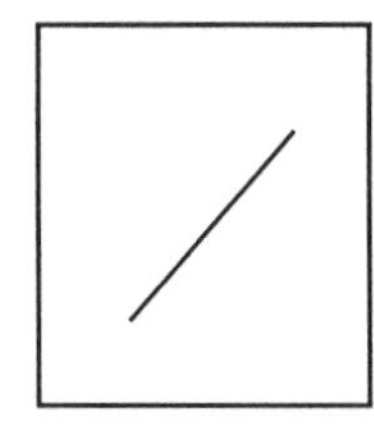 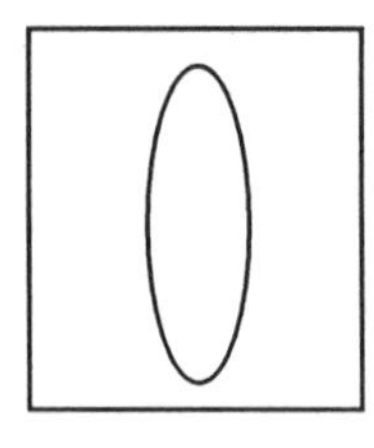

  The candidate states what he or she believes to be on the opposite side of the card as another person (who does not know the candidate) looks at the design on the card. A record is kept as to how many the candidate guesses correctly.

  a. For each type of card, if a candidate is just guessing, what is the probability that the candidate will guess correctly? Explain.

  b. For the average person, not necessarily having ESP, what is the expected number of correct guesses? Explain.

c. Suppose a candidate guessed 25 correct. What would you think? If a candidate guessed 78 correct, what would you think? Explain completely.

a. $\frac{1}{5}$

b. Expect to get about 20 out of 100 correct.

c. Answers will vary. With 25 correct, the person probably does not have ESP, but just happened to guess better than average. With 78 correct, it could be luck as well, but one might begin to believe the person has ESP.

Group Problems

- Your school's mathematics club needs to raise money, so they have decided to set up a booth at this year's spring carnival. They have also decided to devise a game similar to the "Pennies on a Grid" game in Investigation 8.4.1. Each player will throw his or her pennies on a grid laid out on a table within the booth. For each penny that does not cover a line of the grid, the player (that is, the thrower of the coin) will receive a prize. Otherwise, the grid is swept clean and the club gets those coins.

  Help the club out by discussing each of these issues.

  a. After 100 players have thrown a coin, about how many prizes will the club expect to give away?

  b. About how much should the club spend on each prize?

  c. What suggestions do you have for the club to make this more profitable, yet still have people play? (For instance, having each player throw five dollar bills at the grid would certainly be very profitable for the mathematics club, but, very few people would be willing to play the game if the prize was a stick of gum. What is the balance?) Explain completely and clearly, why your ideas are profitable.

  a. The theoretical probability is ≈ 0.0625 so you would expect them to give away about 6 prizes.

  b. The club would only collect $1.00 in 100 plays, but would have given away about 6 prizes. Spending about 17¢ per item would be fair.

  c. Answers will vary.

- You are in charge of ordering pizzas for a party. As you speak to each one of the guests, you record each person's first-name initial across the top of a table. Then, you put an "X" next to the items that person *does not* like combined on one pizza.

	P	M	H	PA	G	B	O
Pepperoni				X			X
Mushrooms				X		X	
Ham						X	
Pineapple	X	X				X	X
Green pepper						X	
Black olives		X	X	X	X		
Onions	X			X			

  a. Is it possible to please everyone?

  b. If it is possible, explain how. If it isn't possible, come up with the best solution. (*Note:* You will need to explain how you interpret "best.")

a. Yes, by getting a pizza with *no* toppings or by getting more than one pizza.

b. Answers will vary.

The following is adapted from an article titled "Graph Chasing Across the Curriculum: Paths, Circuits, and Applications" by Althoen, Brown, and Bumcrot in the *NCTM 1991 Yearbook.*

- Huffman Codes

A teacher intercepts a note in class, and she quickly realizes that at least two of her students have done some additional research into encoding messages. She recognizes the tree and sequences of ones and zeroes as a *Huffman Code*.

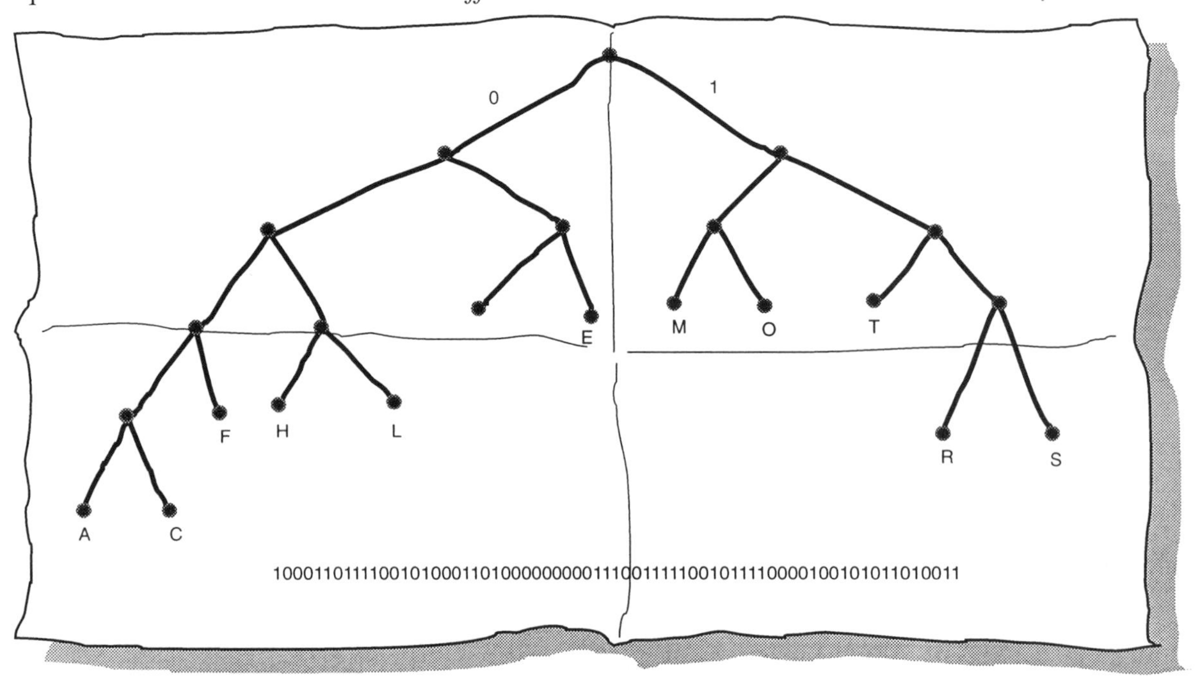

She remembers from her study of codes in her mathematics class that the zeros and ones just tell her whether or not to go left or right on the tree's branches. She begins to decipher the code: **1**-right, **0**-left, **0**-left, and she's at "M." That's the first letter. To find the second letter, she will continue with the next **0**.

a. Decipher the code for the teacher.

b. After cracking this code, the teacher decides to do a little coding herself! Knowing that her principal loves solving different types of puzzles, she decides to send him this message:

I DESERVE A RAISE

Code this message for the teacher using a Huffman Code. Devise an appropriate tree and the correct sequence of zeros and ones. *Note:* There is more than one way to code this message, but you want to make the tree as small as possible and the sequence of zeros and ones as short as possible.

c. A little research: When, where, and how were Huffman Codes used?

a. Meet me after school. **b. Answers will vary.**

Chapter 9: Systems of Equations

Journal Questions

- The title of this chapter is Systems of Equations, and although this title is appropriate, come up with another title that is more interesting yet still conveys what the chapter is about. Explain your title and justify why you think it is a good title.

  Answers will vary.

- Describe how a graph can be used to solve a system of equations.

  Answers will vary, but look for specifics, perhaps an example.

- If you were going to write the test for this chapter, what would you cover? Why?

  Answers will vary.

- In this chapter, you looked at solving systems of equations for both two and three variables. Explain the similarities and differences of the graphs of equations with two variables and the graphs of equations with three variables.

  Answers will vary. Solutions are similar: no solution when they don't cross; one solution means one point of intersection; infinitely many solutions can be a line, a curve, or a plane.

- What graphing calculator skills have you mastered during this chapter? Explain thoroughly and use examples. What graphing calculator skills have you not yet mastered? Provide an example for which you need a calculator skill that you have not yet mastered.

  Answers will vary.

- How has your ability to do mathematics changed throughout the year? Do you feel you have improved? Explain.

  Answers will vary.

- Find three problems in the chapter that you feel are representative of the chapter. Write out the problem and the solution. For each problem, explain why you feel it is representative of the chapter. Please use complete, coherent sentences.

  Answers will vary.

- What ideas or topics were introduced in this chapter that you feel you do not quite understand yet or for which you do not see the purpose? Give examples.

  Answers will vary.

- Throughout this year, we have been asking you to find a problem that you cannot solve. Look over the problems you have chosen in the past as difficult, or "unsolvable," problems. Can you solve them now? What is still keeping you from solving them? Explain.

  Answers will vary.

- If you had to choose a favorite problem from this unit, what would it be? Why?

Open-ended Problems

- How often in the "real world" do you think systems of equations are used? Explain.

Answers will vary, but since an answer is meaningless without an explanation, be sure to read the explanations carefully.

- How many different methods do you know to solve a system of equations? What are they? Which do you prefer? Why?

  Answers will vary. Students may count substitution and elimination as two different methods; others may just say "Algebra" as the method.

- Use a straightedge to neatly draw a polygon on graph paper. Label the vertices. Write the set of inequalities that, when graphed, will produce the polygon. *Note:* The kind of polygon you choose will be taken into account when graded. You can do a very simple figure, or you can impress your teacher and choose a more complex polygon.

  Answers will vary.

- Write equations of two lines for which the intersection is

  a. one point.

  b. no points.

  c. more than one point.

  Answers will vary.

- Why can't you find the inverse of the matrix below? Explain

$$\begin{bmatrix} 1 & ^{-}2 \\ 2 & 1 \\ ^{-}1 & ^{-}4 \end{bmatrix}$$

  To have an inverse, the matrix must have the same number of rows as columns.

- Fred and Ethel are working on a very long mathematics assignment in which they are to solve all kinds of problems. In some problems they must just solve for x. In others, they must solve for x and y. After one hour of hard work and only being halfway through the assignment, Ethel is very frustrated.

  "This is ridiculous!" Ethel exclaims. "I'm spending all my homework time on math. Doesn't our teacher realize we have other classes too!"

  "Calm down, Ethel," Fred says. "We only have 25 more problems to go. It should only take another couple of hours."

  "Maybe for you, Fred, but not for me!" With that, Ethel gets up and finds her graphing calculator.

  "Ethel! That's not going to help!" Fred yells.

  "Sure it is," Ethel replies. "I'll whiz through the rest of these problems."

  "No you won't! How do you intend to do this problem?" With that, Fred tears off a piece of the homework assignment and shoves it into Ethel's face. The paper has this problem on it.

$$3(1.04)^x = 17$$

Is Fred right? Is Ethel doomed to slowly work out all of the problems? Or is Ethel correct that she can use the graphing calculator to help solve the problem? Explain.

Ethel can solve it by graphing $y = 3(1.04)^x$ and $y = 17$ and tracing to find where the graphs intersect.

- Create your own problem that covers the material you have studied so far and that you think would make a good assessment question. Write out the complete solution to your problem and explain why you believe it to be a good problem. *Note:* Please make sure that it is a problem or question and not just an explanation or description.

  Answers will vary.

- Describe two different possible situations that this 2×3 matrix could represent:

$$\begin{bmatrix} 3 & 4 & 5 \\ 1 & 2 & 3 \end{bmatrix}$$

  Answers will vary. One possibility: it could represent the solution to the problem "Where do the lines $3x + 4y = 5$ and $x + 2y = 3$ cross?"

- Write three chapter-appropriate, interesting questions about the graph at the right.

  Answers will vary.

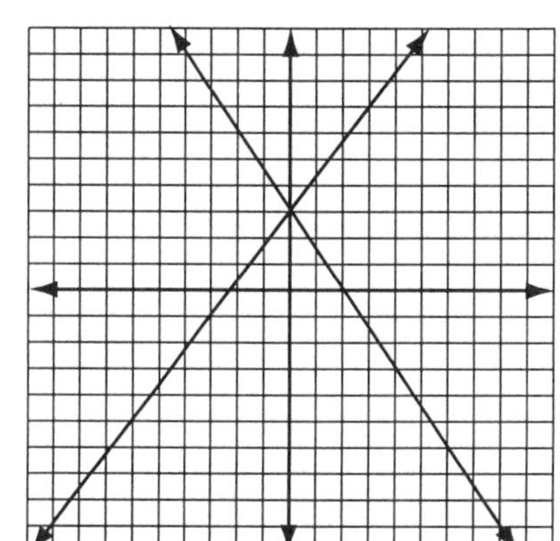

- Explain in your own words *why* matrices can be used to solve systems of equations. (*Note:* The question is *why*, not *how*.)

  The matrices hold the coefficients in the correct place. Since you don't change the variables, you don't need to keep writing them down.

- You and a friend were supposed to go to the movies, but she calls you to say she won't be able to go because of her mathematics homework. (It seems she is not as fortunate as you and does not have as reasonable a teacher as you do!) The instructions for her homework are the following:

  > For each of the following 100 systems of equations, identify each system as being dependent, independent, or inconsistent.

  Your friend would like to go to the movies, but doesn't think it will be possible with 100 systems to solve. Help your friend by explaining a quick way to determine whether the system is dependent, independent, or inconsistent. Explain clearly and completely. She will be tested on this!

  Graph the lines. If they are parallel, then the system is inconsistent. If the two lines intersect, then the system is independent; and if there is only one line, then the system is dependent.

- For the following problem, please follow this format.
  - i. State the problem.
  - ii. What do you already know that would help you solve this problem? Who (in your group) knows it and how does he or she know it?
  - iii. What information do you need to assume? Why are you assuming it?
  - iv. Record all your steps in solving the problem.

v. State your answer clearly and completely.

vi. How good is your answer? Remember: "A chain is only as strong as its weakest link!" What are your most unreliable approximations and weakest assumptions?

Consider an average, college-bound student. Would it be better to take out a loan from a bank to pay for college, or work part-time while going to school?

Answers will vary.

Projects

- Build three-dimensional models that represent the graphs of equations with three variables and the various numbers of solutions possible.

  Answers will vary.

- On a full sheet of graph paper, draw a set of axes in the middle of the page. Using a straightedge, plot, label, and connect the following three points: $A(-2, 3)$, $B(-1, 1)$, and $C(-5, 2)$.

  a. For each of the points *A*, *B*, and *C*, rewrite the coordinates as a 2×1—matrix, for example, point *A* would be written as $\begin{bmatrix} ^-2 \\ 3 \end{bmatrix}$. Call these new matrices by their point names—for example, $[A] = \begin{bmatrix} ^-2 \\ 3 \end{bmatrix}$.

  b. Calculate $R \bullet A$, $R \bullet B$, and $R \bullet C$, where $[R] = \begin{bmatrix} 0 & 1 \\ ^-1 & 0 \end{bmatrix}$. Label the new matrices A', B', and C'.

  c. Plot, label, and connect the new points A', B', and C'.

  d. Is ΔABC congruent to $\Delta A'B'C'$? Justify your answer.

  e. Something geometrical happened to ΔABC to produce $\Delta A'B'C'$. Experiment with other shapes until you can describe in detail what is happening geometrically. *Note:* This means that someone should be able to produce $\Delta A'B'C'$ without performing the matrix multiplication.

  f. What happens if you multiply by the matrix $S = \begin{bmatrix} 0 & ^-1 \\ 1 & 0 \end{bmatrix}$ instead of $[R]$?

  g. Try to figure out what is happening geometrically if you multiply by the matrix

  $$T = \begin{bmatrix} \frac{\sqrt{2}}{2} & \frac{\sqrt{2}}{2} \\ -\frac{\sqrt{2}}{2} & \frac{\sqrt{2}}{2} \end{bmatrix}.$$

  a. $[B] = \begin{bmatrix} ^-1 \\ 1 \end{bmatrix}$, $[C] = \begin{bmatrix} ^-5 \\ 2 \end{bmatrix}$

b. $[A'] = \begin{bmatrix} 3 \\ 2 \end{bmatrix}, [B'] = \begin{bmatrix} 1 \\ 1 \end{bmatrix}, [C'] = \begin{bmatrix} 2 \\ 5 \end{bmatrix}$

d. **Yes, by SSS; side lengths: $\sqrt{10}$, $\sqrt{5}$, and $\sqrt{17}$.**

e. **Rotated clockwise 90° about the origin.**

f. $[A'] = \begin{bmatrix} ^-3 \\ ^-2 \end{bmatrix}, [B'] = \begin{bmatrix} ^-1 \\ ^-1 \end{bmatrix}, [C'] = \begin{bmatrix} ^-2 \\ ^-5 \end{bmatrix}$**, rotated counterclockwise 90° about the origin.**

g. $[A'] \approx \begin{bmatrix} 0.71 \\ 3.54 \end{bmatrix}, [B'] \approx \begin{bmatrix} 0 \\ 1.41 \end{bmatrix}, [C'] \approx \begin{bmatrix} ^-2.12 \\ 4.95 \end{bmatrix}$**, rotated clockwise 45° about the origin.**

Skill Questions: Appropriate for Quizzes or Tests

- Solve the following system of equations in as many ways as possible. Explain each method as you do it. You will be graded on the thoroughness and clarity of your explanations as well as on the mathematical correctness. Use as many methods as possible, showing everything you know about systems of equations.

$$3x + 7y = -3$$
$$5x - 6y = 48$$

Methods will vary. Solution: (6, ⁻3).

- Woody Planck is starting a business of manufacturing cutting boards. He has two designs that he will make. The first is a checkerboard pattern made of cherry and maple. It takes 8 strips of cherry and 12 strips of maple. He can sell it to the local gift shop for $9. The second pattern is a striped board. It takes 9 strips of cherry and 8 strips of maple. The gift shop will pay $7.50 for this board. Woody has 105 strips of cherry and 107 strips of maple in stock.

How many cutting boards of each pattern should Woody make in order to maximize his profit? What is that profit? Show all work and explain your steps.

Four checkerboards with seven stripes, or two checkerboards with nine stripes. Each choice will bring in $88.50.

- Consider the following two equations:

$$y = 2(2.5)^x$$
$$y = x^2 + 3$$

a. Find the x-coordinate of the point of intersection of these two curves. Give your answer accurate to the nearest thousandth.

b. Write an equation for which the x-coordinate that you found in part a is a solution. Explain how you know.

a. $x \approx 0.546$ **b.** $2(2.5)^x = x^2 + 3$.

- Solve the following system using substitution. Show all your work.

$$y = 6x - 26.2$$
$$4x + 3y = 24.8$$

(4.7, 2)

- Solve the following system, using elimination. Show all your work.

$$x - 2y = {}^-5$$
$$3x + 4y = 26$$

$\left(\frac{16}{5}, \frac{41}{10}\right)$

- Classify the following system as inconsistent or dependent. Justify your conclusion.

$$2.4x - 3.6y = 8$$
$$\frac{2}{9}(3x - 9) = y$$

Inconsistent

- Locate all points of intersection of $y = \sqrt{4 - x^2}$ and $y = \frac{1}{2}x^2$. Give answers to the nearest hundredth.

($\pm$1.57, 1.23)

- Solve for w, x, y, and z. Show or explain your work.

$$w + 2x - y + z = 2$$
$$3w - x + 2y - 4z = {}^-7$$
$$2w + 6x - y + 5z = 18$$
$${}^-5w + 3x - 6y + 7z = 4$$

(8, ⁻7.8, 0.2, 9.8)

- Describe two different ways to determine if a system of two linear equations is inconsistent.

If the graphs are parallel, or by solving and coming up with a false statement.

- Write an equation that forms a dependent system with $3x - 2y = 7$.

Any multiple: $3kx - 2ky = 7k$

- Explain two different ways to find the solution to the system:

$$4x - 3y = 7.9$$
$$2x + y = 6.7$$

Algebraically and by graphing are two possibilities.

- Write a system of equations that has (2, 3) as a solution.

Answers will vary.

- One day as young Clark Kent was walking home from school he saw a train headed for the crossing 6 miles down the road. As the engine crossed the road, he took off running at a 60° angle to the road. Clark runs at 60 mi/hr and the train travels at 50 mi/hr. How far ahead of the train does Clark cross the track? Record the equations you used to solve this problem.

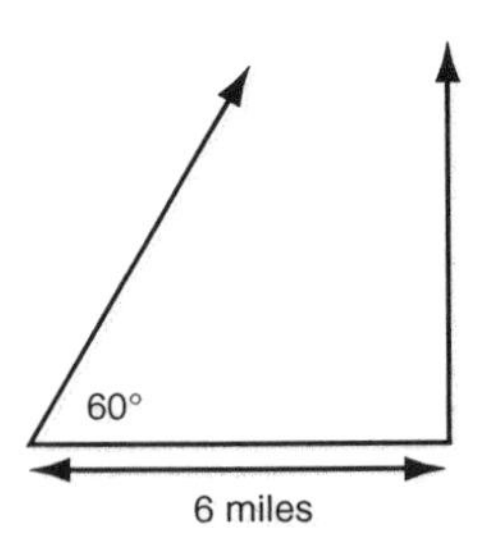

In 12 minutes, Clark reaches the tracks. At that point the train has gone 10 miles. Clark crosses just ≈ 0.39 miles down the track from the train.

- Sales clerks at Gracy's Department Store earn \$4.40 an hour plus 10% of all their sales. Those who work at Mumbles Department Store earn \$4.65 an hour plus 7.5% of their sales. All clerks work 40 hours each week. What amount of sales will a Gracy's clerk need to make in order to take home a bigger paycheck than a Mumbles' clerk?

  A weekly total of \$400 in sales is the "break-even" point; at this level both stores offer the same wage. With greater sales, working at Gracy's is the better-paying job.

- The relief organization, Food for Folks, plans to fly a plane of supplies to a small nation that is suffering from famine. The plane will carry bags of powdered milk, rice, and beans. The milk will come in 50-pound bags, the rice in 50-pound bags, and the beans in 40-pound bags. The plane can safely carry 100,000 pounds. However, the plane has only 9225 cubic feet available for the cargo. Each bag of milk requires 5 cubic feet, each bag of rice requires 4.5 cubic feet, and each bag of beans requires 3 cubic feet of space. The planned budget for the cargo is \$27,800. Checking with their suppliers they find that they can purchase bags of milk for \$18 each, bags of rice for \$8 each, and bags of beans for \$9 each. How many bags of each item should they put on the plane?

  Milk: 1050 bags; rice: 550 bags; and beans: 500 bags.

- Find values for f and g so that the matrix below has no inverse.

$$\begin{bmatrix} 5 & f \\ g & {}^{-}4 \end{bmatrix}$$

  Answers will vary. Any f and g such that $f \cdot g = 20$.

- Find the inverse of each matrix if it exists.

a. $\begin{bmatrix} 12 & 8 \\ {}^{-}4 & {}^{-}3 \end{bmatrix}$ b. $\begin{bmatrix} 3 & 2 & 1 \\ 4 & 2 & 3 \\ {}^{-}1 & {}^{-}2 & 1 \end{bmatrix}$

a. $\begin{bmatrix} \frac{3}{4} & 2 \\ {}^{-}1 & {}^{-}3 \end{bmatrix}$ **b.** $\begin{bmatrix} 2 & {}^{-}1 & 1 \\ {}^{-}1.75 & 1 & {}^{-}1.25 \\ {}^{-}1.5 & 1 & {}^{-}0.5 \end{bmatrix}$

- Give the definition of an identity matrix.

  An $n \cdot n$ matrix with entries of zero everywhere except on the diagonal, where there are only ones. If you multiply any other $n \cdot n$ matrix [A] by the identity matrix, the result is always [A].

- Graph the region described by the inequations. Identify the coordinates of each vertex.

  $y \geq 5 - 2x$

  $y \geq 0.6x - 3$

  $y \leq 0.6 + 0.2x$

  $y \geq 0$

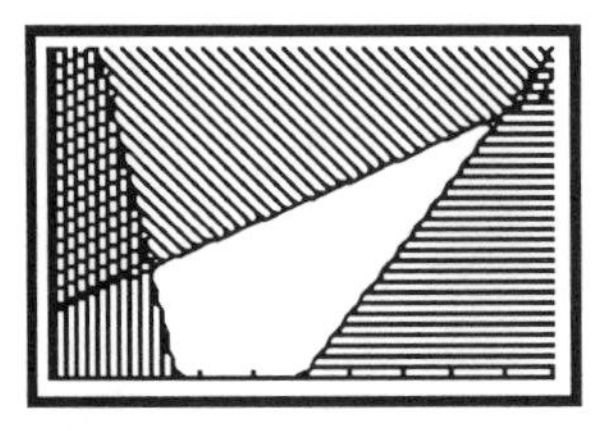

[0, 10, 1, 0, 3, 1]

(2, 1), (2.5, 0), (5, 0), (9, 2.4)

- a. Graph the following system of inequations.

  $x + y \le 8$

  $2x - y \le 4$

  $x + 2y \ge 8$

  $x \ge 0$

  $y \ge 0$

  b. Within the region bounded by the inequations, find the point whose coordinates give the maximum value for the expression $2x - 3y$. What is that maximum value?

  c. Within this region, find the point whose coordinates give the minimum value for the expression $2x - 3y$. What is that minimum value?

a.

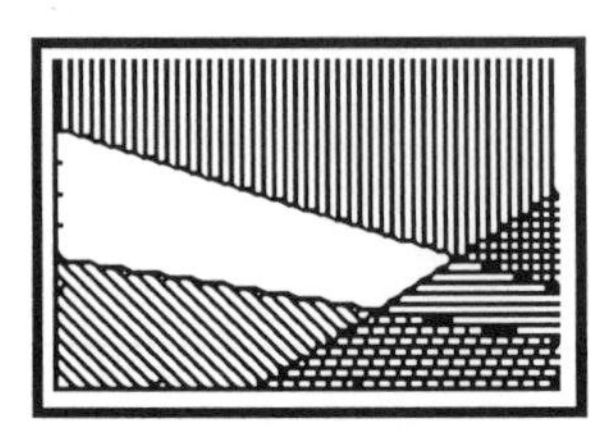

[0, 5, 1, 0, 10, 1]

b. Max of $\frac{^{-}4}{5}$ at $\left(\frac{16}{5}, \frac{12}{5}\right)$ **c. Min of $^{-}24$ at (0, 8)**

- Bea Phlatt, manager of the Monotown Symphony Orchestra, is planning to order new filing cabinets for music storage. There are two companies that make cabinets that Bea feels are suitable. She knows that Acme cabinets each cost \$40, require 6 square feet of floor space, and hold 8 cubic feet. On the other hand, Zenith cabinets each cost \$80, require 8 square feet of floor space, and hold 12 cubic feet of stuff. Her budget allows her to spend no more than \$560 on the cabinets. The Symphony Library room has no more than 72 square feet of floor space for cabinets. Bea wants to get the greatest storage capacity possible within the limitations imposed by her budget and available space. How many of each type should she order?

  Eight Acme cabinets and three Zenith cabinets will give 100 cubic feet of storage.

- Wanda Part is trying to get across L.A. to the movie studio. This time she must reach her destination within 90 minutes. Cabs travel a mile in 2 minutes and buses travel a mile in 5 minutes. The cab will cost \$1.10 each mile and the bus will run 30¢ for each mile. She has only \$20 to spend. The first bus stop is 5 miles away, so she must ride a cab at least to that point. The far east gate of the movie lot is 21 miles away and the far west gate is 25 miles away. The producer will meet her at any of the dozens of gates on the lot. As she travels she can memorize six lines from her script for each mile she rides in a cab and five for each mile riding in the bus. How can she maximize the lines memorized and stay within her constraints? How many lines has she memorized?

  The vertices (c, b) of the feasibility region are: ($11\frac{2}{3}$, $13\frac{1}{3}$), (15.625, 9.375), (5, 16), (17.125, 3.875). Max at (15.625, 9.375) with 140 lines (not quite 141).

- The Fumbling Feet dance company is given two choices of how they will be paid for a performance. Either they will receive \$15,000 plus 3% of the ticket sales or they will receive \$7,000 plus 17% of the ticket sales. The company will give three performances, and the hall seats 2400 persons. All tickets to the concerts will cost \$15. What audience do they need to draw to make both plans pay the same?

  At 3809 tickets for all three shows, the first plan gives \$16,714.05 while the second plan gives \$16,712.95. At 3810 tickets, plan 1 gives \$16,714.50 and plan 2 gives \$16,715.50. So you cannot make both plans exactly the same.

- Consider the graph at right. (Each grid line represents one unit.)

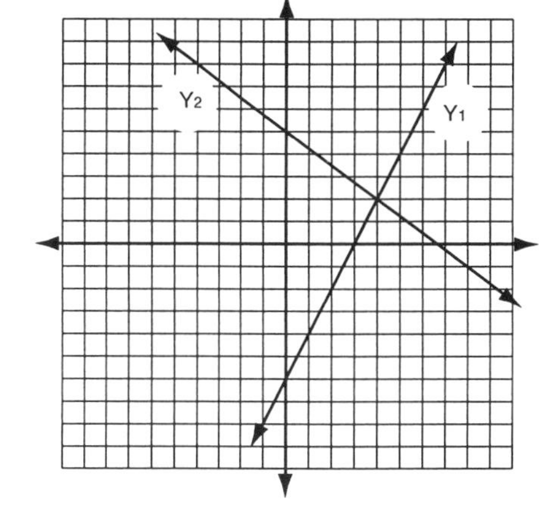

  a. What is the solution to the system pictured? Explain how you know.

  b. Is the system inconsistent? Is the system dependent? Explain.

  c. Write equations for the pictured lines in this system.

  a. (4, 2) because that's where the graphs intersect.

  b. Neither inconsistent nor dependent; the lines intersect and there are two distinct lines.

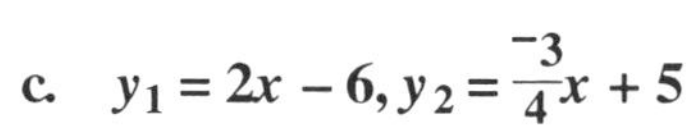

  c. $y_1 = 2x - 6, y_2 = \frac{-3}{4}x + 5$

- a. Write two linear equations such that the solution to the system is the point (3, ⁻2).

  b. Carefully graph and label the two equations from part a.

  a. and b. Answers will vary.

- The equations $Y1 = 3^x$ and $Y2 = x^3$ form a system.

  a. Find *all solutions* (x, y) for this system, correct to 0.001.

  b. Graph Y1 – Y2.

  c. What is the connection between the x-intercepts of Y1 – Y2 and the answer to part a? Be clear.

  a. 2.476 and 3.000 **c. They are the same.**

- Find the point where the graphs of $3x + 4y = -11$ and $5x - 6y = 45$ meet. What method did you use? Why?

  (3, ⁻5)

- Explain why (0.5, 4.75) a solution of the system of equations given below.

$$7x - 2y = -6$$
$$5x + 2y = 12$$

  7(0.5) – 2(4.75) = ⁻6 and 5(0.5) + 2(4.75) = 12

- The line pictured, passing through the points (0, 6) and (6, 1), has the equation $5x + 6y = 36$. Write a system of inequations that describes the shaded region.

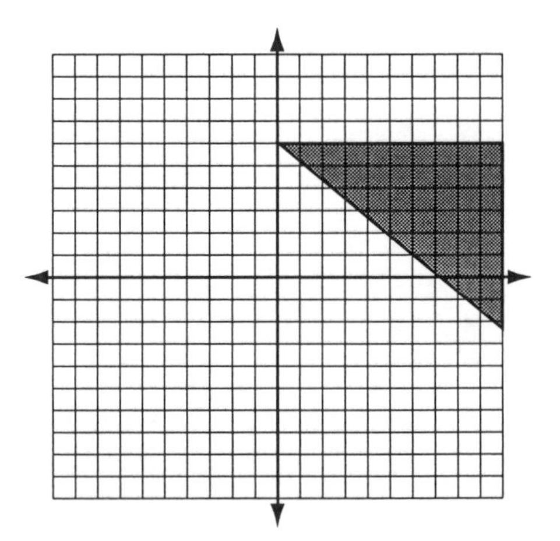

  $5x + 6y \geq 36 \quad x \leq 10 \quad y \leq 6$

- a. What is the 2×2 identity matrix?

  b. Prove that it is an identity matrix using $\begin{bmatrix} -4 & 3.5 & 7 \\ -8.5 & 2 & -10 \end{bmatrix}$.

  c. Find the inverse matrix of

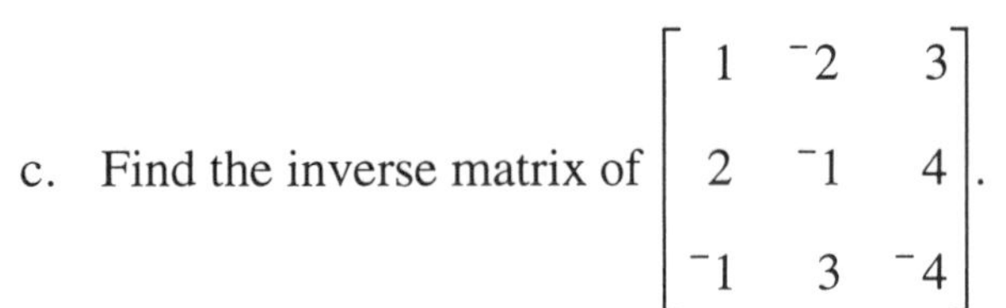

$$\begin{bmatrix} 1 & -2 & 3 \\ 2 & -1 & 4 \\ -1 & 3 & -4 \end{bmatrix}.$$

  d. Prove that your answer to part c is correct.

  a. $\begin{bmatrix} \mathbf{1} & \mathbf{0} \\ \mathbf{0} & \mathbf{1} \end{bmatrix}$ **b. Multiply and it will stay the same.** **c.** $\begin{bmatrix} \mathbf{8} & \mathbf{-1} & \mathbf{5} \\ \mathbf{-4} & \mathbf{1} & \mathbf{-2} \\ \mathbf{-5} & \mathbf{1} & \mathbf{-3} \end{bmatrix}$

- Solve the system

$$7x + 3y - 5z + u + 4v = 120$$
$$10x + 2y + 4z - 3u + v = 225$$
$$9x - 8y + z + 5u + 3v = 345$$
$$6x + y + 8z + 9u + 5v = 830$$
$$-2x + 7y + 3z + 4u - v = 325$$

  $x = 20, y = 15, z = 30, u = 45, v = 10$

- Suppose that you go into business raising thoroughbreds and quarterhorses. Having studied linear programming, you decide to maximize the profit you can make. Let x be the number of thoroughbreds, and let y be the number of quarterhorses you raise each year.

  a. Write inequalities expressing each of the following requirements:

     i. Your supplier can get you at most 20 thoroughbreds and at most 15 quarterhorses to raise each year.

     ii. You must raise a total of at least 12 horses each year to make the business profitable.

iii. A thoroughbred eats 2 tons of food per year, but a quarterhorse eats 6 tons per year. You can handle no more than 96 tons of food per year.

iv. A thoroughbred requires 1000 hours of training per year, and a quarterhorse only 250 hours per year. You have enough personnel to do at most 10,000 hours of training per year.

b. Draw a graph of the feasible region.

a. **i.** $\mathbf{x \le 20, y \le 15}$

ii. $\mathbf{x + y \ge 12}$

iii. $\mathbf{2x + 6y \le 96}$

iv. $\mathbf{1000x + 250y \le 10{,}000}$

b.

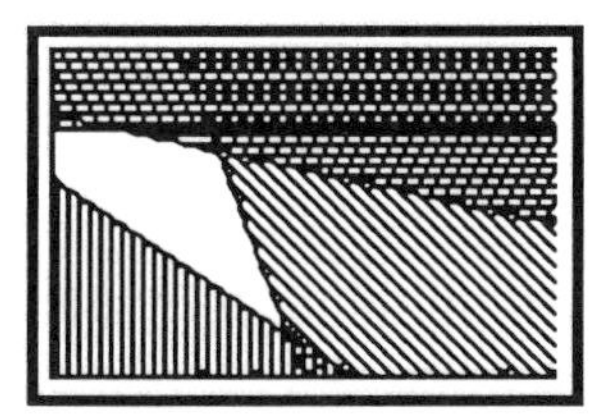

[0, 20, 2, 0, 20, 5]

- To keep track of his merchandise, a dealer in old pinball machines uses matrices and his computer. In his computer he can store information about his stock, the number of sales, and his costs and profits. Below is his selling matrix, S, for April.

	Brand	Wizard	ADK	Davis
Date of manufacture	1956	2	1	0
	1958	0	3	1
	1960	1	2	3

= S (selling matrix)

The average cost and profit for April is shown in the matrix (in dollars) below

	Cost-price	Profit
Wizard	5000	2000
ADK	3500	1500
Davis	3000	1500

= D (dollar matrix)

Calculate $[S] \bullet [D]$ and explain the meaning of this matrix product.

$$\begin{bmatrix} 13{,}500 & 5{,}500 \\ 13{,}500 & 6{,}000 \\ 21{,}000 & 9{,}500 \end{bmatrix}$$

The matrix shows the money taken in and the profit for each of the three years.

- Find the equation of the parabola passing through the points $(-3, 6)$, $(1, -7)$, and $(5, 9)$.

$\mathbf{y = 0.90625x^2 - 1.4375x - 6.46875}$

- Use the determinant of the coefficient matrix to determine whether or not each system has a unique solution.

a. $2x + 3y = 32$
$5x + 4y = 59$

b. $3x + 4y = 19$
$2y + 3z = 8$
$4x - 5z = 7$

c. $15x + 12y = 8$
$10x + 8y = 13$

d. $15x - 12y = 18$
$10x - 8y = 12$

a. Det = $^-7 \neq 0$, unique solution.

b. Det = $18 \neq 0$, unique solution.

c. Det = 0, not unique, no solution.

d. Det = 0, not unique, infinitely, many solutions.

Group Problems

- The Mathematics Club has decided to raise money by charging for helping students with their homework and with studying for a test. Unfortunately, the Student Council, recognizing this potential money-making scheme, has put some strange restrictions on the Mathematics Club's venture. (The Student Council is planning to have a bake sale about the same time; they don't like competition.) Let x be the number of hours of homework help each day, and let y be the number of hours of help studying for a test each day. The list of conditions they must meet each day are listed below in parts a–d. Translate each condition into an inequality and graph each result. After all inequations have been graphed, darken the region that satisfies all conditions.

a. The total number of helping hours for both homework and studying for tests must be at least 10.

b. The number of hours of homework help must be between 5 and 20, inclusive.

c. The number of hours of test-studying help must be not more than twice the number of homework hours, but at least one-sixth the number of homework hours.

d. Ten times the number of homework hours plus thirteen times the number of studying hours must be at most 260.

e. If the Mathematics Club charges \$5.00 per hour for homework help, and \$7.00 per hour for help studying for a test, how can the Mathematics Club maximize their daily earnings?

a. $x + y \geq 10$

b. $5 \leq x \leq 20$

c. $y \leq 2x, y \geq \frac{1}{6}x$

d. $10x + 13y \leq 260$

e.

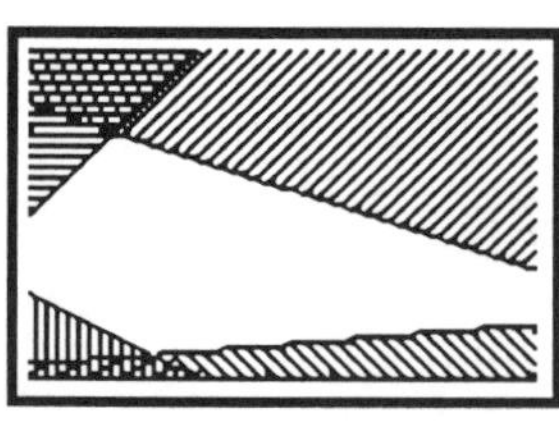

[5, 20, 2, 0, 20, 5]

$\left(\frac{65}{9}, \frac{130}{9}\right)$ gives \$137.22.

- Little Danny Q. Ale has decided to open his own business building potato-head aliens he calls YesEs and NoEs. Danny has all the potatoes he needs for his business venture, but he has only a limited supply of the essential alien potato-head body parts. In his toy box he has a total of 36 eyes, 14 noses, and 15 mouths. He builds each YesE with four eyes, two noses, and one mouth. A NoE has six eyes, one nose, and three mouths. He makes $1.00 on each YesE and $2.00 on each NoE.

  a. How many YesEs and NoEs should he build in order to maximize the amount of money he makes selling them? Show all work.

  b. News flash! People want YesEs! He can now make $3.00 on a YesE and $2.00 on a NoE. Now, how many of each type of potato-head aliens should Danny make to maximize his profit? Show all work.

  a. Make three YesEs and four NoEs to make $11.00.

  b. Make six YesEs and two NoEs to make $22.00.

Chapter 10: Polynomials

Journal Questions

- The title of this chapter is Polynomials, yet you start off by examining finite differences. In your own words, explain how these two ideas are related. Are they really the same thing?

  Answers will vary.

- In this chapter you studied polynomial functions. Describe the different types of functions you have looked at so far this year. Explain the similarities and differences between these different types of functions.

  Answers will vary.

- If you were going to write the test for this chapter, what would you cover? Why?

  Answers will vary.

- What graphing calculator skills have you mastered during this chapter? Explain thoroughly and use examples. What graphing calculator skills have you not yet mastered? Provide an example for which you need a calculator skill that you have not yet mastered.

  Answers will vary.

- How has your ability to do mathematics changed throughout the year? Do you feel you have improved? Explain.

  Answers will vary.

- Find three problems in the chapter that you feel are representative of the chapter. Write out the problem and the solution. For each problem, explain why you feel it is representative of the chapter. Please use complete, coherent sentences.

- What ideas or topics were introduced in this chapter that you feel you do not quite understand yet or for which you do not see the purpose? Give examples.

  Answers will vary.

- Throughout this year, we have been asking you to find a problem that you cannot solve. Look over the problems you have chosen in the past as difficult, or "unsolvable," problems. Can you solve them now? If not, what is still keeping you from solving them? Explain.

  Answers will vary.

- If you had to choose a favorite problem from this unit, what would it be? Why?

  Answers will vary.

Open-ended Problems

- How can you recognize that a function is a polynomial function? Explain.

  A polynomial function is the sum of terms whose variables have only positive whole-number exponents.

- Clearly explain the differences between real numbers, imaginary numbers, and complex numbers.

Complex numbers include real and imaginary numbers as well as sums of these ($a + bi$). Real numbers are what you have used most of your life. Imaginary numbers are real numbers times $\sqrt{-1}$.

- In trying to find the x-intercepts of $y = x^2 + x + 2$, Macario came up with $x = \frac{-1 \pm i\sqrt{7}}{2}$.

a. What method must Macario have used to come up with this strange answer? Explain completely.

b. What does this answer tell Macario about the x-intercepts? Explain completely.

a. Set $x^2 + x + 2 = 0$ and use the quadratic formula to solve for x.

b. There are none.

- In your friend Hakin's mathematics class, they are also studying polynomial functions, and Hakin has come to you for some help. It seems that in his group, they were given a polynomial to work with. They were supposed to fill in a table of values and then answer some questions. He has the table of values and the questions, but he has lost the original problem with the polynomial. Here's what he has:

Complete the table of values below and answer the questions.
Do not graph the points!

x	y
−728	−1290
−673	−334
−543	−211
−412	−98
−376	12
−301	114
−242	198
−198	175
−101	67
−87	22
−31	−6
9	−81
92	−67
102	−59
324	312
543	1093

NOTE: For $x < -728$, all y-values are less than −1290, and for all $x > 543$, we know $y > 1093$.

1. How many zeros does this polynomial have? Explain how you know.

2. Based on the table, what are your best guesses for the zeros? Justify your guess.

3. What is the degree of the polynomial? Explain how you know.

4. How many local maxima and minima does this polynomial have? Explain how you know.

Help Hakin by answering the questions for him and explain why he can answer each question without knowing the polynomial equation.

1. **Three because the y-values change sign in three places. To do this, the graph must have crossed the x-axis.**
2. **($\approx -380, 0$), ($\approx -40, 0$), ($\approx 140, 0$)**
3. **Three zeros implies degree three.**
4. **One local max and one local min. You can see this by sketching the graph.**

- Explain the similarities and differences of the graphs of the following equations.

$y = x^2$ $y = x^8$
$y = x^4$ $y = x^{10}$
$y = x^6$ $y = x^{12}$

Answers will vary. All have a "U" shape. As the exponent increases, the bottom of the graph gets flatter.

- Explain the similarities and differences of the graphs of the following equations.

$y = x^3$ $y = x^9$
$y = x^5$ $y = x^{11}$
$y = x^7$ $y = x^{13}$

Answers will vary. All have "S" shape. As the exponent increases, the graph gets flatter around $x = 0$.

- How many different methods do you know that enable you to find the zeros of a polynomial? What are they and how do they work? What are the advantages and disadvantages of the different methods? Which do you prefer? Why?

Answers will vary. Set equal to zero and solve.

- One day, your friend Deniz was fiddling around with your graphing calculator when she stumbled onto something (she thought was) remarkable. She asked you, "Which is bigger: x^2, x^4, or x^6?" Deniz was certain that you would get this wrong. On the calculator she has this display, which she says proves that x^2 is the biggest.

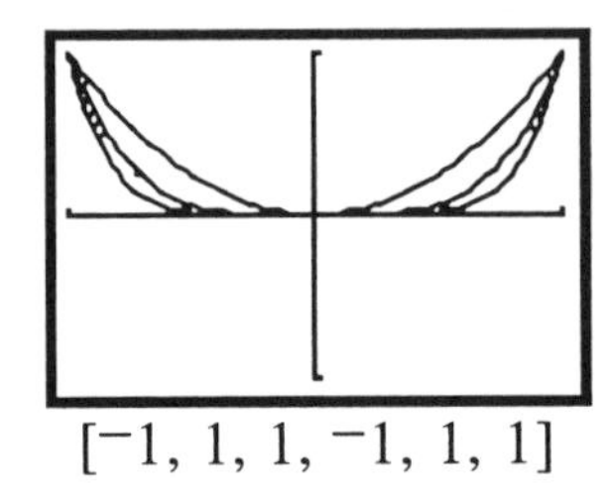

[⁻1, 1, 1, ⁻1, 1, 1]

"The graph on top is $y = x^2$, so see, it is the biggest."

Is Deniz correct? Analyze this situation completely.

This graph only shows $^-1 \le x \le 1$ and in this interval x^2 is the largest, but outside this interval x^6 is the largest.

- Draw a sketch of a polynomial function that satisfies each of these criteria. If it is not possible, explain why. *Note:* Each part is a separate problem.

a. A polynomial function with exactly two real zeros.

b. A polynomial function with exactly one real zero.

c. A polynomial function with one real zero and two complex zeros.

d. A polynomial function with two real and three complex zeros.

e. A polynomial function with six complex zeros.

f. A seventh-degree polynomial function with exactly two real zeros and exactly four complex zeros.

Answers will vary.

a.

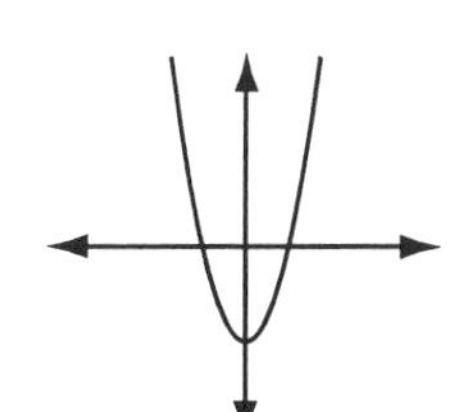

b.

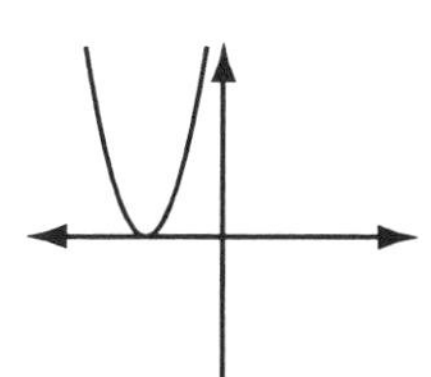

c.

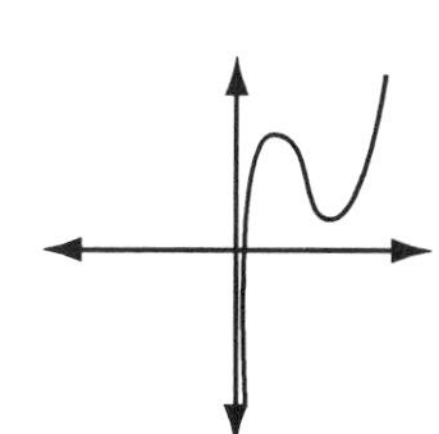

d. Impossible, since complex zeros must always occur in conjugate pairs.

e.

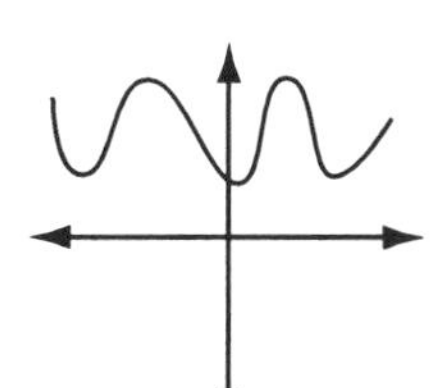

f.

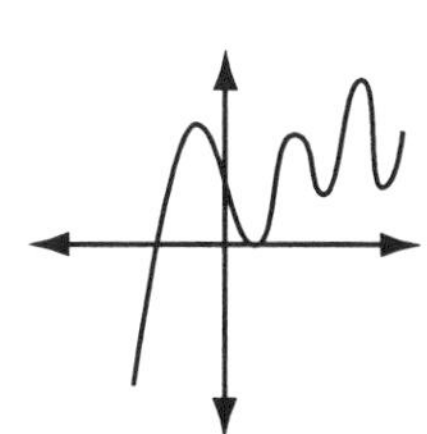

- Come up with an equation and graph of a polynomial function that satisfies *all* of the requirements below. *Note:* One equation must meet them all! Justify your response.
  i. The polynomial is degree six.
  ii. It has exactly two real roots (zeros).
  iii. It has exactly two complex zeros, one of which is $\frac{-1 + i\sqrt{3}}{2}$.
  iv. For all $x < {}^{-}2$, the function is strictly negative, and for all $x > 1$, the function is strictly negative.

  $y = {}^{-}(x^2 + x + 1)(x + 2)^2(x - 1)^2$ works.

- Why can't you graphically find the zeros of the polynomial equation $y = x^2 + x + 1$? Explain completely.

  Because it does not cross the x-axis, so there are no real zeros.

- The graph of a polynomial function has three real zeros. Could the degree of the polynomial be
  a. one? Explain.
  b. two? Explain.
  c. three? Explain.
  d. four? Explain.
  e. greater than four? Explain.

  a. No, three real zeroes implies at a degree of at least three.

  b. No, same reason as in part a.

  c. Yes

  d. No, if there are only three real zeros, the fourth would be complex, but you know there is always an even number of complex zeros.

  e. It could be 5, 7, 9, . . . , so that there is an even number of complex zeros.

- Is it possible for a polynomial with a degree that is an even number to have *no* x-intercepts? Is it possible for a polynomial with a degree that is an odd number to have *no* x-intercepts? Justify your answers.

  Even degree: yes, for example, $y = x^2 + 6$. Odd degree: No. Odd-degree polynomials will have at least one real zero. This can be explained by the shape of the graph as well as by the fact that complex roots come in pairs.

- Create your own problem that covers the material you have studied so far and that you think would make a good assessment question. Write out the complete solution to your problem and explain why you believe it to be a good problem. *Note:* Please make sure that it is a problem or question and not just an explanation or description.

  Answers will vary.

- Describe two different real-world situations in which a cubic polynomial could be used as an appropriate model.

  Answers will vary.

- Write three interesting, chapter-appropriate questions about the graph at the right. Answer your questions.

  Answers will vary.

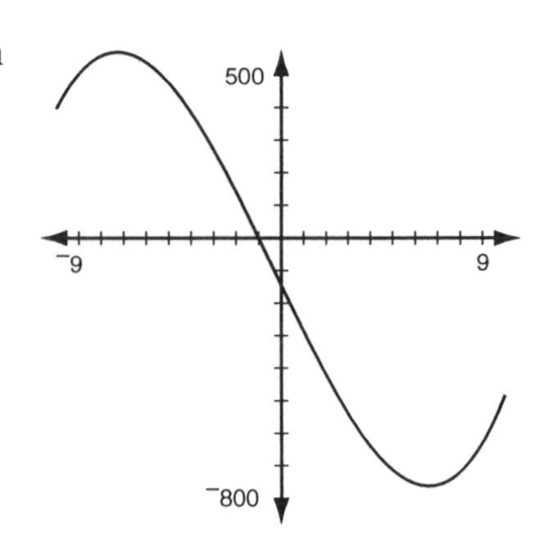

- The graph at the right shows the graphs of these two functions:

  $y = x^3 + x^2 - 144x - 144$

  $y = x^3 + x^2 - 144x$

  a. How do you know which graph represents which function? Justify your response.

  b. How many solutions does this system of equations have? Justify your answer.

  c. If you were to solve this system algebraically, what would happen? Explain.

  d. Is this system independent, dependent, or inconsistent? Explain.

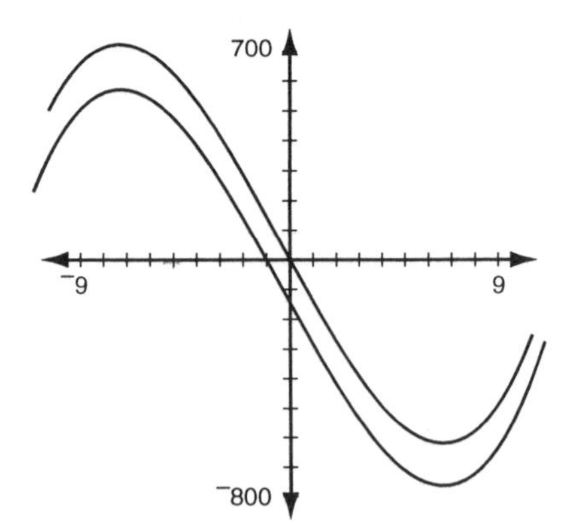

  a. The top graph represents the second equation because the y-intercept is zero.

  b. Zero; the two curves do not cross.

  c. You would come up with an untrue statement, such as $0 = {}^{-}144$.

  d. Inconsistent

- Your friend Nelson is not as fortunate as you and does not have a graphing calculator, yet his mathematics teacher has given him this problem.

  The graph at the right is of the function $y = 0.5(x - 2)^2 - 6$.

  Draw the graph of the function $y = |0.5(x - 2)^2 - 6|$.

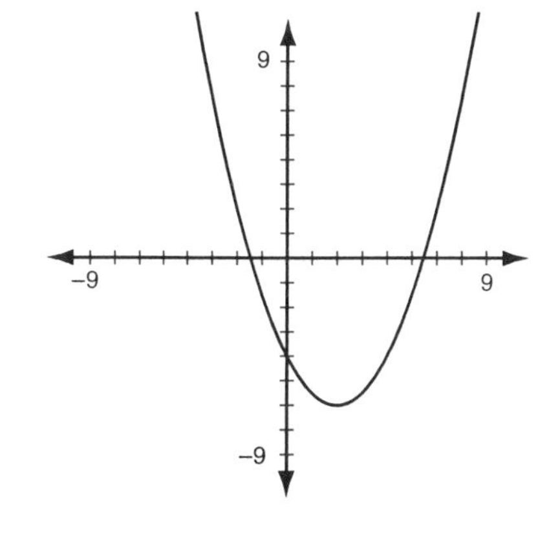

  Nelson does not have a clue as to how to do this problem, and even if he did have a graphing calculator, he doesn't know how to use it. Help Nelson out by explaining how he can graph the new function by using only what he is given here and not doing any extra work.

  The absolute value function makes all negative values positive, so where the graph is negative (that is, below the x-axis) it will become positive, and will be "flipped" or mirrored above the axis.

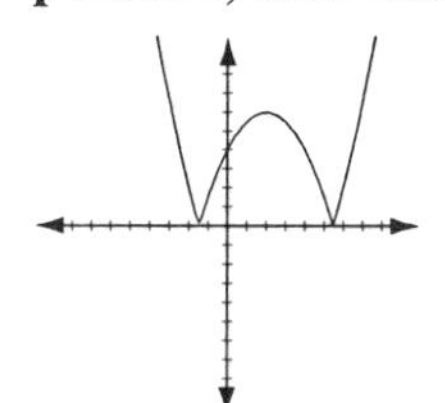

- For the following problem, please use this format.
  - i. State the problem.
  - ii. What do you already know that would help you solve this problem? Who (in your group) knows it and how does he or she know it?
  - iii. What information do you need to assume? Why are you assuming it?
  - iv. Record all your steps in solving the problem.
  - v. State your answer clearly and completely.
  - vi. How good is your answer? Remember: "A chain is only as strong as its weakest link!" What are your most unreliable approximations and weakest assumptions?

  When an object is thrown upward with an initial velocity and with gravity acting upon it, it travels upward for a period of time, slows, stops, and then returns to the ground. What initial velocity and acceleration would an object (such as a rocket) need in order for it to *not* come down (that is, to move out of the atmosphere and come down elsewhere as intended, as a rocket does).

  Answers will vary.

Projects

- On one side of a 1-mile-wide river is a power plant. On the other side, 4 miles upstream, there is a factory. It costs \$3.00 per foot to run cable over land and \$5.00 per foot to run the cable underwater. (One possible route is shown with the darker line.)

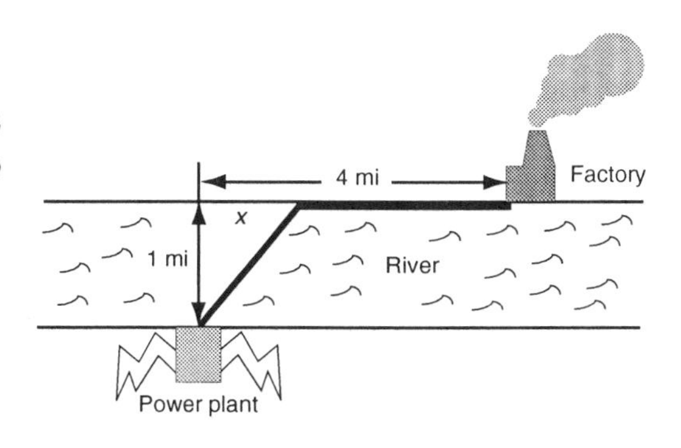

  - a. Draw the routes for $x = 0.5$, 1, 1.5, and 2. Make the drawings accurate and to scale.
  - b. Calculate the cost of each route you drew in part a.

c. What is the cost for the route shown with an arbitrary distance x?

d. Will minimizing the length of the cable minimize the cost? Explain.

e. What value of x will minimize the cost of installing the cable? Explain.

f. What happens if the factory is 6 miles upstream? 7 miles? 10 miles? Write a conjecture about the distance the factory is from the power plant and the cost of the cable installation.

a.

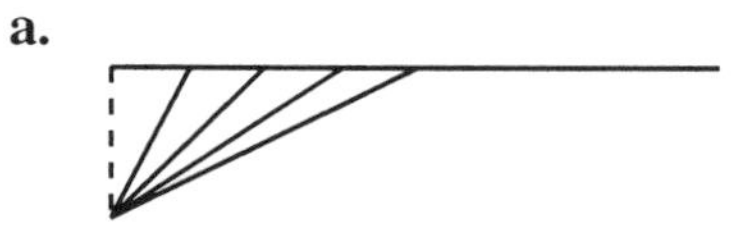

b. **≈ $84,956.10, $84,855.24, $87,193.28, $90,712.19**

c. $5\sqrt{5280^2 + (5280x)^2} + (4 - x)(5280)(3)$

d. **Not necessarily. The shortest distance would be a straight line, but a straight line would be entirely underwater and would be more expensive.**

e. **The minimum cost is at $x = 0.75$ miles.**

f. **No matter how much farther upstream the factory is located, $x = 0.75$ miles gives the minimum cost.**

- For this project you will need the following equipment: a ramp, a marble or ball bearing, stopwatch, and a meter stick. You will measure various distances along the ramp and measure the time it takes for the ball to travel that distance.

On the ramp, mark a place to start rolling the ball and another indicating a place to start timing. Then mark off another distance, such as 50 centimeters, from the place where you will start timing the ball. Time how long it takes for the ball to travel this far. Repeat this so that you have four time measurements for that length. Average these values and record them in a data table like the example below. Measure another distance on the ramp and repeat the procedure. Continue to collect data for different distances until you have at least six data points.

Time	Distance

In your project you must include a write-up of your data along with a brief, but clear explanation of what each person in your group did. Indicate any problems or questions you had while doing the lab, along with how you resolved them. Then include the following.

a. Graph your data points on your calculator and make a plot on paper for your report.

b. What degree of polynomial do you predict will fit the data? Why?

c. Use the method of finite differences to investigate your guess.

d. Find the equation for this curve, and explain how you found that equation.

e. Respond to the following questions using your model.

  i. If the ramp were 500 centimeters long, how much time does your equation predict it would take for the ball to roll down the ramp?

  ii. How far down the ramp would the ball travel in 7.4 seconds?

iii. Compare your equation to that of another group. Are they the same? If not, explain why they are different.

iv. How would you improve the design of this lab?

All parts: answers will vary. The degree should be two.

- Find an occupation (not a mathematics teacher or professor) in the "real world" that makes use of complex numbers, imaginary numbers, or both. Describe how and why this occupation makes use of them and what facts about complex numbers a person in this occupation would utilize. Write up a complete report.

  Answers will vary.

- To ship the new Annie Oakley Action Dolls, a rectangular box with a square base is needed. Your company, named Just Boxes, has been contracted to build the box.

  The box must hold 100 cubic inches. The material to make the sides of the box cost 3¢ per square inch, while the material for the top and bottom costs twice as much. Let x represent the side of the base and h represent the height of the box.

  a. Write an equation representing what you know about the volume.

  b. Write an equation that represents the cost to make the box.

  c. Use the equation in part a to rewrite the equation in part b with x as the only variable.

  d. What box dimensions should you use to make the cheapest box?

  e. Write a professional business letter to the president of the company selling the Annie Oakley Action Doll, explaining the exact dimensions needed and the cost of each box. Be complete! The president of this company is very skeptical!

  a. $x^2h = 100$

  b. $0.12x^2 + 0.12xh = C$

  c. $h = \frac{100}{x^2}$ so $C = 0.12x^2 + 0.12x\left(\frac{100}{x^2}\right)$.

  d. $x \approx 3.684$, $h \approx 7.368$

  e. **Answers will vary.**

Skill Questions: Appropriate for Quizzes or Tests

- Consider the equation $y = {}^{-}3x^2 + 16x - 12$.

  a. Find the y-intercept.

  b. Find the x-intercept(s).

  c. Find the minimum or maximum point.

  d. Sketch a complete graph and indicate the graphing window used.

  e. Write the equation in vertex form.

  f. Write the equation in factored form.

  a. $(0, {}^{-}12)$

  b. $\left(\frac{8 \pm 2\sqrt{7}}{3}, 0\right)$

c. **max at $\left(\frac{8}{3}, \frac{28}{3}\right)$**

d. **One possible window: Xmin = $^-2$, Xmax = 8, Xscl = 1, Ymin = $^-15$, Ymax = 10, Yscl = 1.**

e. $y = {}^-3\left(x - \frac{8}{3}\right)^2 + \frac{28}{3}$

f. $y = {}^-3\left(x - \frac{8+2\sqrt{7}}{3}\right)\left(x - \frac{8-2\sqrt{7}}{3}\right)$

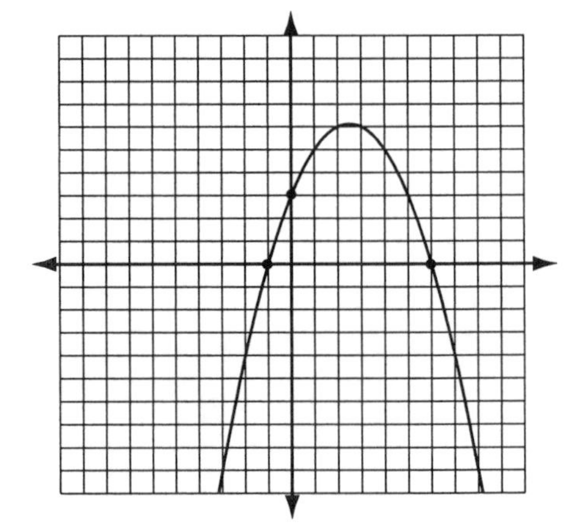

- Write an equation that describes the graph at right. (Each grid line represents one unit.)

  $y = {}^-0.5x^2 + 2.5x + 3$

- Homer Uhn hits the ball with an initial speed of 130 feet per second. The ball is 3 feet high when he hits it at an angle of 26° with horizontal.

  a. Write the equations that simulate this motion.

  b. How high is the ball when it gets to the wall, which is 400 feet away? Is it a home run? Describe why it is or isn't a home run.

a. $x = 130t \cos 26°, y = {}^-16t^2 + 130t \sin 26° + 3$

b. **The ball is approximately 10.579 feet high; if this is higher than the fence, the hit is a home run.**

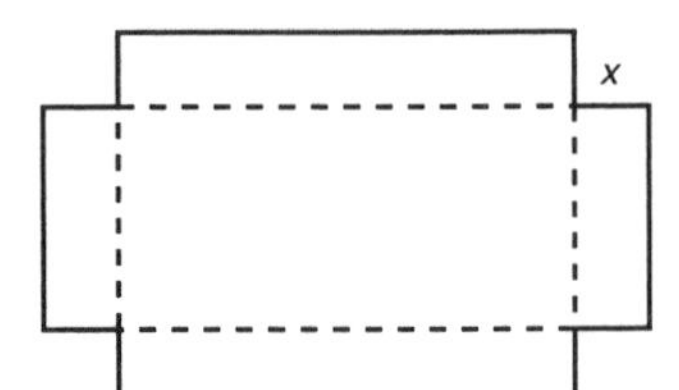

- Four congruent squares are cut from the corners of a rectangular piece of paper 18 inches by 11 inches. Let x be the side length of each one of the cut-out squares. The paper is folded into an open-top box.

  a. Write an expression representing the length of the box.

  b. Write an expression representing the width of the box.

  c. Write an expression representing the height of the box.

  d. Try six values for x and make a table of values (x, V), V being the volume of the box.

  e. What degree is the relationship (x, V)? Explain how you know.

  f. Write an equation representing the volume of the box.

  g. Find the value of x that gives the box with largest volume.

a. $18 - 2x$

b. $11 - 2x$

c. x

d. **Answers will vary.**

e. **3**

f. $V = x(18 - 2x)(11 - 2x)$

g. $x \approx 2.214$

- Consider the following data.

x	0	1	2	3	4	5	6
y	4	2	−6	22	176	594	1462

  a. What degree of polynomial will best fit this data? Justify your answer.

  b. Find the equation that best fits the data.

a. **Degree 4 because it takes four differences to get a constant.**

b. $y = 2x^4 - 5x^3 - 2x^2 + 3x + 4$

- Find the coordinates of the vertex of $y = {}^-3x^2 + 4x - 1$ to the nearest hundredth (or in exact fraction form).

  $\left(\frac{2}{3}, \frac{1}{3}\right)$

- Change to polynomial form and to factored form: $y = \frac{1}{2}(x + 4)^2 - 2$

  $y = 0.5x^2 + 4x + 6 \quad y = (0.5x + 3)(x + 2)$ **or** $y = \frac{1}{2}(x + 6)(x + 2)$

- Write an equation for the graph pictured.

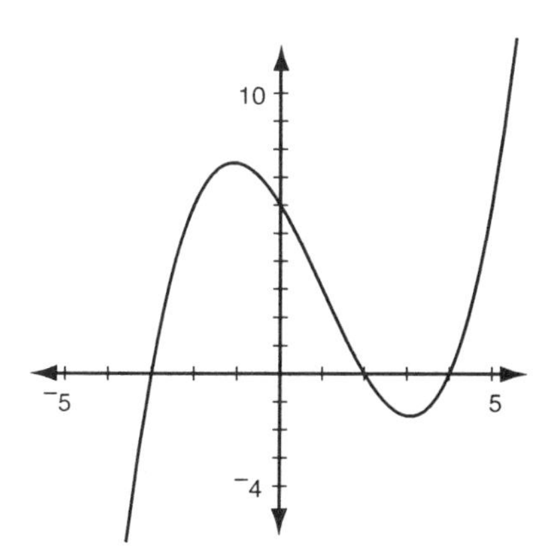

$y = \frac{1}{4}x^3 - \frac{3}{4}x^2 - \frac{5}{2}x + 6$

- Woody Irons hits a golf ball with an initial speed of 150 feet per second. It goes up at a 38° angle with respect to the ground.
  a. How far away does it come down?
  b. How high does it go?

  a. $\approx$ **682.2 feet** **b.** $\approx$ **133.26 feet**

- Use the method of finite differences to complete the table below.

x	3	6	9	12	15	18	21
y	−12	−15	−6	15	48		150

93

- Find a cubic equation that contains the points (2, 82), (4, 66), (6, 66), (8, 58), and (10, 18). Show all your work.

  $y = {}^-0.5x^3 + 8x^2 - 42x + 138$

- Suppose you know that $y = ax^2 + bx + c$ and $y = A(x - r)(x - s)$ are two forms of the same equation. Explain why $\frac{-b}{2a} = \frac{r + s}{2}$ and what this has to do with the graph.

  Both equations provide the *x*-coordinate of the vertex.

- Sketch a graph of the function $y = (x + 2)(x - 4)$. Label the coordinates of the vertex and all roots.

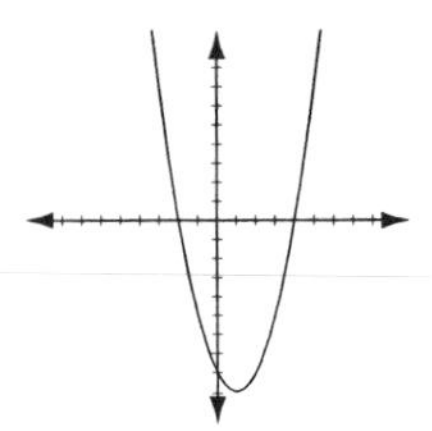

Roots ($^-2$, 0), (4, 0); Vertex (1, $^-9$).

- True or false. If the statement is false, explain why.
  a. A third-degree polynomial *can* have exactly one real root.
  b. Cubic equations *can* be shaped like a W.
  c. A polynomial with real coefficients *can* have exactly one nonreal root.
  d. Fifth-degree equations *can* have two relative maximums.
  e. You cannot tell the difference between a single root and a repeated root from the graph.

  a. True

  b. False, they have a side-turned "s" shape.

  c. False, complex roots come in pairs.

  d. True

  e. False, a repeated root is also a local max or min.

- Find all roots, real and complex, of the polynomial $y = 2x^3 - 7x^2 - 9$. Show all your work.

  $\approx$ 3.81, $^-0.155 \pm 1.0757i$

- The graph at the right is a polynomial function.
  a. Write the equation of the polynomial in factored form.
  b. Write the equation of the polynomial in polynomial form.

  a. $y = 2(x + 3)^2(x - 2)(x - 5)$

  b. $y = 2x^4 - 2x^3 - 46x^2 - 6x + 180$

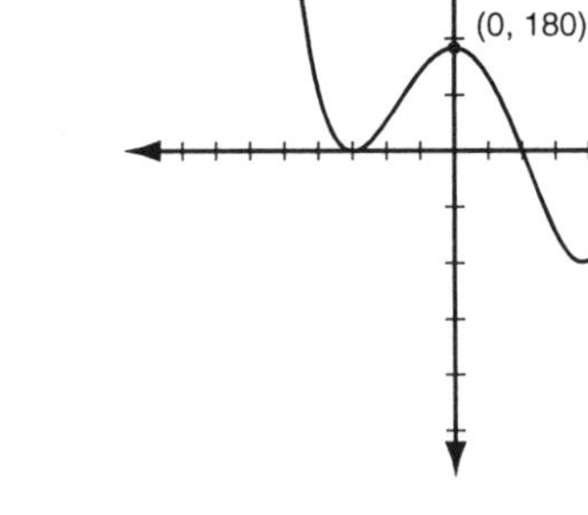

- An object is thrown vertically with a initial upward velocity of $v_0 = 96$ feet per second from an initial height of $s_0 = 128$ feet. The equation that relates the vertical height of the object to the time in flight is $H(t) = {}^-16t^2 + v_0t + s_0$.
  a. At what time will the object reach its greatest height?
  b. How high will it be at this point?
  c. At what time will it reach the ground?

  a. At 3 seconds **b. 272 feet** **c. $\approx$ 7.123 seconds**

- What must k be for $(x + 2)$ to be a factor of $x^4 - 2x^3 - 3x^2 + kx - 6$? Explain your reasoning.

  Using division, you want $r = 0$. So $14 - 2k = 0$, or $k = 7$.

- Big Bird is on a rigorous diet and exercise program. The following is a chart of his progress over the first week.

Day	0	1	2	3	4	5	6	7
Weight	188.5	180.75	175	171	168.5	167	166.25	166

a. What is the degree of the best polynomial model for this data? Justify your answer.

b. Which points would you select to find the equation of this data? Why?

c. Find a best-fit equation.

d. What will his weight be in another week if it continues to follow your model?

a. Three, third difference.

b. Answers will vary. Perhaps the first three.

c. One possibility: $y = {}^{-}0.0543x^3 + 1.195x^2 - 8.922x + 188.508$

d. $\approx$ 148.821 pounds using this model.

- Find all of the zeros (real and complex) of the following equations.

a. $(x-4)^2 - 9 = 0$ b. $4.7(x+3)(x-5) = 0$

c. $x^2 + 3x - 40 = 0$ d. $4x^2 + 3 = 6x$

a. 1, 7 **b. $^{-}3, 5$**

c. $^{-}8, 5$ **d. $\frac{3 \pm i\sqrt{3}}{4}$**

- Write the equation of each graph.

a.

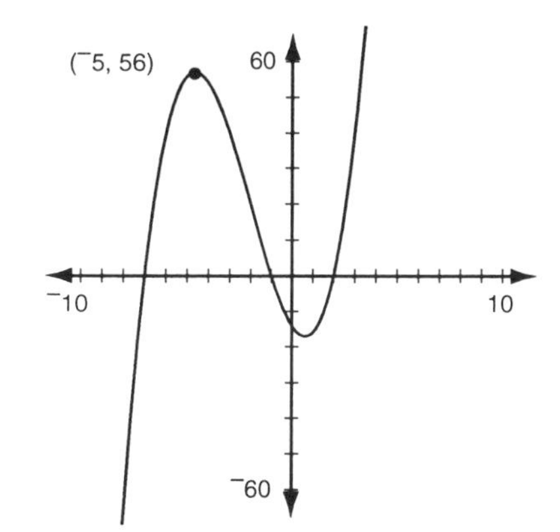

b.

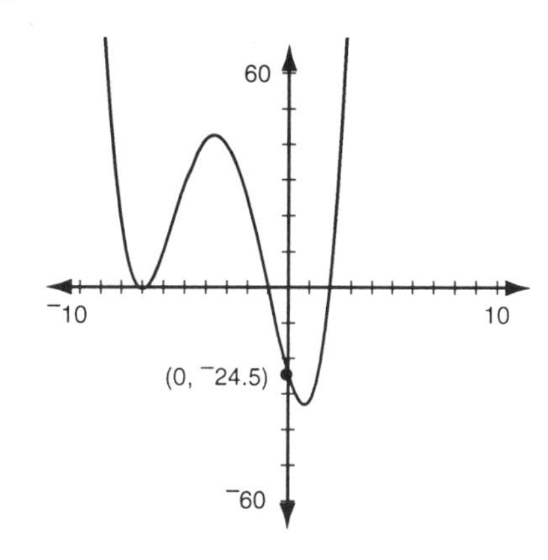

a. $y = 1(x+7)(x+1)(x-2) = x^3 + 6x^2 - 9x - 14$

b. $y = 0.25(x+7)^2(x+1)(x-2) = \frac{1}{4}x^4 + \frac{13}{4}x^3 + \frac{33}{4}x^2 - \frac{77}{4}x - \frac{98}{4}$

- Classify each expression as a linear, quadratic, cubic, or higher degree polynomial. Justify your answer.

a. $3x^2 - 5x + 2x^3 - 8$ b. $2x - 7$

c. $3^4x + 5x^2 - 1$ d. $x^4 + x^2$

a. cubic **b. linear**

c. quadratic **d. quartic**

- The data below fits a quadratic equation.

x	0	1	2	3	4	5	6
y	4.8	1.5	2.4	7.5	16.8	30.3	48

a. How do you know it fits a quadratic equation? Explain.

b. Find the quadratic equation.

a. Second difference **b.** $y = 2.1x^2 - 5.4x + 4.8$

- Change the following equation to polynomial form: $y = \frac{1}{2}(x+4)^2 - 5$

$y = 0.5x^2 + 4x + 3$

- If $(x - 2)$ is a factor of $x^3 + 6x^2 - x - 30$, find all other factors.

$(x + 5)$ and $(x + 3)$

- Mora Muny opens a savings account by depositing $20,000, and she vows to add some money to the account at the end of each month. At the end of the first month, she adds $10,000. At the end of the second month, she adds $5,000. By the end of the third month, she can only add $2,500, and at the end of the fourth, only $1,250. The annual interest rate is 5% compounded monthly.

a. What is the balance in the account at the end of the fourth month?

b. If this pattern continues, what is the balance in the account at the end of 8 months?

a. ≈ $39,262.11 **b. ≈ $41,104.58**

- Name the vertex of the parabola $y = {}^-8x^2 + 6x - 7$.

$\left(\frac{3}{8}, \frac{^-47}{8}\right)$

- Consider the quadratic $y = 2(x + 7)^2 - 3$.

a. Graph the equation.

b. Remove the parentheses and write the equation in polynomial form. Graph it to be sure you removed the parentheses correctly.

a.

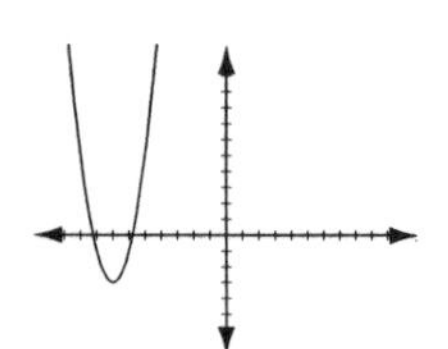

b. $y = 2x^2 + 28x + 95$

- Consider the three points $A(-2, 3)$, $B(1, -5)$ and $C(4, p)$.

a. What value of p will make these points lie on a line? What is the equation of that line?

b. What value of p will make these points lie on a parabola? What is the equation of that parabola?

c. Is there a value of p that will make these points lie on the graph of a cubic function? Explain.

a. $p = {}^{-}13$, $y = \frac{-8}{3}x - \frac{7}{3}$

b. **For $p \neq {}^{-}13$ there are infinitely many quadratic equations.**

c. **There are infinitely many cubic equations even if $p = 13$.**

- Sketch a graph that is
  a. quadratic and has no x-intercepts.
  b. cubic with no x-intercepts.
  c. cubic with two x-intercepts.

a.

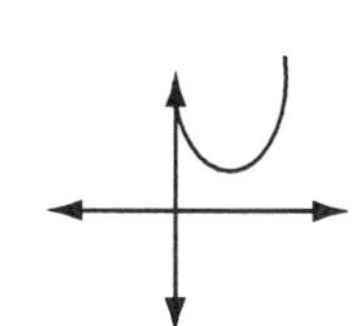

b. Not possible.

c.

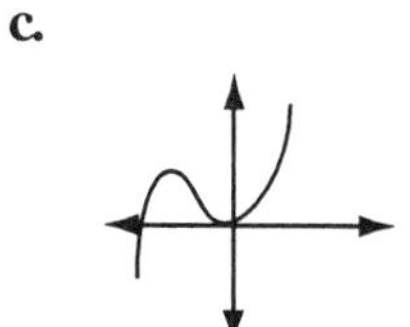

- Can you use the quadratic formula when solving the equation $x^2 - 3ix - 4i = 0$? If you can, does that mean you are finding the x-intercepts of $y = x^2 - 3ix - 4i$? Explain.

You will get $\sqrt{i}$ in your solutions. The solutions satisfy the equation, but they are not the x-intercepts.

- At time zero, a football player kicks the football off the ground and into the air. It returns to the ground 3.2 seconds later. Write a quadratic polynomial to model this situation.

$y = {}^{-}x(x - 3.2)$ will work.

- The Terre Haute Discount Mart is going to begin selling the Annie Oakley Action Doll. The store will charge $15.50 for each doll and expects to sell an average of 300 each day. A survey indicates that the sales will decrease by an average of five per day for each $1.00 increase in price.
  a. Write an equation that describes the relationship between the income, y, and the selling price, x, charged per doll.
  b. What selling price will yield the maximum income?

a. **$y = (15.50 + x)(300 - 5x)$**

b. **$x = 22.2$, which gives 189 dolls at $37.70 each, for an income of $7125.30.**

- The graph at the right has two x-intercepts. Is it degree two? Explain.

No, both appear to be repeated roots, so the graph represents fourth-degree polynomial.

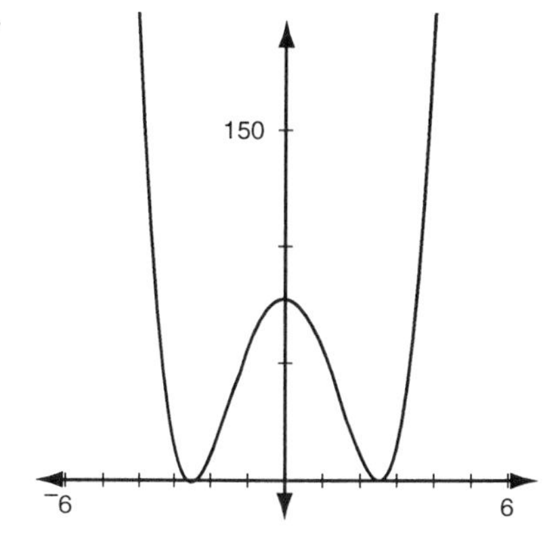

- Write a quadratic equation with $4 + 3i$ as a solution. Show that it is a solution.

$x^2 - 8x + 25 = 0$

- Is $(x + 2)$ a factor of $x^3 - 28x - 48$? Explain why or why not. Is $(x - 4)$ a factor? Explain why or why not.

Yes. No, but $(x + 4)$ is a factor.

Group Problems

- How many small squares are there in an $n \times n$ grid? *Hint:* It is **not** n^2.

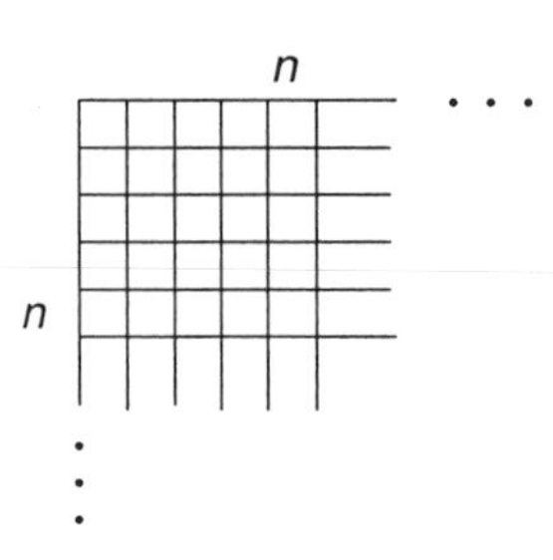

$\mathbf{n^2 + (n-1)^2 + \ldots + 1}$

- How many **rectangles** are in an $n \times n$ grid?

$\mathbf{1 + 2^2 + 3^2 + \ldots + n^2 = \frac{1}{3}n^3 + \frac{1}{2}n^2 + \frac{1}{6}}$

- Rectangle ABCD must have two vertices on the semicircle with center (0, 0) and radius 4, and two vertices on the x-axis, as shown, but these four points can be anywhere as long as a rectangle is formed and the conditions stated above are met.

What are the dimensions of the rectangle when it is at its maximum area? What is the maximum area?

$\mathbf{b = 4\sqrt{2}, h = 2\sqrt{2}, A = 16}$

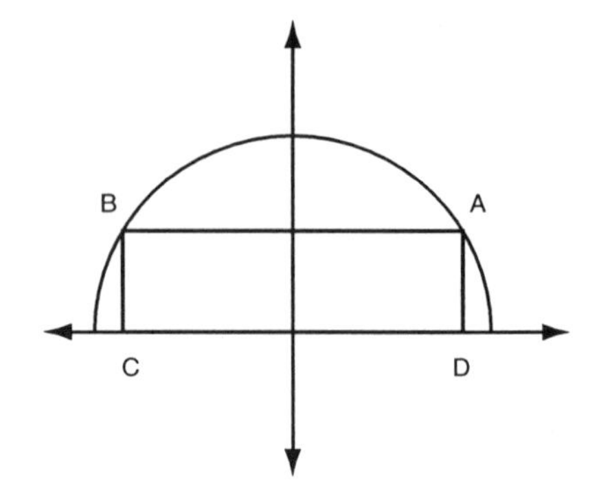

Chapter 11: Probability and Statistics

Journal Questions

- The title of this chapter could be More Probability and Statistics. How is this chapter different from the other lessons on probability and statistics?

  Answers will vary.

- Describe the similarities and differences between combinations and permutations. Do you find that one of these concepts is easier to understand than the other? Which one? Why do you think that is? Explain.

  Answers will vary.

- If you were going to write the test for this chapter, what would you cover? Why?

  Answers will vary.

- What graphing calculator skills have you mastered during this chapter? Explain thoroughly and use examples. What graphing calculator skills have you not yet mastered? Provide an example for which you need a calculator skill that you have not yet mastered.

  Answers will vary.

- How has your ability to do mathematics changed throughout the year? Do you feel your skills and understanding have improved? Explain.

  Answers will vary.

- Find three problems in the chapter that you feel are representative of the chapter. Write out the problem and the solution. For each problem, explain why you feel it is representative of the chapter. Please use complete, coherent sentences.

  Answers will vary.

- What ideas or topics were introduced in this chapter that you feel you do not quite understand yet or for which you do not see the purpose? Give examples.

  Answers will vary.

- Throughout this year, we have been asking you to find a problem that you cannot solve. Look over the problems you have chosen in the past as difficult, or "unsolvable," problems. Can you solve them now? What is still keeping you from solving them? Explain.

  Answers will vary.

- If you had to choose a favorite problem from this unit, what would it be? Why?

  Answers will vary.

Open-ended Problems

- When reading a counting problem, how do you know whether or not you are counting a permutation or a combination? Explain and be clear.

  A problem asking for a permutation will state that order matters, or this will be implied in the problem statement. Order is not important in a combination.

- Cham has been working on his mathematics assignment for several hours when he calls you for clarification on something.

  "When we compute the standard deviation," he says, "we square the deviations, but in the end we just take the square root. It seems to me that since we square, but then take the square root, this really is not any different from the mean absolute deviation we studied in Chapter 3. Am I correct?"

  Answer Cham and be sure to justify your response completely.

  Cham is forgetting that you square the deviations and then <u>sum</u> them before taking the square root, so you are not just "undoing" the squaring. They are two different things.

- Explain completely to your friend's little sister why her three sweaters, five skirts, and two pairs of tights gives her $5 \cdot 3 \cdot 2 = 30$ different outfits.

  Answers will vary, but you want to see more than just "because you are supposed to multiply."

- For each of the following, write a separate real-world application that has each of these as answers.

  a. ${}_9P_2$ b. ${}_9C_2$ c. 9^2 d. 2^9

  a. One possibility: How many ways can Miss Covered Bridge Festival and the first runner-up be chosen from nine finalists?

  b. One possibility: How many ways can Ms. Wootton choose two of her nine laziest students to wash classroom desks?

  c. I need to choose a secret code to be able to listen to my telephone answering machine messages. The code must be two digits, each from the set 1, 2, 3, . . . , 9, and I can repeat the digits if I want. How many possible codes are there to choose from?

  d. Nine pennies are to be arranged in a straight line with some of them heads up, others tails up. How many different arrangements are there?

- Name a set of six elements that you would expect to have

  a. a small mean and a large standard deviation.

  b. a large mean and a small standard deviation.

  a. Answers will vary. The numbers should all be small, but very different from each other.

  b. Answers will vary. The numbers should all be large, but close to each other in value.

- What is so *normal* about the normal distribution? Explain.

  Answer will vary.

- You know that you can represent certain counting problems with tree diagrams. For instance, this problem, "A coin is flipped twice. How many different outcomes are there?" can be represented by the diagram at the right. Give a different way to demonstrate that there are four different outcomes.

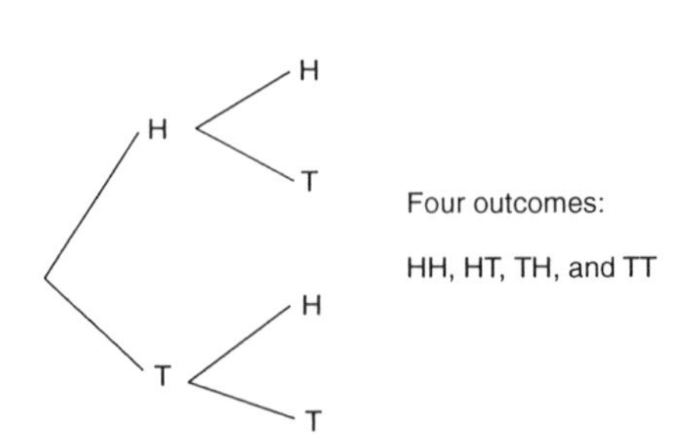

  Answers will vary. One possibility:

	H	T
H	HH	HT
T	TH	TT

- Marco and Polo are each using their graphing calculators to create a histogram of a set of data. Marco has been struggling to make sense out of his graph when Polo says, "Boy, this data is really normal!" Marco's histogram looks like the one at the right. Does Marco's data look "really normal"? Explain. What do you think is going on here? Explain.

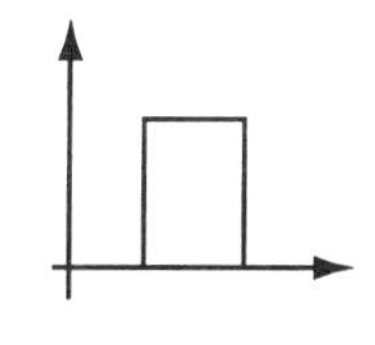

  Marco probably has used an Xscl that is too large so the data is classified in only one group.

- Throughout the year you have studied different types of relations, such as $y = 7x + 2$ or $y = (x - 5)^2 + 8$. For each of these relations you know that x represents the input and y represents the output. Tell me everything you can about this relation: $y = {}_{10}C_x$. How would it be different from the relation $y = {}_{10}P_x$? Explain completely.

  Answers will vary. Students should discuss domain, range, continuity, and so on, to be complete.

- Why is it convenient to have the area under the graph of the normal distribution to be one square unit? Be clear and complete.

  With the area equaling one, you can quickly determine probabilities by finding the area of specific regions, since 1 represents 100%.

- The night before the big statistics project is due in her mathematics class, Dee Lay is quickly trying to start *and* finish the project! As she was just finishing up, the batteries in her graphing calculator die. She had been analyzing a set of data and all she had written down before the calculator quit was this equation

$$y = \left(\frac{1}{3.25\sqrt{2\pi}}\right)\left(1 - \frac{1}{2(3.25)^2}\right)^{(x-15)^2}$$

  Dee calls you at 11:00 pm, begging for some help. "If I could have just written down the mean, standard deviation, and the graph before the stupid calculator quit, I would be in good shape. But without those things I am lost!"

  Is Dee really lost? Help her out. Be clear. (The alternative is for you to meet her at school at 5:00 a.m. tomorrow so she can borrow your calculator and finish her project.)

  Dee can find the mean and standard deviation from the equation and should also then be able to make a reasonable sketch of the graph. Mean = 15, s.d. = 3.25.

- Some teachers say they use the normal distribution to determine their grades. What do you suppose this means? How would it work? Be clear and complete. What would be the advantages and disadvantages of assigning grades using this method?

  Answers will vary.

- Mrs. Peacock is president of the Get a Clue Widget factory, manufacturing beautifully colored widgets. Mrs. Peacock demands quality work, so she has every twentieth widget taken from the assembly line and thoroughly inspected by an independent widget quality control engineer. In three years of inspections, this engineer has found virtually nothing wrong with the widgets coming off the assembly line. However, widget dealers complain that most widgets reaching their showrooms have something wrong with them. Could there be something wrong with the sampling method? Explain these results.

  Answers will vary, but a likely answer would be that something in the assembly line works correctly at least for every twentieth widget.

- Create your own problem that covers the material you have studied so far, that you think would make a good assessment question. Write out the complete solution to your problem and explain why you believe it to be a good problem. *Note:* Please make sure that it is a problem or question and not just an explanation or description.

- Write three interesting, chapter-appropriate questions about the graph at right. Answer your questions.

  Answers will vary.

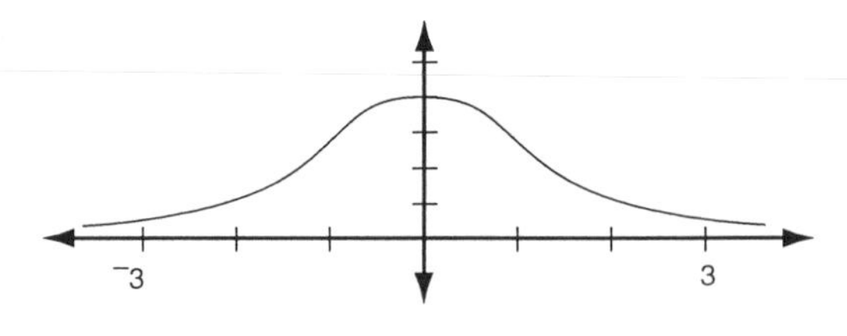

- Give an example illustrating how probability and statistics are connected.

  Answers will vary.

- For the following problems, please use this format.

  i. State the problem.

  ii. What do you already know that would help you solve this problem? Who (in your group) knows it and how does he or she know it?

  iii. What information do you need to assume? Why are you assuming it?

  iv. Record all your steps in solving the problem.

  v. State your answer clearly and completely.

  vi. How good is your answer? Remember: "A chain is only as strong as its weakest link!" What are your most unreliable approximations and weakest assumptions?

  1. Create a histogram showing the number of people of each age in the world.

  Answers will vary.

  2. What is the minimum number of phone numbers your hometown would need?

  Answers will vary.

Projects

- Research magazines, newspapers, or journal articles to find two instances where the normal distribution is mentioned. How is it used? Is it explained clearly and completely? Does the article use statistics correctly or does it distort the information? Explain completely.

  Extra Credit: Rewrite the article, using the same statistics, but to support a position contrary to the original article's intent.

  Answers will vary.

The next project is an extension of the Trinomial Distribution Project at the end of Section 11.3.

- As you studied binomial distributions in this chapter, you found out that the binomial coefficients are represented in Pascal's triangle. You also found an easy way to determine the numbers in Pascal's triangle by summing the two numbers above a desired entry.

  Come up with a "triangle" of sorts that gives the "trinomial coefficients" described in Project 11.3.

```
          1
        1   1
      1   2   1
    1   3   3   1
  1   4   6   4   1
1   5  10  10   5   1
```

If your students need a hint, offer this one: For the bi nomial coefficients, you created a two-dimensional figure, namely a triangle, in which you summed the two terms above an entry. What should you do for trinomial coefficients? Answer: A tetrahedron can be built with the nodes representing the coefficients; sum the three nodes that join to a node on the level below. An easy way to build this model is with gumdrops for the nodes and toothpicks showing the connections.

- In Investigation 11.4.1, Measuring a Cord Length, you might have noticed that the histogram you created looked "normal." Does this make sense to you? Explain. Think of some set of data that you suspect would look like a normal distribution when graphed. Clearly define the set of data and then collect the data (clearly explain how you do this as well). Graph your data. Is it normal? Show how you can change the bar widths on the histogram to make the data appear more or less "normal."

  Answers will vary.

- Collect data for the past ten or more years on some topic that interests you. For instance, you may wish to investigate the number of students applying to different colleges. Analyze the data. Is it normally distributed? Justify your answer.

  Answers will vary.

Skill Questions: Appropriate for Quizzes or Tests

- Explain why outliers strongly influence the mean and standard deviation of a set of data.

  Since every piece of data is used in the computation of each of these, outliers are not excluded as anomalies.

- Sketch the graph of a normal distribution with a mean of 100 and a standard deviation of:

  a. 5 b. 20 c. 50

  a. Peak at 100, narrow curve. Points of inflection at $x = 95$ and 105.

  b. Peak at 100. Points of inflection at $x = 80$ and 120.

  c. Peak at 100, wide curve. Points of inflection at $x = 50$ and 150.

- a. In how many ways can Allaina, Barika, Chin, Duy, and Everett sit in a row of desks?

  b. If Allaina and Duy must sit next to each other, how many ways are there?

  c. If Barika and Chin *cannot* be seated next to each other, how many ways are there?

  a. $5! = 120$ b. $2 \cdot 4! = 48$ b. $120 - 48 = 72$

- The ten digits 0, 1, 2, 3, . . . , 9 are arranged randomly with no repetition of digits.

  a. How many arrangements create a number less than one billion?

  b. What is the probability the number formed is even *and* greater than five billion?

  a. 9! b. $\frac{21}{90}$

- How many different five-digit zip codes are there?

  a. Zip codes are not assigned randomly. For instance, all zip codes in the state of Indiana begin with 46 or 47 (47803, for example). At most, how many different zip codes can there be for Indiana?

  b. California's zip codes all begin with either 90, 91, 92, 93, 94, 95, or 96. At most, how many different zip codes are there in California?

c. **Extra credit:** Find out how the post office decided to assign the zip codes. Does it seem like a logical or natural way to assign them? Can you come up with a better method? Justify that your method is better.

There are 10,000 possible zip codes.

a. 2000 **b. 7000** **c. Answers will vary.**

- Find n if $\frac{n!}{(n-3)!\,3!} = 56$.

$n = 8$

- In Vigo County in western Indiana, all car license plates begin with the number 84. These digits are then followed by one letter and four more digits; repetition is allowed. The county has a population close to 128,000. Do you think there are enough license plates for the county? Justify your answer.

There are 260,000 different license plates, which is more than enough, especially considering not every person owns a car.

- In the Powerball Lottery drawing, a machine randomly chooses five balls, without replacement, from a bin of balls numbered 1 through 45. Then another machine chooses a "powerball" from a different bin with the same set of numbered balls. To win, a player must match all five balls plus the powerball. (Order is not important.)
  a. What is the probability of winning the Powerball Lottery?
  b. A player will win $1.00 if he or she matches just the powerball. What is the probability of that happening? (Don't worry about any other numbers.)
  c. A player will win $100,000 if he or she matches *only* the five "non-powerballs." What is the probability of that happening?

a. $\frac{1}{54{,}979{,}155}$ **b.** $\frac{1}{45}$ **c.** $\frac{44}{1{,}221{,}759 \cdot 45}$

- Mr. Dredge is going to choose five of his thirty-six students to wash desktops after school.
  a. How many ways are there to select these five students from the thirty-six?
  b. Bobby Dogoody really wants to wash desks! What is the probability that he is selected?
  c. If the class has 19 boys and 17 girls, what is the probability that three girls and two boys will be chosen?
  d. If Mr. Dredge lets Bobby volunteer to wash desks, what is the probability that the four other students chosen will all be girls?

a. ${}_{36}C_5 = 376{,}992$ **b.** $\frac{{}_{35}C_4}{{}_{36}C_5} = \frac{5}{36}$

c. $\frac{{}_{19}C_2 \cdot {}_{17}C_3}{{}_{36}C_5} = \frac{95}{308}$ **d.** $\frac{{}_{17}C_4}{{}_{36}C_5} = \frac{5}{792}$

- A trick coin is slightly weighted so that the probability of tossing a head is 0.75.
  a. What is the probability of tails coming up?
  b. Draw a tree diagram showing the possible outcomes if the coin is flipped three times.
  c. What is the probability that all three flips come up tails?

d. When flipping a fair coin many times, you would expect the coin to come up heads about half the time and tails the other half. Explain why this is so. Then state and explain how often you would expect to see heads and tails if the trick coin is tossed many times.

a. 0.25

b. HHH, HHT, HTH, THH, TTT, TTH, THT, TTH

c. $(0.25)^3 = 0.015625$

d. With the trick coin, you would expect tails to come up only one-fourth of the time, heads three-fourths of the time.

- A 1-pound bag of M&Ms contains approximately 250 M&Ms. To promote the new blue M&Ms, the bags of candy contain quite a few of these new tidbits. The probability of reaching in and drawing out a new blue M&M is 0.45.

a. What is the probability that you will find exactly 100 blue M&Ms in a 1-pound bag?

b. What is the probability that a bag promoting the new blue M&Ms will have *no* blue M&Ms in it?

c. On average, how many blue M&Ms would you expect to find in a 1-pound bag?

d. **Extra credit:** What was given up so that the blue M&Ms could exist?

a. $_{250}C_{100} \cdot (0.45)^{100} \cdot (0.65)^{150} \approx 0.0148$

b. $_{250}C_{0} \cdot (0.45)^{0} \cdot (0.65)^{250} \approx 0$

c. About 113

d. The light brown M&Ms were retired.

- In a recent classroom experiment, each group was supposed to take very precise measurements in centimeters. Once all the measurements were taken, the teacher collected all the items and the rulers. Then the students were supposed to calculate the mean and standard deviation of the measurements. At this point, Ima Ditz realized that she had taken all the measurements in millimeters. Has Ima ruined her group's chance of succeeding on this project? Explain.

No, once the mean and standard deviation have been computed in millimeters, they can be converted to centimeters.

- Greg DeWorld wants to determine the total value of all the bicycles in his town. He goes door to door in his neighborhood, asking all 32 families the value of their bicycles. He finds that the average value for the bikes in his neighborhood is $78.00, with a standard deviation of $4.80. He then goes to the bicycle licensing branch and finds that there are 9834 bicycles within the city limits. He then concludes that the total value of all bicycles within the city limits is about $767,052 (that is, $78 · 9834), and that he could be off by as much as $47,203.20 (that is, $4.80 · 9834).

a. Do you think his method of sampling is the best way to determine random results? Explain.

b. If Greg doubled his sample size by also going door to door in the adjacent neighborhood, would that improve his results?

c. If Greg's mean and standard deviation were in fact correct, would there be any other problems? Explain.

a. Probably not; his neighborhood might be richer or poorer than most.

b. Probably not; he really needs a random sampling over the whole town.

c. **Answers will vary, but one problem is that Greg is assuming that no bike has a value more than one standard deviation away from the mean. If the values of several bikes were two standard deviations away from the mean, then his error could be even greater.**

- Duzz Prettygood loves his mathematics class. Here are his scores for the tests he has taken so far in mathematics:

93	89	89	89	90	86	88	84	91	92
88	87	88	90	95	94	86	87	96	89
93	94	91	90	87	90	91	92	90	94

a. Create a histogram representing this data.

b. Find the mean and standard deviation.

c. Does the data appear to be normally distributed?

d. Write an equation of a normal distribution that would approximate this data.

a.

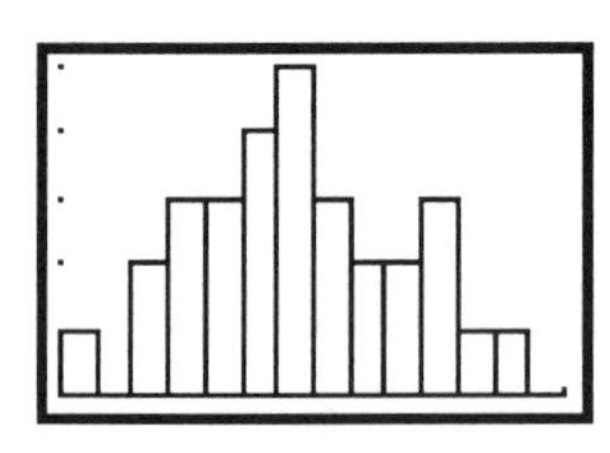

[84, 98, 1, 0, 5, 1]

b. mean = 90.1, s.d. ≈ 2.879

c. somewhat normal

d. $y = (0.13857)(0.93968)^{(x-90.1)^2}$

- No matter how his class performs, Mr. Wanna B. Fare uses a normal distribution when determining his course grades. Every student who has a score within one standard deviation from the mean receives a grade of C. A student with a grade more than one standard deviation, but less than or equal to two standard deviations, above the mean receives a B. A student with a grade more than one standard deviation, but less than or equal to two standard deviations, below the mean receives a D. The letter grades A and F are reserved for students whose scores are more than two standard deviations above or below (respectively) the mean.

a. Using Mr. Fare's grading scheme, what percentage of the class will receive the grade of A? B? C? D? F?

b. In a special studies course, Mr. Fare had only ten students. Their final course scores were:

88	85	87	92	88
96	86	90	89	91

Calculate the mean and standard deviation for these scores. What grades did each score receive?

c. What do you think of Mr. Fare's grading method? When do you think his method is best used? Explain.

a. Roughly 2.28% will receive an A, 13.6% B, 68% C, 13.6% D, and 2.28% F.

b. mean = 89.2, s.d. ≈3.06, Grades: 88 - C, 85 - D, 87 - C, 92 - C, 96 - A, 86 - D, 90 - C, 89 - C, 91 - C, (> 95.32 = A, > 92.26 = B, > 86.14 = C, > 83.06 = D)

c. The method does not seem very fair. It is probably best used in a very large class.

- Define a function $f(x)$ as follows: $f(x)$ = the probability of x heads in six tosses of a fair coin. Graph $f(x)$. What do you notice about the graph? Explain this.

  It looks like a normal curve.

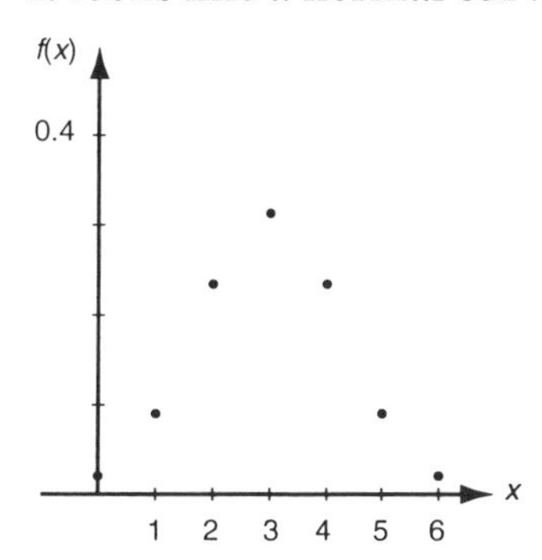

Group Problems

- Some people believe that there should be mandatory testing for HIV for people working in the health services. Suppose the test for HIV is 99% accurate (the current tests are not this accurate). Statistically, it has been documented that an average of 100 out of every 100,000 people actually are HIV positive. Suppose 100,000 people are going to be tested. How many people will have a true result from the test? What is the probability that someone who tests positive for HIV actually does not have it (a false-positive result)? Based on this, do you think that there should be mandatory testing? Support your conclusion in a clearly written paragraph.

  In 100,000 people, 99 people who actually have HIV will be told they have it; 98,901 people who don't have it will be told they do not have it; 1 person with HIV will be told he or she doesn't have it; and 999 people who actually do not have HIV will be told they do.

- Par Tickular and Maya Way go to Raskin Bobbins for ice cream after work. Both are very picky about their ice cream. Par *must* have his ice cream on a cone and Maya *must* have hers in a dish. Par wants chocolate mousse on top, cherry truffle in the middle, and double Dutch chocolate on the bottom. Maya wants strawberry, banana, and vanilla. They walk into the ice cream parlor and they don't even need to look at the list of 31 flavors offered, they know what to order! Just when they finish ordering, the lights go off and it is completely dark. The ice cream scooper can find the dishes and the cones, but must scoop the ice cream at random due to the darkness. Scooping at random, what is the probability that:

  a. Maya gets *exactly* what she wants?

  b. Par gets *exactly* what he wants (order and all)?

  c. Par *does not* get exactly what he wants?

  d. If Par decides to order his ice cream in a dish rather than a cone keeping the same ice cream flavors, does he have a better chance of getting what he wants? Explain.

  a. $\frac{1}{4495}$ **b.** $\frac{1}{26{,}970}$ **c.** $\frac{26{,}969}{26{,}970}$

  d. Yes, because order is not important.

Chapter 12: Functions and Relations

Journal Questions

- Some new ideas and concepts were introduced in Chapter 12: Functions and Relations. What do you think is the point of Chapter 12? What do you think you should learn about functions and relations from this chapter? Be clear and justify your response.

  Answers will vary.

- Find three problems in the chapter that you feel are representative of the chapter. Write out the problem and the solution. For each problem, explain why you feel it is representative of the chapter.

  Answers will vary.

- Find and solve a problem (or perhaps write one of your own) that shows that you understand how the mathematics in this chapter is useful in a real-world setting.

  Answers will vary.

- Find and solve a problem (or perhaps write one of your own) that shows that you understand how the mathematics you learned in this chapter is connected to mathematics you have studied previously this year.

  Answers will vary.

- What ideas or topics were introduced in this chapter that you feel you do not quite understand yet or for which you do not see the purpose? Give examples.

  Answers will vary.

- Consider again the role of the graphing calculator in this course for this chapter. Have you discovered new advantages or disadvantages of using the graphing calculator? If so, what are they? Has your perspective or feeling changed toward the use of the graphing calculator as you have moved through the year? Be clear and explain your response.

  Answers will vary.

- What graphing calculator skills have you mastered during this chapter? Explain thoroughly and use examples. What graphing calculator skills have you not yet mastered? Provide an example for which you need a calculator skill that you have not yet mastered.

  Answers will vary.

- Previously, you were asked to think about the purpose of working in groups within your class. Also, you were asked to think about the role you played in your group. Why do you think you should work in groups? Be clear and explain your response.

  Answers will vary.

- In your own words, explain what a function is and what a relation is, and compare and contrast the two. Explain why you think it is important to study both. Be clear and complete.

  Answers will vary.

- Explain everything you know about functions and relations.

  Answers will vary.

Open-ended Problems

- Your task is to convince the reader (you may choose a reader, but explain who your reader is) that you understand functions and relations and how they can be used in real-life situations.

  Answers will vary.

- For each type of function listed below, give a real-life situation that is best modeled by that type of function. Justify your statement.

  a. quadratic (parabola)

  b. exponential

  c. logarithmic

  d. rational

  Answers will vary, depending most on what you covered and/or emphasized in your class.

- Come up with a real-world situation that can be represented graphically, in which the graph will have:

  a. a hole (discontinuity) in it.

  b. a vertical asymptote.

  c. a horizontal asymptote.

  d. at least two of the above simultaneously.

  Answers will vary.

- Define a function (an equation with x and y) that will fit each condition given below. (Each is a separate problem.) Verify that each is correct.

  a. A graph that has holes (discontinuities) at $x = 3$ and $x = -2$.

  b. A graph that has a hole (discontinuity) at $x = 0$ and a vertical asymptote at $x = -9$.

  c. A graph that has a vertical asymptote at $x = 7$ and a horizontal asymptote at $y = 3$.

  d. For at least one of the above, come up with a different function fitting the same conditions.

  Answers will vary, but here are some samples that work.

  a. $y = \frac{x(x-3)(x+2)}{(x-3)(x+2)}$ **b.** $y = \frac{x}{x(x+9)}$ **c.** $y = \frac{1}{x-7} + 3$

  d. Answers will vary.

- When Ima Lost was working on her algebra assignment, she hit a stumbling block. To help remedy the situation, she went to her friend Crystal Claire.

  "I just don't get it, Crystal," Ima whined. "I understand completely how to find the roots of an equation such as this one," and she wrote the equation

$$y = x^2 + x - 6$$

  on a piece of paper. "But I have problems with this type of equation," and she wrote the equation

$$y = \frac{x^2 + x - 6}{x + 4}.$$

  "Why do I have such problems with algebra!"

Crystal immediately jumped in. "Are you sure you really understand the first one? Explain to me how to find the roots."

"Roots are x-intercepts," Ima explained. "At x-intercepts, $y = 0$. So I set the equation equal to zero and solve for x."

"Sounds pretty good," Crystal replied. "So what's the trouble with the second equation?"

"Everyone keeps saying I should just set the numerator equal to zero and solve to find the roots of that one," Ima stated. "I can do that, but why? Why do I just forget about the denominator?"

"Aha! Now I see the problem," Crystal replied. "You don't have a problem with algebra. You have a problem with fractions!"

What is Ima's problem? Explain to her completely why she can just use the numerator to find the roots.

Answers will vary. Be sure the student is clear that for a fraction to equal zero, the numerator must equal zero, thus giving a quick way to find the x-intercepts of the rational function.

- Do you think $f(x) = \frac{1}{x}$ is the parent of $f(x) = \frac{1}{x^2}$? Justify your answer.

Answers will vary. There is no simple way to manipulate the graph of the first to get the graph of the second.

- Les Payshence cannot use a graphing calculator in his mathematics class. He is also studying rational functions, having to sketch the graphs of many of them for homework. Offer Les some guidance by giving him some general guidelines for graphing equations in the following forms.

a. $y = \frac{a}{x - b}$ b. $y = ax + b + \frac{c}{x}$ c. $y = \frac{(x + a)(x + b)}{(x + a)(x + c)}$

Answers will vary.

- For the following problem, please follow this format.
  - i. State the problem.
  - ii. What do you already know that would help you solve this problem? Who (in your group) knows it and how does he or she know it?
  - iii. What information do you need to assume? Why are you assuming it?
  - iv. Record all your steps in solving the problem.
  - v. State your answer clearly and completely.
  - vi. How good is your answer? Remember: "A chain is only as strong as its weakest link!" What are your most unreliable approximations and weakest assumptions?

How far does the earth travel through space in 1 year?

Answers will vary.

Projects

- You have studied several types of functions this year and have seen how they can be used to model real-world situations. For each function type listed below, you need to find a person and a profession that uses the function somewhat regularly. Give the person's name and job title, and a detailed description of how the function is used. When possible, include items from the job that show how he or she uses the function.

a. linear function

b. exponential function

c. quadratic function

d. logarithmic function

e. rational function

Answers will vary.

The following project allows students to investigate the *xy*-term in a general quadratic relation. To do this project by hand (that is, without the aid of a graphing utility) would be quite tedious. Some algebraic work would be needed to be done, however, to use a graphing calculator.

- In this project, you will be guided to discovering a mathematical fact. Use a graphing utility to create the graphs, but also record the graph on paper to be included in your project. An organized project should include (at least) the following:

  i. Neat replicas of all graphs, organized and accurately and appropriately labeled.

  ii. An explanation of the graphing utility you used and how you used it. (Did you have to make any adjustments in the equations?)

  iii. A description of the process you went through—both the solving process and your thinking process. (This would entail descriptions such as "First I graphed . . . by doing this . . . This made me think that. . . .")

  iv. A clear statement and explanation of your conjectures and conclusions.

  a. Graph all of the equations below on the same set of coordinate axes.

  Equation 1: $x^2 + y^2 = 16$

  Equation 2: $x^2 + xy + y^2 = 16$

  Equation 3: $x^2 + 4xy + y^2 = 16$

  b. How are the equations related? How are the graphs related? Come up with another equation that is similar to the ones above. Before graphing it, predict what the graph will look like. Verify your prediction.

  c. Graph each equation below and name the conic section represented by the graph.

  Equation 4: $x^2 + y^2 - 8x - 10y + 16 = 0$

  Equation 5: $x^2 + xy + y^2 - 8x - 10y + 16 = 0$

  Equation 6: $x^2 + 2xy + y^2 - 8x - 10y + 16 = 0$

  Equation 7: $x^2 + 4xy + y^2 - 8x - 10y + 16 = 0$

  d. Each of the equations above is written in general form:

  $$Ax^2 + Bxy + Cy^2 + Dx + Ey + F = 0$$

  When writing in this form, the discriminant is

  $$B^2 - 4AC$$

  Calculate the discriminant for each of the numbered equations (1 through 7) above.

  e. What does the discriminant tell you? Be clear. Test your conjecture.

a.

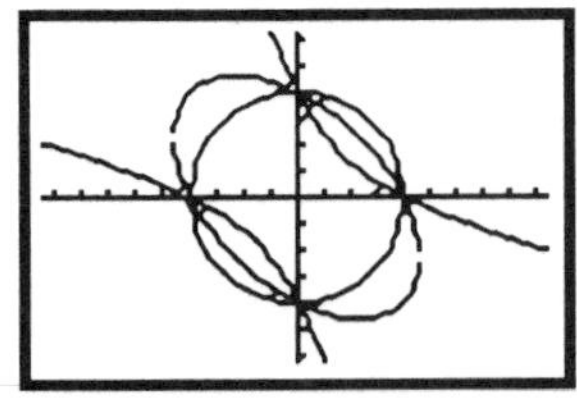

[−9.4, 9.4, 1, −4.7, 4.7, 1]

b. **Answers will vary. All equations intersect in the same four points.**

c. **Equation 4**

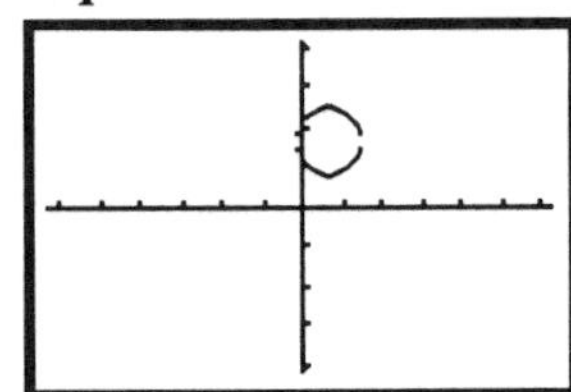

[−37.6, 37.6, 6, −24.8, 24.8, 6]
a circle

Equation 5

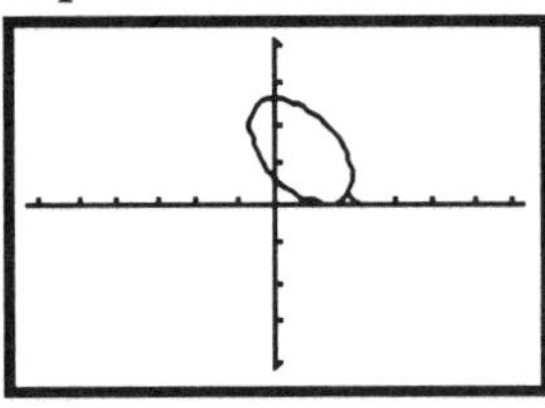

[−18.8, 18.8, 3, −12.4, 12.4, 3]
an ellipse

Equation 6

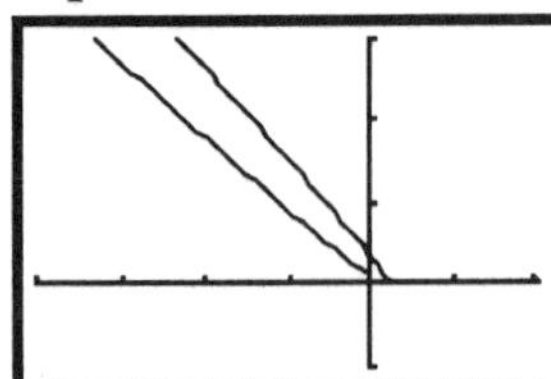

[−100.8, 50.8, 25, −25, 75, 25]
a parabola

Equation 7

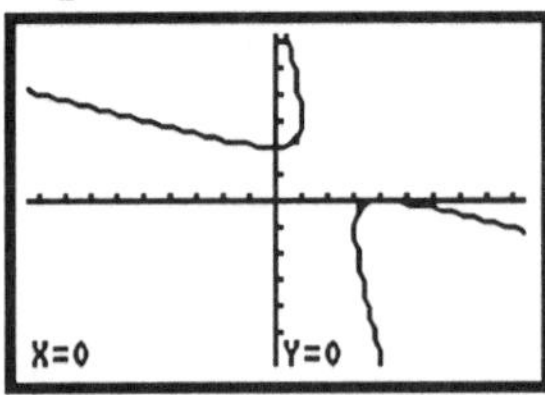

[−9.4, 9.4, 1, −6.2, 6.2, 1]
a hyperbola

d. **Equation 1: −4** **Equation 2: −3** **Equation 3: 12**
Equation 4: −4 **Equation 5: −3** **Equation 6: 0**
Equation 7: 12

e. **What the students should discover is that if the discriminant < 0, the graph is a circle or ellipse, if the discriminant is = 0, the graph is a parabola, and if the discriminant is > 0, the graph is a hyperbola.**

Skill Questions: Appropriate for Quizzes or Tests

- If the graph of $f(x) = \frac{1}{x}$ is shifted 5 units down and 2 units right, what is the equation of the graph?

  $\mathbf{f(x) = \frac{1}{x-2} - 5}$

- Consider the graph of $y = \frac{1}{x}$.

  a. Is this a function? Justify your answer.
  b. Does it have a vertical asymptote? If so, where? If not, why not?
  c. Does it have a horizontal asymptote? If so, where? If not, why not?
  d. Change the equation so that the graph has a vertical asymptote at $x = {}^-6$.
  e. Change the equation so that the graph has a horizontal asymptote at $y = 3$.
  f. What equation would give both the vertical and horizontal asymptotes of the last two parts?

a. Yes, it passes the vertical line test.

b. Yes at $x = 0$.

c. Yes, at $y = 0$.

d. $y = \frac{1}{x+6}$

e. $y = \frac{1}{x} + 3$

f. $\frac{1}{x+6} + 3$

- Izzy Tolate is having a lot of trouble with algebra. He scored 45% on each of the first five tests. To pass the class (and graduate) he must have a 65% average on his tests. How many 100% scores must he earn to be sure he graduates?

  He would have to have three 100% and then nothing lower than a 65%.

- a. Graph each equation on a separate set of axes.

  $y = \frac{x^2 + x - 2}{x^2 - x}$ $\qquad$ $y = \frac{x + 2}{x}$

  b. How are the graphs similar? How are they different? Be clear and explain the similarities and differences.

  a.

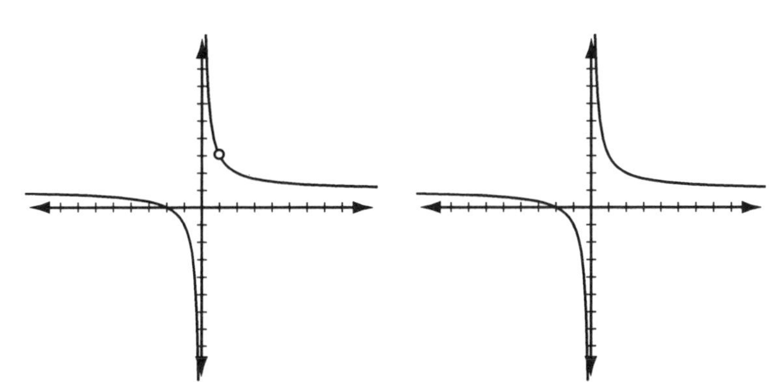

  b. The graphs are the same except the first has a hole at $x = 1$.

- What are the roots of each equation?

  a. $y = 3x + 6$

  b. $y = (3x + 6)(x - 4)$

  c. $y = \frac{(3x + 6)(x - 4)}{x + 7}$

  a. $x = {}^{-}2$

  b. $x = {}^{-}2, 4$

  c. $x = {}^{-}2, 4$

- Write the equation of a function that satisfies each of the following conditions simultaneously.

  a. It has a vertical asymptote at $x = 4$.

  b. It has roots at $x = {}^{-}1$ and $x = 9$.

  c. It has a tilted asymptote of $y = \frac{2}{3}x - 2$.

  $y = \frac{(x+1)(x-9)}{x^2(x-4)} + \frac{2}{3}x - 2$

- Solve each equation or inequation for x.

  a. $\frac{5}{x - 6} - 2 = 10$

  b. $\frac{5}{x - 6} - x = 10 + 3x$

  c. $\frac{x + 5}{x - 6} \geq 10$

  a. $x = \frac{77}{12}$

  b. $x = \frac{14 \pm \sqrt{1236}}{8} = \frac{7 \pm \sqrt{309}}{4}$

  c. ${}^{-}6 \leq x \leq \frac{65}{9}$

- A square-based box is to have a volume of 100 cubic centimeters.
Complete the table below, which compares the length of the sides of the base and the height, for at least five values.

x = side of base					
h = height					

a. Plot the points (x, h) and draw a smooth curve through them.

b. Explain what happens to the height of the box as the length of the side of the base gets smaller. How small can x be? Explain.

c. Write a formula for volume in terms of x and h.

d. Solve the formula in part c for h. What type of function is this?

a. Answers will vary. The graph is $y = \frac{100}{x^2}$.

b. The height gets larger. Positive x can be as close to zero as desired without actually being zero.

c. $V = x^2h$, $100 = x^2h$ **d. $h = \frac{100}{x^2}$, hyperbola.**

- A 13-foot ladder is held upright against a wall. The top of the ladder slides down while the foot of the ladder is dragged outward along the ground at a steady rate of 1.5 feet per second.

a. How long will it take before the entire ladder is lying on the ground?

b. Complete the table showing the height of the ladder top at 1-second intervals while the ladder slides down the wall.

Time in seconds	0	1	2	. . .
Height in feet	13			

c. Does the ladder slide down the wall at a steady rate of 1.5 feet per second? Support your answer.

d. Write a pair of parametric equations, one that graphs the location of the foot of the ladder and the second to graph the location of the top of the ladder.

a. $\approx$ 8.7 seconds **b. $\approx$ 12.9, 12.6**

c. No, see the last answer. During the first second it dropped $\approx$ 0.1 feet. In the second second, it dropped $\approx$ 0.3 feet.

d. $x = 1.5t, y = \sqrt{169 - (1.5t)^2}$

- Sketch a graph of each equation. Label any important items, for instance, a focus (foci), directrix, asymptotes, and so on.

a. $\begin{cases} x(t) = 5\cos t + 6 \\ y(t) = 5\sin t - 1 \end{cases}$

b. $(x + 4)^2 + (y + 3)^2 = 4$

c. $\begin{cases} x(t) = 6\cos t + 2 \\ y(t) = \sin t - 4 \end{cases}$

d. $\frac{x^2}{16} + \frac{(y - 4)^2}{36} = 1$

e. $9(x - 2)^2 - 16(y + 4)^2 = 144$

f. $\begin{cases} x(t) = \frac{6}{\cos t} - 8 \\ y(t) = 3\tan t + 3 \end{cases}$

a. **A circle whose center is (6, ⁻1) with a radius of 5.**

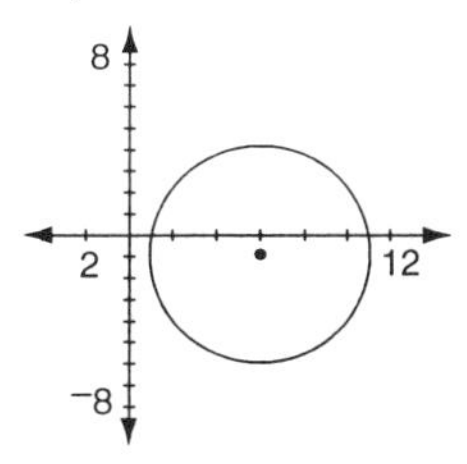

b. **A circle whose center is (⁻4, ⁻3) with a radius of 2.**

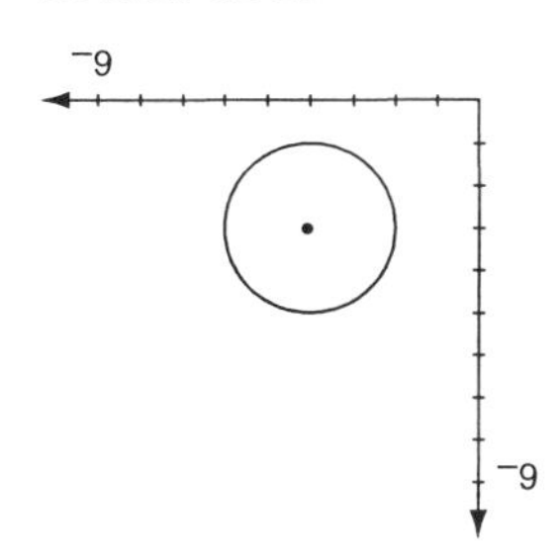

c. **An ellipse whose center is (2, ⁻4). The length of the major axis is 12, and the length of the minor axis is 2. The coordinates of the foci are $(2 + \sqrt{35}, {}^{-}4)$ and $(2 - \sqrt{35}, {}^{-}4)$.**

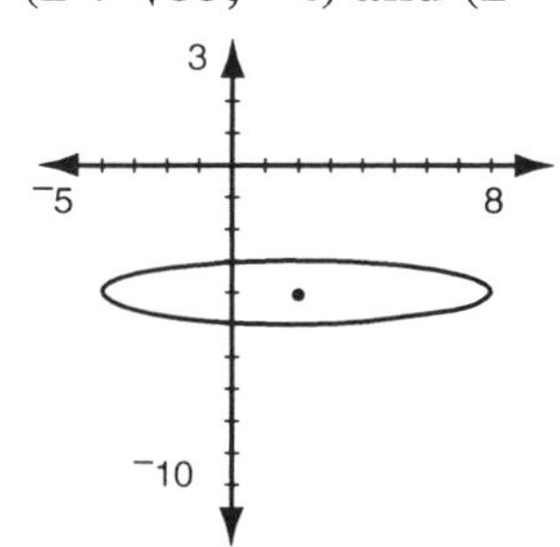

d. **An ellipse whose center is (0, 4). The length of the major axis is 12, and the length of the minor axis is 8. The coordinates of the foci are $(0, 4 + 2\sqrt{5})$ and $(0, 4 - 2\sqrt{5})$.**

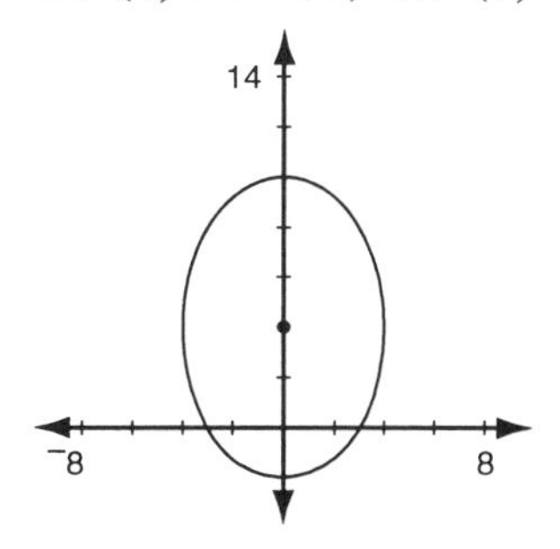

e. **A hyperbola whose center is (2, ⁻4). The equations of the asymptotes are $y = \frac{3}{4}x - \frac{11}{2}$ and $y = \frac{-3}{4}x - \frac{5}{2}$. The coordinates of the foci are (⁻3, ⁻4) and (7, ⁻4).**

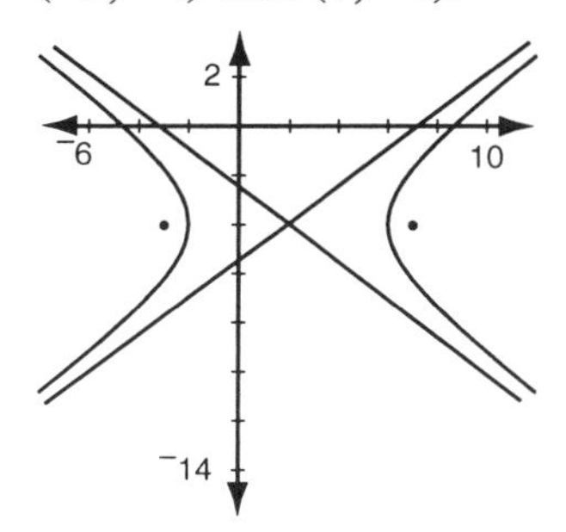

f. **A hyperbola whose center is (⁻8, 3). The equations of the asymptotes are $y = 0.5x + 7$ and $y = {}^{-}0.5x - 1$. The coordinates of the foci are $({}^{-}8 + 2\sqrt{5}, 3)$ and $({}^{-}8 - 2\sqrt{5}, 3)$.**

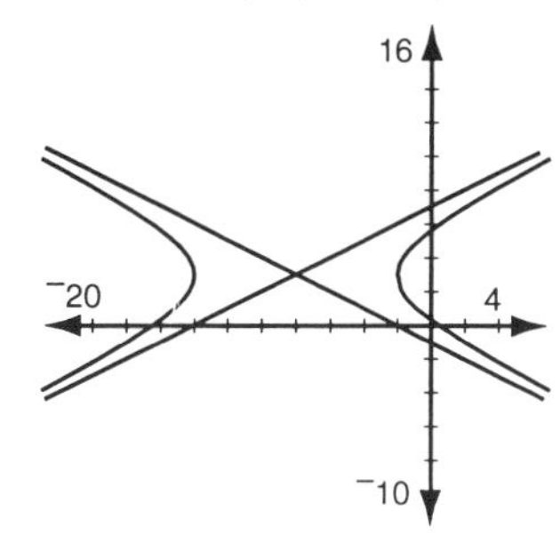

- A point moves in the plane so that it is always five units from the point (−3, 7). What is the equation of the path of this point?

  $x(t) = 5 \cos t - 3, y(t) = 5 \sin t + 7$ or $(x + 3)^2 + (y - 7)^2 = 25$

- A point moves in the plane so that it is always the same distance from the point (4, −6) as it is from the line $y = -2$. What is the equation of the path of this point?

  $y = \frac{1}{8}x^2 + x - 6$

- A point moves in the plane so that the sum of the distances from (3, 8) and (3, −2) is always 15. What is the equation of the path of this point?

$$\frac{(x-3)^2}{56.25}+\frac{(y-3)^2}{31.25}=1 \text{ or } \frac{4(x-3)^2}{225}+\frac{4(y-3)^2}{125}=1$$

- A point moves in the plane so that the difference of the distances from (7, −3) and (2, −3) is always 3. What is the equation of the path of this point?

  $$\frac{(x-4.5)^2}{2.25}-\frac{(y+3)^2}{4}=1$$

- Find the equation of the parabola containing these points: (5, 3), (−1, 1), and (7, 5).

  $$y=\frac{1}{12}x^2+\frac{11}{12}$$

- Find the equation of the circle that contains the points (−1, 4), (5, −4), and (5, 4).

  $$(x-2)^2+y^2=25$$

- Rewrite each equation in *general quadratic form.*

  a. $(y-4)^2=3(x+3)$
  b. $(x+5)^2+(y-6)^2=81$
  c. $\frac{(x-3)^2}{36}+\frac{(y-1)^2}{121}=1$
  d. $\frac{(y+5)^2}{25}-\frac{(x-4)^2}{9}=1$

  a. $y^2-3x-8y+7=0$
  b. $x^2+y^2+10x-12y-20=0$
  c. $121x^2+36y^2-726x-72y-3231=0$
  d. $^-25x^2+9y^2+200x+90y-400=0$

- Rewrite each equation in *center-vertex form* and identify the curve.

  a. $8x^2+16x+3y^2-9y=0$
  b. $x^2-y^2-5y=2.25$
  c. $2y^2-5x+8y+18=0$

  a. $\frac{(x+1)^2}{3}+\frac{(y-1.5)^2}{8}=\frac{14.75}{24}$, **ellipse**

  b. $\frac{(y+2.5)^2}{4}-\frac{x^2}{4}=1$, **hyperbola**

  c. $x=\frac{2}{5}(y+2)^2+2$, **parabola**

- Graph this system of inequations.

  $$y \ge x-4$$
  $$y \ge -\frac{7}{2}x+5$$
  $$y \le -\frac{1}{3}x+5$$

  a. What shape is formed by the inequations?
  b. Name the coordinates of the vertices of the shape you found in part a.
  c. Rotate this shape counterclockwise 90° and 120° about the origin. Sketch the rotated shapes.
  d. Name the coordinates of the vertices of the rotated shapes.

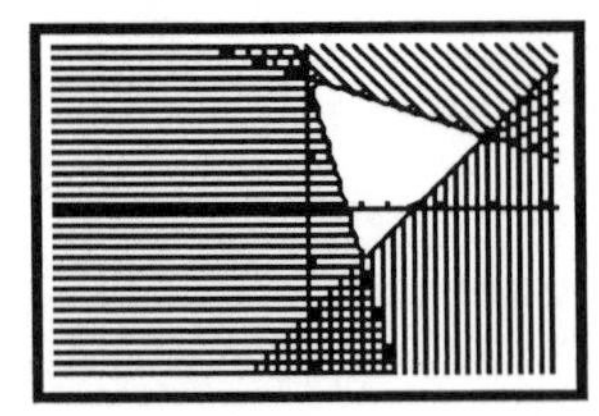

[$^-$9.4, 9.4, 1, $^-$3.1, 3.1, 1]

a. A triangle

b. (0, 5), (2, ⁻2), (6.75, 2.75)

c.

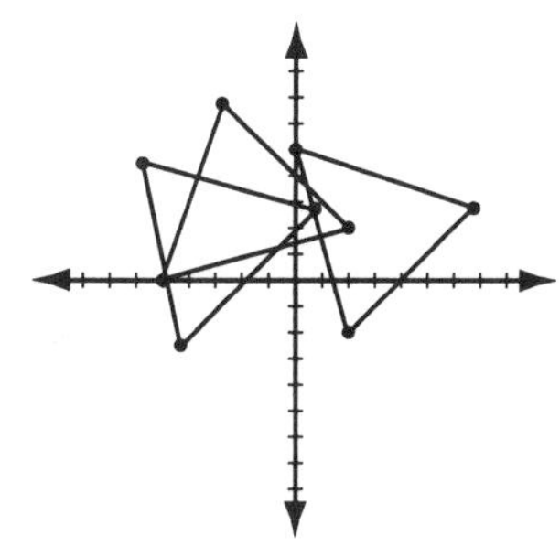

d. rotated 90°: (⁻5,0), (2, 2), (⁻2.75, 6.75); rotated 120°: (⁻4.33, ⁻2.5), (0.73, 2.73), (⁻5.76, 4.47)

- Graph the curve defined parametrically by $\begin{cases} x(t) = 5\cos t \\ y(t) = 2\sin t \end{cases}$.

  a. What conic section is this?

  b. Rotate this graph through an angle of 45°. Graph the new curve.

  c. Write the parametric equations of the new curve.

a. ellipse

b.

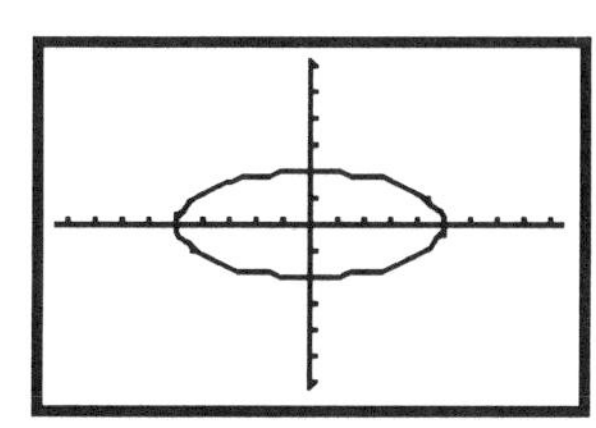

[⁻9.4, 9.4, 1, ⁻6.2, 6.2, 1]

c. $x(t) = \frac{5\sqrt{2}}{2}\cos t - \sqrt{2}\sin t,\ y(t) = \frac{5\sqrt{2}}{2}\cos t + \sqrt{2}\sin t$

- The graph of $x^2 + y^2 = 36$ is a circle. How can you tell this without actually graphing it? Where is the center of this circle?

It fits the form for the equation of a circle. The center is (0, 0).

- For each of the following, make *one* change in the equation $x^2 + y^2 = 36$ so that its graph will

  a. be the region *outside* the circle.

  b. have a radius one unit larger.

  c. have a center at (0, −2).

  d. be an ellipse.

  e. be a hyperbola.

a. $x^2 + y^2 > 36$ **b.** $x^2 + y^2 = 49$ **c.** $x^2 + (y + 2)^2 = 36$

d. $ax^2 + y^2 = 36$ **or** $x^2 + ay^2 = 36$**, where** $a \neq 0$ **or 1.**

e. $x^2 - y^2 = 36$ **or** $^-x^2 + y^2 = 36$

- For each of the following, transform the equation or inequation by completing the square. Find the center, radius, and/or vertex of each (where applicable) and sketch the graph.

a. $x^2 + y^2 + 4x - 10y + 20 < 0$

b. $4x^2 + y^2 - 8x + 6y - 3 = 0$

c. $y^2 + 2x - 6y - 7 = 0$

d. $9x^2 - 4y^2 - 72x + 40y + 80 = 0$

a. $(x + 2)^2 + (y - 5)^2 < 9$**, inside circle with center (⁻2, 5), radius 3.**

b. $\frac{(x-1)^2}{4} + \frac{(y+3)^2}{16} = 1$**, ellipse with center (1, ⁻3),** $r_x = 2$, $r_y = 4$**.**

c. $x = -\frac{1}{2}(y - 3)^2 + 8$**, parabola with vertex (3, 8) opening to the left.**

d. $\frac{(y-5)^2}{9} - \frac{(x-4)^2}{4} = 1$**, hyperbola with center (4, 5).**

- If the equation of a quadratic relation has an *xy*-term, you can use the discriminant to tell which conic it will be. Find the discriminant and tell which conic section the graph will be. *Note:* You do *not* need to graph it!

a. $4x^2 + 9y^2 + 7x - 2y - 100 = 0$

b. $4x^2 + 10xy + 9y^2 + 7x - 2y - 100 = 0$

c. $4x^2 + 12xy + 9y^2 + 7x - 2y - 100 = 0$

d. $4x^2 + 14xy + 7x - 2y - 100 = 0$

a. D = ⁻144, ellipse **b. D = ⁻44, ellipse**

c. D = 0, parabola **d. D = 196, hyperbola**

- Intersections of two conics can be found by solving the system of equations. Use algebra to solve each of the following systems. Show all your work.

a. $x^2 - 6y = 34$
$x^2 + y^2 = 25$

b. $y = x^2 + 8x + 9$
$x - y = {}^-3$

a. (±4, ⁻3) **b. (⁻6, ⁻3), (⁻1, 2)**

- Write the equation of the conic section pictured below.

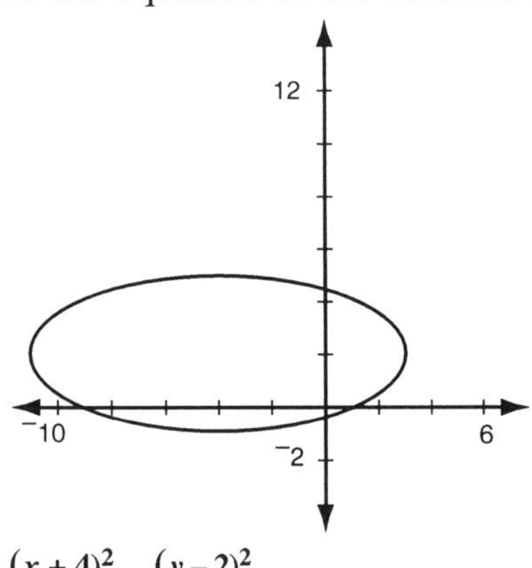

$\frac{(x+4)^2}{49} + \frac{(y-2)^2}{9} = 1$

- Carefully sketch a graph of each equation, showing the important features. Determine if the graph is a function, and name both the domain and range.

  a. $y = \sqrt{x + 4} - 2$ b. $y = \dfrac{3}{x - 2}$

  c. $y = \dfrac{2(2x - 1)}{(2x - 1)}$

  a. yes, $x \geq {}^-4, y \geq {}^-2$ **b. yes, $x \neq 2, y \neq 0$** **c. yes, $x \neq 0.5, y = 2$**

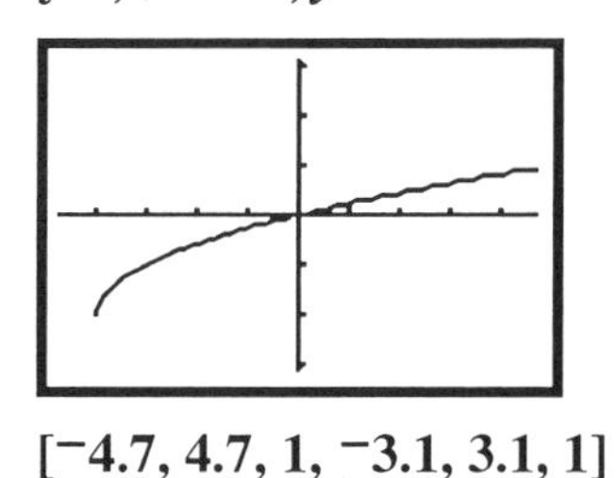

[⁻4.7, 4.7, 1, ⁻3.1, 3.1, 1]

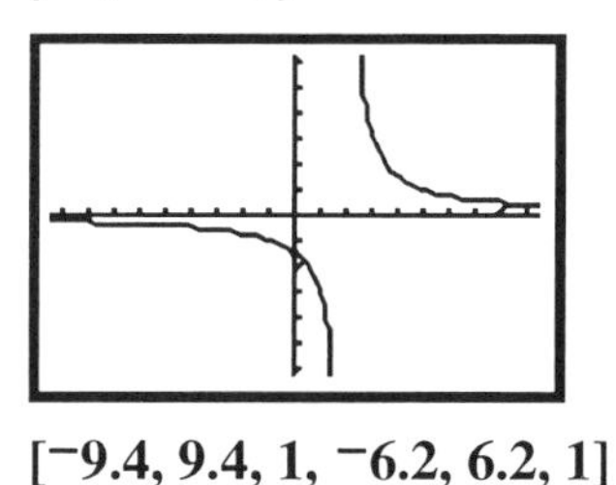

[⁻9.4, 9.4, 1, ⁻6.2, 6.2, 1]

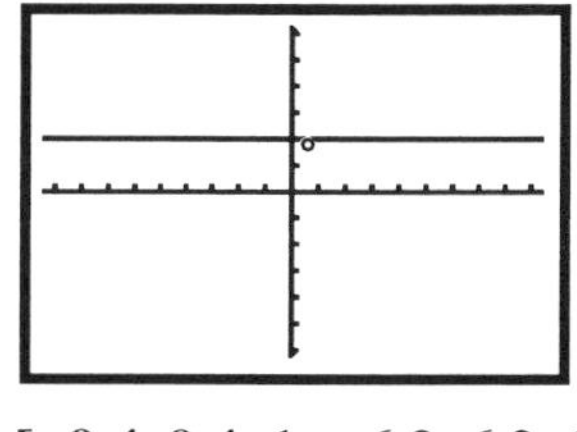

[⁻9.4, 9.4, 1, ⁻6.2, 6.2, 1]

Group Problems

The next problem is listed as a project in the Chapter 10 assessment materials. Using only the ideas of Chapter 10, this problem is fairly difficult, but using the ideas in this chapter, the problem is somewhat less difficult.

- On one side of a 1-mile-wide river is a power plant. On the other side, 4 miles upstream, there is a factory. It costs \$3.00 per foot to run cable over land and \$5.00 per foot to run the cable underwater. (One possible route is shown with the darker line.)

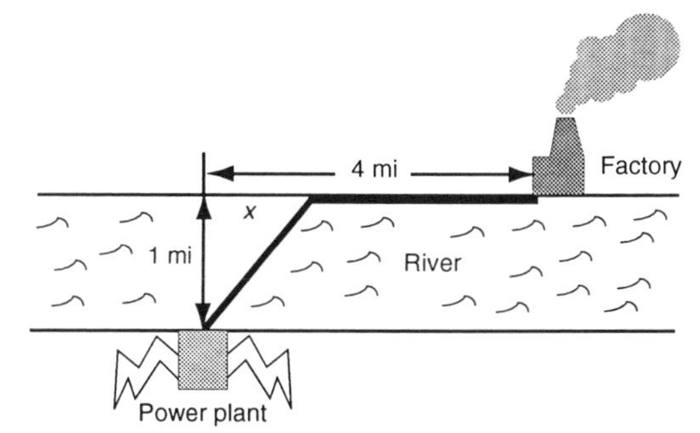

  a. Draw the routes for $x = 0.5$, 1, 1.5, and 2. Make the drawings accurate and to scale.

  b. Calculate the cost of each of the routes you drew in part a.

  c. What is the cost for the route shown with an arbitrary distance x?

  d. Will minimizing the length of the cable minimize the cost? Explain.

  e. What value of x will minimize the cost of installing the cable? Explain.

  f. What happens if the factory is 6 miles upstream? 7 miles? 10 miles? Write a conjecture about the distance the factory is from the power plant and the cost of the cable installation.

a.

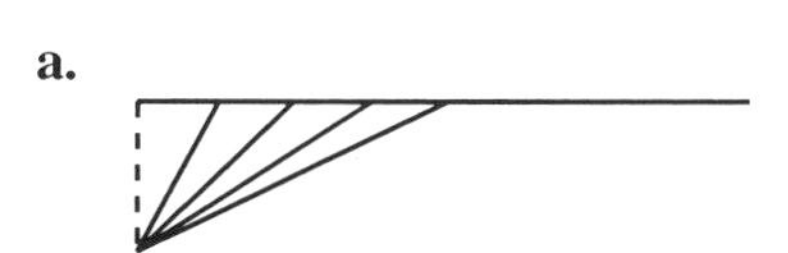

b. **≈ \$84,956.10, \$84,855.24, \$87,193.28, \$90,712.19**

c. $5\sqrt{5280^2 + (5280x)^2} + (4 - x)(5280)(3)$

d. Not necessarily. The shortest distance would be a straight line, but a straight line would be entirely underwater and would be more expensive.

e. The minimum cost is at $x = 0.75$ miles.

f. No matter how much farther upstream the factory is located, $x = 0.75$ miles gives the minimum cost.

- Read the following situations carefully. Your task is to decide which type of function would best model the situation described, justify why you believe it is best modeled by that type of function, and come up with an equation and use it to answer the question stated.

  a. A team of mountain climbers is planning to climb Mt. Everest. Naturally, they are concerned, for as they climb higher and higher (as their elevation increases) they realize that the percent of oxygen (by volume) in the air decreases. This will make it very difficult to breathe as they climb, and can even kill them if the air becomes too thin. Their base camp will be at an elevation of 1056 feet ($\frac{1}{5}$ mile). There, the oxygen will be 20% by volume. They know that when they reach an elevation of 1 mile, the oxygen will then be $\frac{1}{5}$ of what it was at the base camp. The climbers' hope is to reach the peak of Mt. Everest, an elevation of 29,002 feet (approximately 5.5 miles). If a physically fit human's actions are impaired with less than 0.8% oxygen by volume, at what elevation will the climbers be forced to carry oxygen tanks to continue?

  b. You're going to Disneyland! You must pick up one of your friends in Sacramento, California, and then head south on the freeway. As you get onto the freeway, you notice that it is exactly 12 noon and a sign along the road reads "Los Angeles 432 miles." After two hours you pass another sign which reads "Los Angeles 302 miles." Knowing that you always drive *at* the speed limit, what time will it be when you get to Los Angeles?

  c. You climb to the top of a 500-foot building and drop a book off the edge. After one second, it has fallen 16 feet; after three seconds, it has fallen 144 feet; after four seconds, it has fallen 256 feet. When will it hit the ground?
  Extra credit: Explain, in detail, a method to accurately measure the heights of the book at these time intervals.

a. Answers will vary. An inverse variation (hyperbola: $y = \frac{0.04}{x}$) will work, with x in miles. Using this equation, at 5 miles up they will need tanks.

b. Linear model will best work here: $y = ^{-}65x + 432$, arrive at $\approx$ 6:39 p.m.

c. Quadratic works: $y = ^{-}16x^2 + 500$.

- Chuan can walk 3 miles per hour on the grass and 5 miles per hour on the sidewalk. On a hot sunny day, she finds herself in the middle of a large lawn at point A. She wants to get to a shade tree at point B where she can get out of the sun. She's 1 mile from the sidewalk and the tree is 6 miles down the sidewalk. What path should she take to reach point B in the *least* amount of time? Justify your answer.

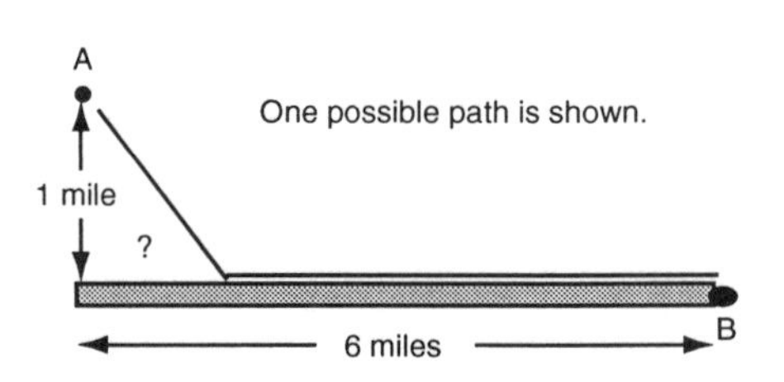

She should walk across the grass to a point $\frac{3}{4}$ mile from the foot of the perpendicular. Then she should walk the remaining $5\frac{1}{4}$ miles on the sidewalk.

Chapter 13: Trigonometric Functions

Journal Questions

- Is the trigonometry you studied in Chapter 13 the same as the trigonometry you studied in Chapter 6? Explain the similarities and differences completely.

  Answers will vary.

- In this chapter you studied six trigonometric functions: sine, cosine, tangent, cosecant, secant, and cotangent. Do any of these belong with a family of functions you studied earlier? Are these trigonometric functions similar to any of the functions you have studied? Explain completely.

  Answers will vary.

- Consider the six trigonometric functions you studied in this chapter: sine, cosine, tangent, cosecant, secant, and cotangent. What is the parent of these functions? Justify your answer completely.

  Answers will vary.

- If you were going to write the test for this chapter, what would you cover? Why?

  Answers will vary.

- If you had to write the final exam for this course, what questions would you ask? Why? Justify your choices.

  Answers will vary.

- What graphing calculator skills have you mastered during this chapter? Explain thoroughly and use examples. What graphing calculator skills have you not yet mastered? Provide an example for which you need a calculator skill that you have not yet mastered.

  Answers will vary.

- How has your ability to do mathematics changed throughout the year? Do you feel you have improved? Explain.

  Answers will vary.

- In a short essay, explain your journey through mathematics this year. Describe your difficult times and your accomplishments. Highlight successes and memorable problems. Discuss things you would do differently if you took a course similar to this one next year.

  Answers will vary.

- In a letter to a student who will be in this class next year, give advice about this course. Inform the future advanced algebra student about how he or she can be successful and enjoy this course.

  Answers will vary.

- Find three problems in the chapter that you feel are representative of the chapter. Write out the problem and the solution. For each problem, explain why you feel it is representative of the chapter. Please use complete, coherent sentences.

  Answers will vary.

- Find five problems that you feel represent the mathematics you have learned this year. Write the problems and the complete solution. For each problem, explain why you feel it is representative of the mathematics you have learned.

  Answers will vary.

- What ideas or topics were introduced in this chapter that you feel you do not quite understand yet or for which you do not see the purpose? Give examples.

  Answers will vary.

- Throughout this year, we have been asking you to find a problem that you cannot solve. Look over the problems you have chosen in the past as difficult, or "unsolvable," problems. Can you solve them now? What is still keeping you from solving them? Explain.

  Answers will vary.

- If you had to choose a favorite problem from this unit, what would it be? Why?

  Answers will vary.

Open-ended Problems

- How can you recognize a function as a trigonometric function by examining the graph? Explain.

  Answers will vary. Look for the student to mention the periodicity of the graph.

- Clearly explain the similarities and differences between the six trigonometric functions you have studied in this chapter.

  Answers will vary. Look for groupings (sine and cosine, same just shifted, and so on.)

- Salvador has come to you with a question. It seems that on his last mathematics quiz, he lost half the points on a problem he is sure he got correct. Since the problem asked for the x-intercepts of $y = \sin x$, Salvador knew he had to set $\sin x$ equal to zero and solve.

  "I know that I solved $\sin x = 0$ correctly. I got the answer by using my calculator to find $\sin^{-1} 0$. It equals 0. Also, when I check, $\sin 0 = 0$. So why did I lose half the points?!"

  a. Is Salvador correct? Explain completely.

  b. Give Salvador some advice for dealing with this situation and future similar situations.

  Salvador probably lost points because he forgot that there are infinitely many x-intercepts.

- Lena thinks that the only trigonometric functions we need are $y = \sin x$ and $y = \tan x$. "All the others you can get by changing the equations of these slightly." What do you think? Justify your answer.

  You can write all the trig functions (including tangent: $y = \frac{\sin x}{\sin (x + 90°)}$ using just the sine function.

- Write a trigonometric function with each of the following characteristics:

  a. No x-intercepts
  b. No y-intercepts
  c. One y-intercept
  d. One x-intercept

  a. $y = \sin x + c$, with $c > 1$, will work.
  b. $y = \csc x$ or $y = \cot x$
  c. Anything but the two in part b.
  d. Not possible unless the domain is restricted.

- Write the equation of a trigonometric function that satisfies both of the following requirements. Justify your response.

  i. The x-intercepts are at . . . , $-20°$, $0°$, $20°$, $40°$, $60°$, ...

  ii. The amplitude is 5.

  $y = 5 \cos (9(x - 30))$ will work, as will $y = 5 \sin 9x$.

- Why can't you find all the x-intercepts when you solve an equation such as $\sin x = 0$ for x? Justify your answers completely.

  To solve the equation, you are calculating $\sin^{-1}(0)$. Your calculator only works with functions, so to keep the inverse of sine a function, it must restrict the domain. Doing this, you lose some solutions.

- In Chapter 6 you learned that if you graphed the parametric equations $x = \cos t$ and $y = \sin t$, the result would be a circle. In light of what you have learned in this chapter—in particular, Investigation 13.1.1, Anne Fibian and the Paddle Wheel—explain why this makes sense.

  Look for students making connections and *understanding* the fact that the coordinates of the points on the unit circle are ($\cos t$, $\sin t$) if t is the angle.

- Write a problem or question that requires the use of the Law of Cosines to solve. Solve your problem.

  Answers will vary.

- Write a problem or question that requires the use of the Law of Sines to solve. Solve your problem.

  Answers will vary.

- Kim and Habib were working together on their mathematics homework, solving for the missing parts of triangles. After solving one problem, Kim states, "Wait a minute! These answers can't be correct! There is no way that these are the lengths and angle measures for this triangle. The triangle looks nothing like what these answers say. We must have done something wrong."

  Habib responds, "No, I think the picture is wrong and we did our work right."

  Who do you think is correct? Comment on this situation.

  Answers will vary.

- Your friend has never seen polar coordinates before. Explain to him what polar coordinates are and how he could plot points and graphs in polar coordinates. Your friend does not have a graphing calculator.

  Answers will vary.

- Throughout this year, you have learned that certain mathematical operations affect the graphs of functions similarly. For instance, the graph of $f(x)$ would be stretched up by a factor of three if you graphed $3f(x)$. Also, the graph of $g(x)$ is shifted to the left 5 units if you graphed $g(x + 5)$. Are these properties (and the other properties you have studied) also true in polar coordinates? (That is, does $r(q + 5)$ shift $r(q)$ to the left as well?) Explain completely.

  No, it rotates the graph 5° clockwise.

- Create your own problem that covers the material you have studied so far and that you think would make a good assessment question. Write out the complete solution to your problem and explain why you believe it to be a good problem. *Note:* Please make sure that it is a problem or question and not just an explanation or description.

  Answers will vary.

- Describe two different real-world situations in which a trigonometric function could be used as an appropriate model.

  Answers will vary.

- Write three interesting, chapter-appropriate questions about the graph at the right. Answer your questions.

  Answers will vary.

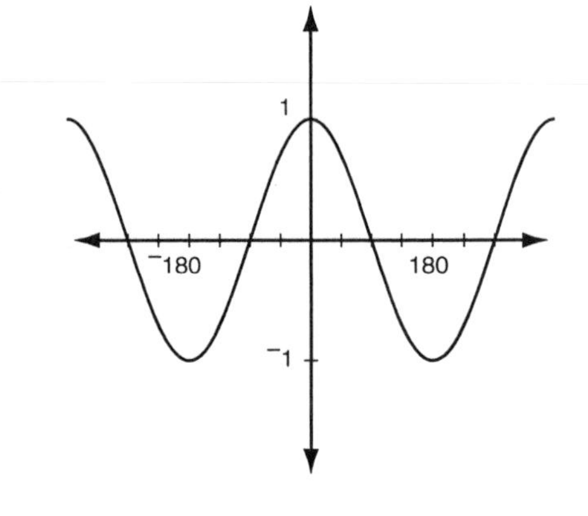

Projects

- In the library, find several books on space flight, orbits of satellites, rocket orbits, path of the space shuttle, and so on. If you were to trace the route a satellite, rocket, or space shuttle would fly over on a map of the world (a *flat* map, not a globe), what would that path look like? Draw such a path. Why is the path this shape? What equation would give the path over time? Support all your work and answers.

  Answers will vary.

- Reread Problem 4, parts a and b, in Problem Set 13.2. As in part b, sketch a graph of the bug's (*time, height from floor*) over the next 20 minutes if all sides of the picture frame are equal in length and the shape of the frame is as given below. Be sure to draw diagrams and state any assumptions that you make.

  a. equilateral triangle
  b. regular pentagon
  c. regular hexagon
  d. regular octagon
  e. Can you generalize to a regular n-gon? Explain.

  Answers will vary depending on the assumptions made and the orientation of the polygons.

- In this chapter, you learned that the Law of Sines is

$$\frac{\sin A}{a} = \frac{\sin B}{b} = \frac{\sin C}{c}$$

  Perhaps there is a "Law of Tangents" that says

$$\frac{\tan A}{a} = \frac{\tan B}{b} = \frac{\tan C}{c}$$

  Find all triangles for which this "Law of Tangents" works.

  This "law" is only true if $\cos A = \cos B = \cos C$, so $A = B = C = 60°$.

- Come up with a method for *measuring* the diameter of the earth. If you need a hint, the Greek scientist Eratosthenes measured the diameter of the earth, with an error of less than 1%, in about 150 B.C. Explain his method and how yours is different and/or better.

  Answers will vary.

Skill Questions: Appropriate for Quizzes or Tests

- Find each of the following values. For each one, draw a diagram showing how the value can be determined. Name the reference angle.

a. $\sin 60°$	b. $\cos 45°$	c. $\sin 135°$
d. $\cos 200°$	e. $\cos 180°$	f. $\sin 180°$

a. ≈ 0.866, ref. angle: 60° **b. ≈ 0.707, ref. angle: 45°**

c. ≈ 0.707, ref. angle: 45° **d. $\approx {}^{-}0.940$, ref. angle: 20°**

e. $^{-}1$, ref. angle: 0° **f. 0, ref. angle: 0°**

- Your friend Reiko does not have a graphing calculator, but she has to graph 100 trigonometric graphs. The first problem says

1. Graph $y = \sin x + c$, for $c = 1, 2, 3, \ldots, 25$

so this one problem has 25 graphs. The next three problems are similar:

2. Graph $y = \sin x - c$, for $c = 1, 2, 3, \ldots, 25$
3. Graph $y = \sin (x - c)$, for $c = 1, 2, 3, \ldots, 25$
4. Graph $y = \sin (x + c)$, for $c = 1, 2, 3, \ldots, 25$

Give Reiko some helpful advice so she won't spend all night graphing these equations by making tables and plotting points.

Answers will vary. Students should be able to tell Reiko that the graphs all look exactly the same, just shifted up, down, right or left.

- Reiko has more problems! She has just mastered what you explained to her earlier when she is given the two graphs at the right. She must write the equation for each of them.

"There's no problem with the first one. I know that's the graph of $y = \cos x$. But how am I supposed to figure out the equation of the second one?"

Help Reiko out by giving her the equation of the second graph and explaining how she can determine the equation of similar graphs in the future.

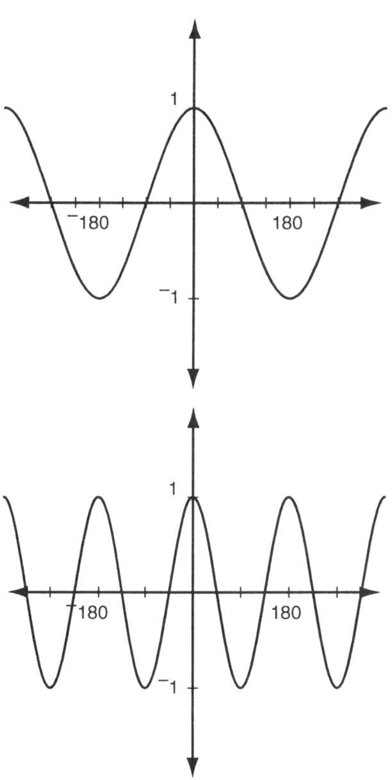

Answer: If the first graph is $y = \cos x$, then the second is $y = \cos 2x$. Be sure students give the explanation as to how to determine the constant that multiplies the variable angle measure.

- In your own words, explain what $\tan x$ equals and why it equals that.

Answers will vary. Because this is open-ended, students may say that $\tan x = \frac{\sin x}{\cos x}$ or it equals the slope of the line formed by the angle. Be sure to read the explanation carefully.

- Name the period of each function below.

a. $y = \cos x$ b. $y = \sin 5x$ c. $y = \sin \frac{1}{4}x$

d. $y = \cos 0.1x$ e. $y = \tan 180x$

a. 360° **b. 72°** **c. 1440°**

d. 3600° **e. 1°**

- For each graph below, write two equations that will produce the graph. Check your equations on your calculator.

a.

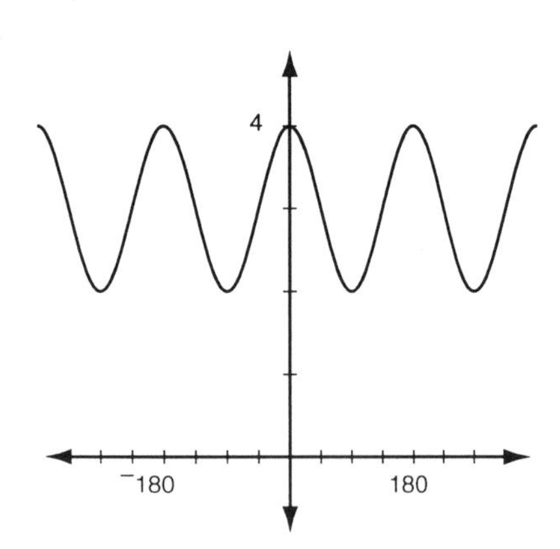

b.

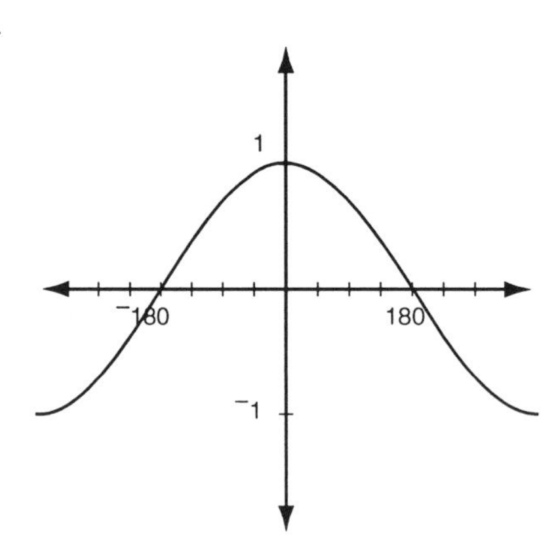

c.

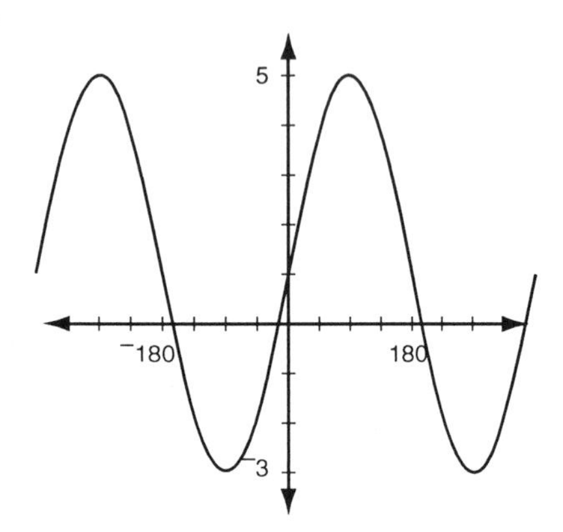

d.

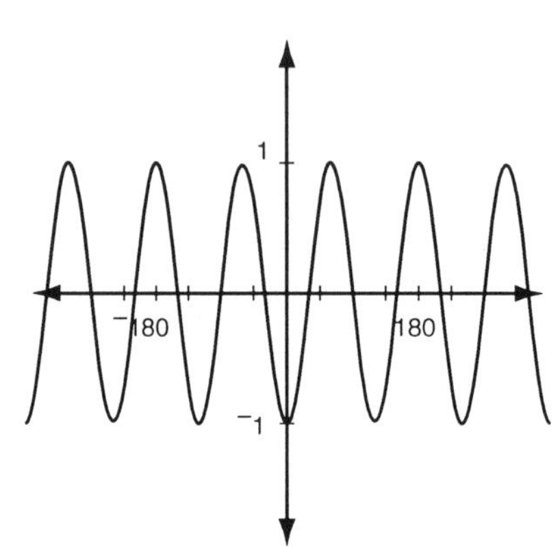

e.

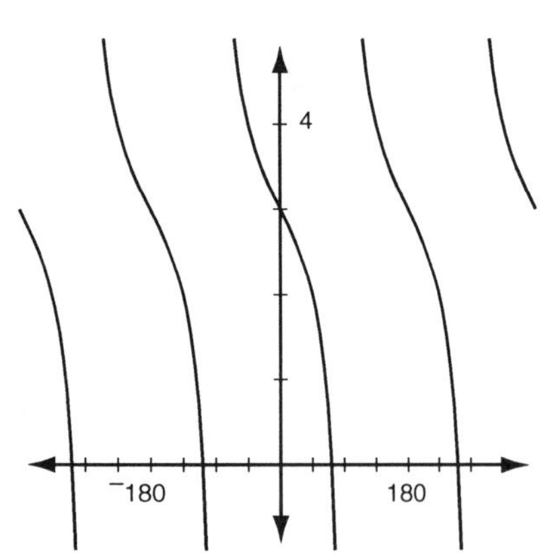

a. $y = \cos(2x) + 3$ **b.** $y = \cos(0.5x)$ **c.** $y = 4\sin x + 1$

d. $y = {}^{-}\cos(3x)$ **e.** $y = {}^{-}\tan x + 3$

- Describe how the constants (in bold) in the equation below will affect the graph of $y = \sin x$.

$$y = \mathbf{4} \sin \mathbf{0.5}(x + \mathbf{30}) - \mathbf{7}$$

The 4 increases the amplitude to 4, the 0.5 means the period is $\frac{360}{0.5} = 720°$, the 30 shifts the graph to the left 30, and the 7 drops the graph down 7 units.

- Examine the four graphs below. If two of the graphs are $f(x)$ and $g(x)$, the other two are the graphs of $\frac{1}{f(x)}$ and $\frac{1}{g(x)}$. Which are which? Write the equations of $f(x)$ and $g(x)$. If possible, give another equation for $\frac{1}{f(x)}$ and $\frac{1}{g(x)}$. Justify your choices and equations.

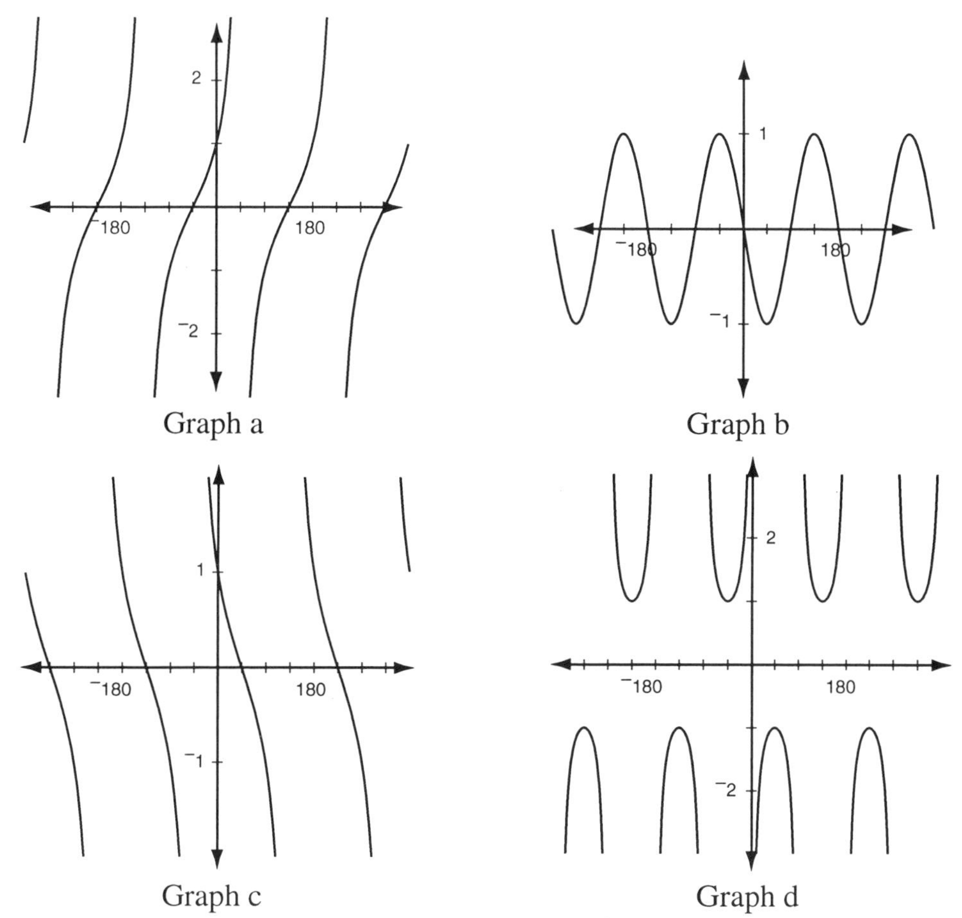

Graph a

Graph b

Graph c

Graph d

Graph a is $y = \tan(x + 45°)$ and graph c is $y = \frac{1}{\tan(x + 45°)} = \cot(x + 45°)$. Graph b is $y = {}^{-}\sin 2x$ and graph d is $y = \frac{1}{{}^{-}\sin 2x} = {}^{-}\csc 2x$.

- Explain *why* $\sin(x - 180°) = {}^{-}\sin x$. (In other words, why are the graphs of $y = \sin(x - 180°)$ and $y = {}^{-}\sin x$ the same?) Be complete.

Look for students discussing both the shifting of the first graph and the flipping of the second. Better students should be able to explain this clearly.

- Your friend Hillary has missed almost a month of school due to the chickenpox. Now that she has returned to school she has a lot of catching up to do. Help her out by giving her some information on how to find the period of functions such as the following:

  a. $y = \sin 6x$ b. $y = \cos \frac{1}{2}x$

  c. $y = \tan \frac{5}{4}x$ d. $y = \sin 6x + \cos \frac{1}{2}x + \tan \frac{5}{4}x$

  a. period: 60° b. period: 720° c. period: 144°

  d. period: LCM(60, 720, 144) = 1440°

- You encountered several trigonometric identities in this chapter. Which of the following equations are identities? Prove your answers.

  a. $\cos 2x = 2\cos^2 x - 1$ b. $\cos 2x = 1 - 2\sin^2 x$

  c. $\tan\left(\frac{x}{2}\right) = \frac{\sin x}{1 + \cos x}$ d. $\sin(x + 30°) = \sin x + \sin 30°$

  Parts a, b, and c are identities.

- When Ahmed first gets on his bike and puts his feet on the pedals, his left foot is as close to the ground as it can be, only five inches above the ground. He pedals at a constant rate, with his foot making one revolution every three seconds.

  The crank arm for the pedal is eight inches long. Write an equation that will give the height of his left foot at any time.

  $\mathbf{y = {}^-8 \cos (120x) + 13}$

- Your kid brother is caught on a merry-go-round that has gone out of control! The merry-go-round, which has a diameter of 22 feet, is 8 feet away from a long wall of mirrors. As the merry-go-round revolves at a constant rate of four revolutions in 5 seconds, your brother tries to see himself in the mirror to see how white (or green!) he looks!

  a. Write an equation that will give your brother's distance from the mirror at any time.

  b. A hose is turned on squirting a stream of water parallel to the mirrors and 14 feet away from them. At what points in time will your brother be squirted?

  a. $\mathbf{y = 11 \sin 288x + 19}$

  b. at approximately 0.22 + 1.25*n* seconds and 1.03 + 1.25*n* seconds, where *n* = 0, 1, 2, 3, ...

- Use the Law of Sines to find the missing parts of each triangle.

  a.

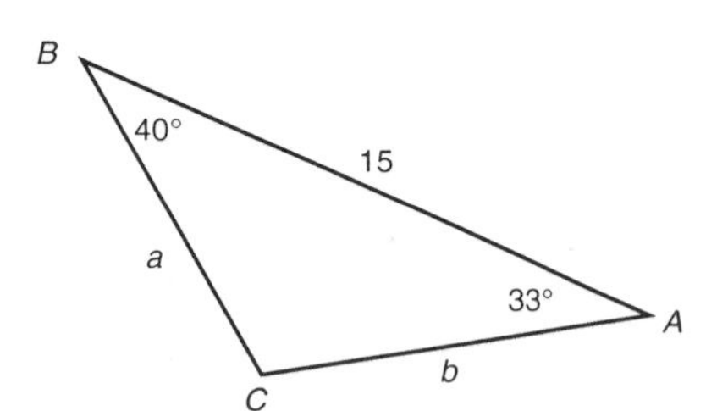

  b.

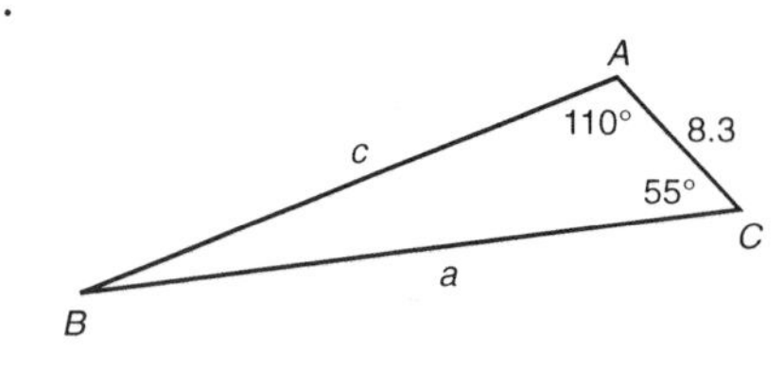

c.

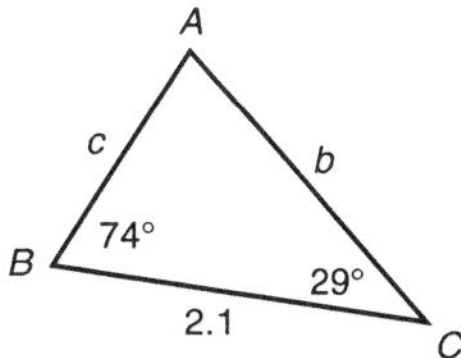

d.

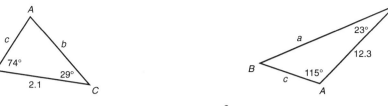

e.

B
8
5
20°
C
A
b

f.

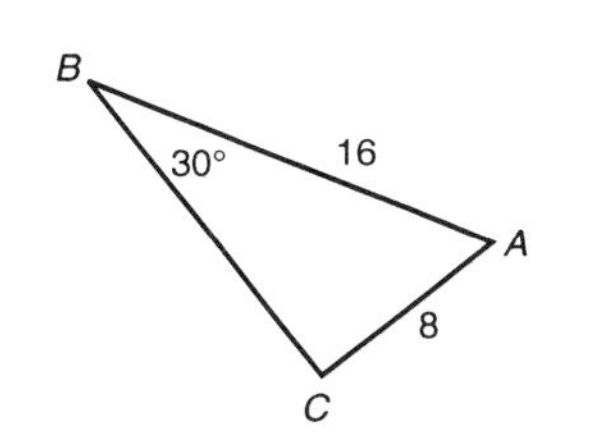

a. $C = 107°$, $a \approx 8.54$, $b \approx 10.1$

b. $B = 15°$, $c \approx 26.3$, $a \approx 30.1$

c. $A = 77°$, $b \approx 2.07$, $c \approx 1.04$

d. $B = 42°$, $c \approx 7.2$, $a \approx 16.7$

e. **This is the ambiguous case:** $C \approx 33.2°$, $B \approx 126.8°$, $b \approx 11.7$ **or** $C \approx 146.8°$, $B \approx 13.2°$, $b \approx 3.33$

f. $A = 60°$, $C = 90°$, $a \approx 13.9$

- Use the Law of Cosines to find the missing parts of the triangle.

a.

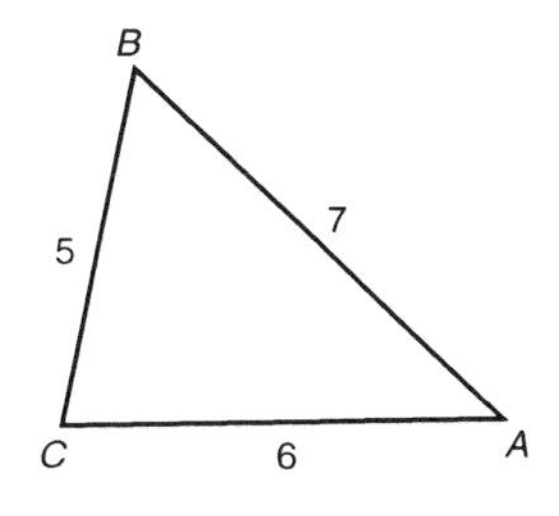

b.

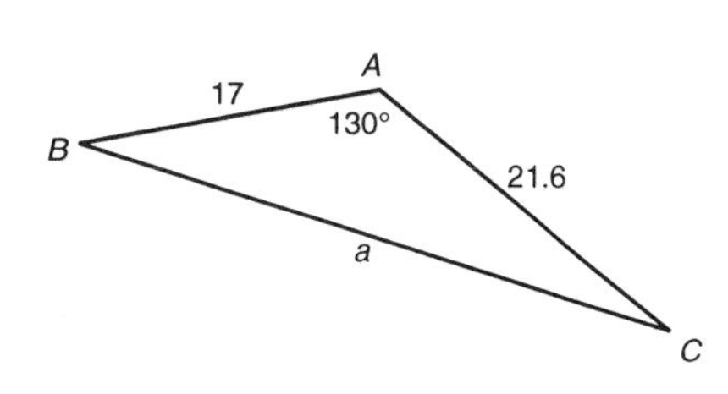

c.

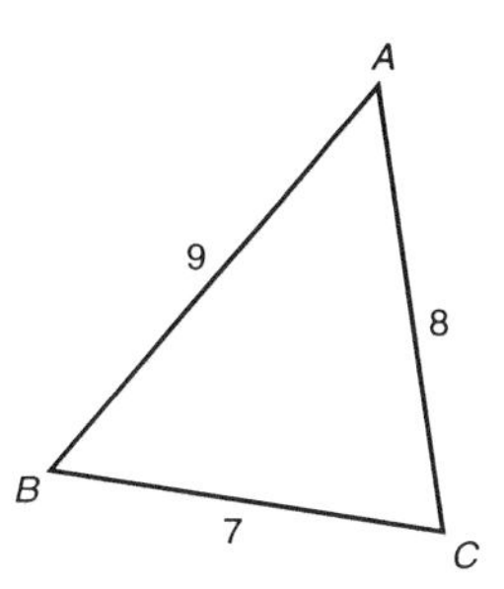

d.

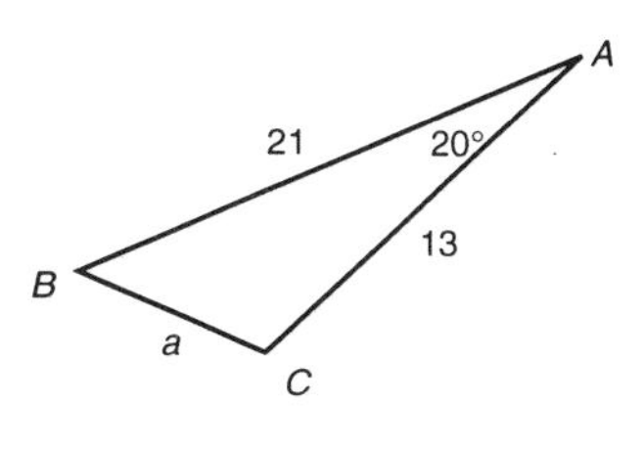

e.

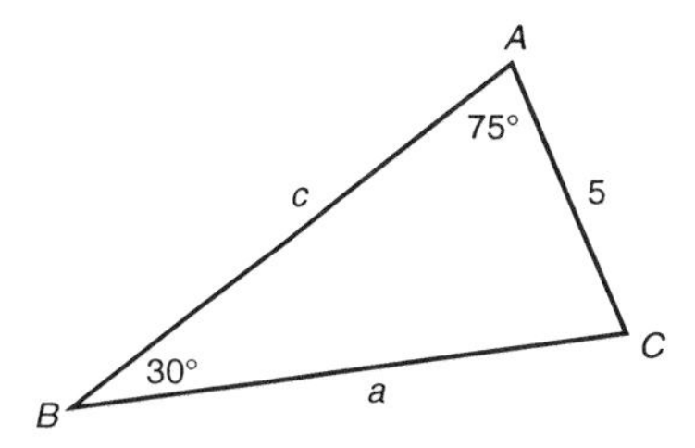

f.

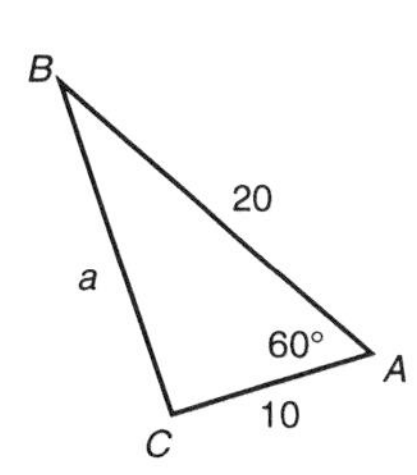

a. $C \approx 78.5°$, $A \approx 44.4°$, $B \approx 57.1°$

b. $C \approx 21.8°$, $B \approx 28.2°$, $a \approx 35.0$

c. $A \approx 48.2°$, $B \approx 58.4°$, $C \approx 73.4°$ **d.** $C = 113.12°$, $B \approx 46.85°$, $a \approx 9.85$

e. $C = 75°$, $a \approx 9.7$, $c \approx 9.7$ **f.** $B = 30°$, $C = 90°$, $a \approx 17.3$

- Use the Law of Sines, the Law of Cosines, or both to show whether or not there is a triangle with side lengths of

  a. 2, 4, and 7. Explain your answer completely.

  b. 4, $\sqrt{33}$, and 7. Explain your answer completely.

  a. no **b. yes**

- Line l passes through the point $(-1, 5)$ and the origin. Find the measure of the angle formed by this line and the x-axis.

  Acute angle is ≈ 78.7°; obtuse, ≈ 101.3°

- Solve for x in each triangle. Show all work.

  a.

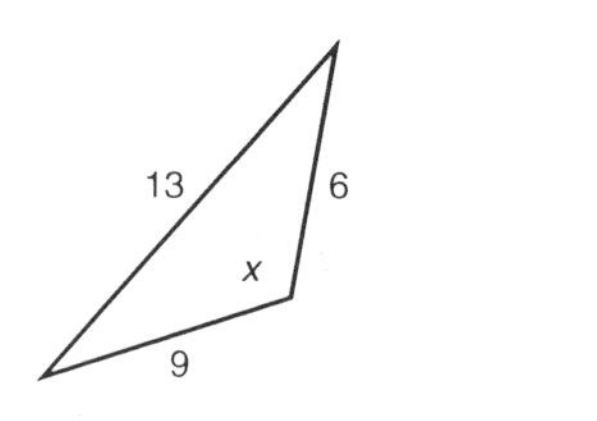

  b.

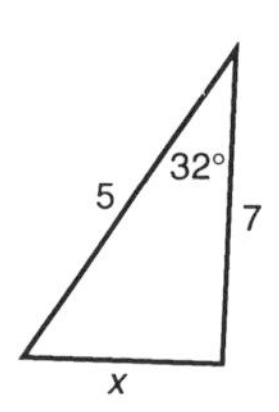

  c.

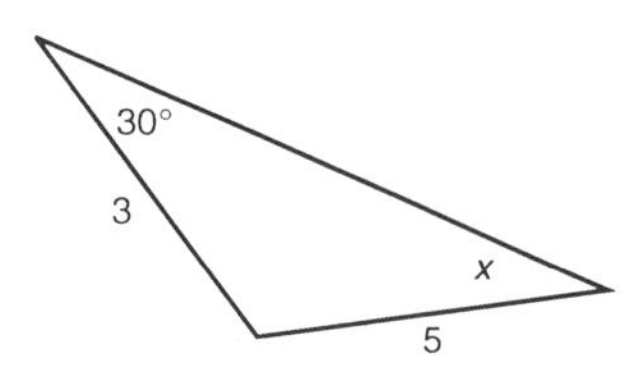

  d.

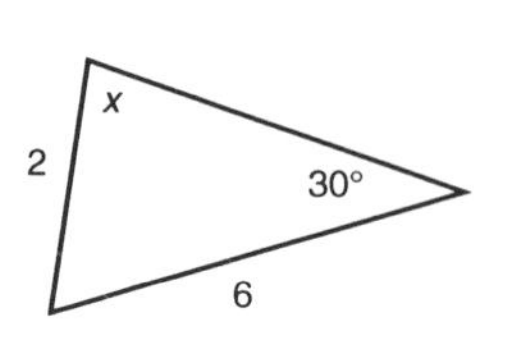

  a. $x \approx 118.8°$ **b.** $x \approx 3.83$ **c.** $x \approx 17.5°$ **d. no solution**

- Explain why you cannot solve for the unknown parts of the triangle.

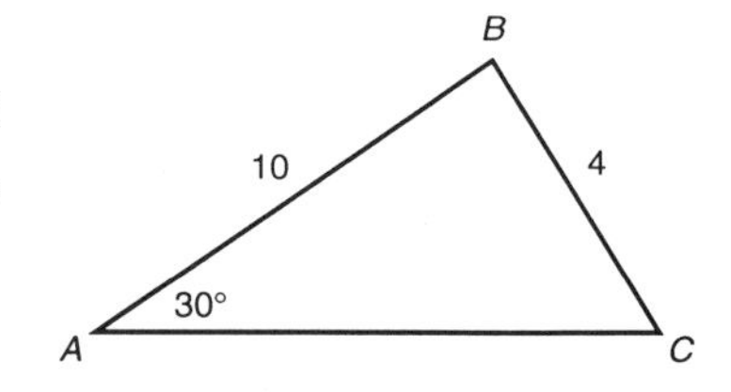

  When trying to solve using the Law of Sines, you get sin $C = 1.25$, which is not possible. This triangle, then, does not exist. (In fact, since $AB = 10$, the shortest that side BC can be is 5, and that is with a right angle at B.)

- A mass on a string is pulled 5 centimeters down from its resting position and then released. It makes nine complete bounces in 5 seconds.

  a. Write an equation that will model the position of the mass.

  b. At what times during the first 4 seconds is the mass 3 centimeters above its resting position? Explain completely how you found all the times and how you know you have *all* the times.

  a. $y = -5 \cos 648x$

  b. ≈ **0.196, 0.360, 0.751, 0.915, 1.31, 1.47, 1.86, 2.02, 2.42, 2.58, 2.97, 3.14, 2.53, 3.70**

- Each of the following are rectangular coordinates. What points do they each represent in polar coordinates?

  a. (4, 5) b. (3, 0) c. (0, −12) d. (−8, 0)

  e. (4, −6) f. (7, −7) g. $(9, 9\sqrt{3})$ h. $(9\sqrt{3}, 9)$

Note: There is more than one correct answer!

a. (6.4, 38.7°) b. (3, 90°) c. (12, 180°) d. (8, 270°)

e. (7.2, 146.3°) f. ($7\sqrt{2}$, 135°) g. (18, 30°) h. (18, 60°)

- Convert each pair of polar coordinates to rectangular coordinates.

a. (6, 35°) b. (16, 210°) c. (4, −72°) d. (−2, 90°)
e. (7, 120°) f. (5, 0°) g. (−5, 375°) h. (5.7, −225°)

a. (3.4, 4.9) b. ($-8, -8\sqrt{3}$) c. (−3.8, 1.2) d. (−2, 0)

e. ($3.5\sqrt{3}, -3.5$) f. (0, 5) g. (−1.3, −4.8) h. (4, −4)

- Sketch each polar graph. When possible, name an interval for θ that provides a complete graph.

a. $r = 0.02\theta$ b. $r = 4 \cos 4\theta$

c. $r = 3((\cos \theta) + 1)$ d. $r = 2 \sin 3\theta$

a.

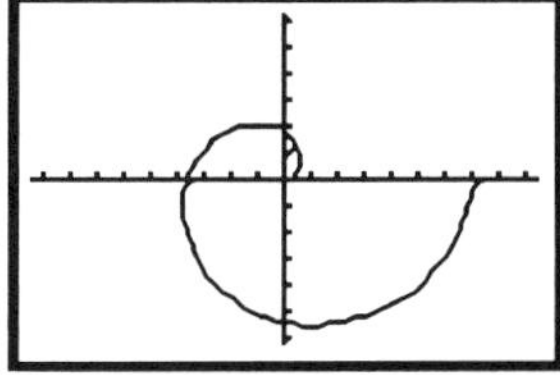

[0, 360, 10, ⁻9.4, 9.4, 1, ⁻6.2, 6.2, 1]
Graph continues to increase.

b.

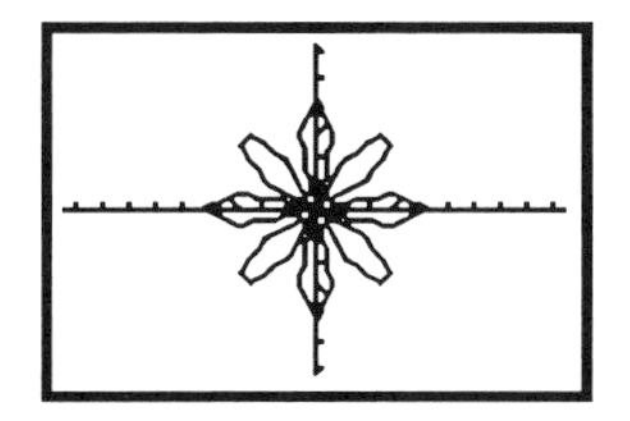

[0, 360, 10, ⁻9.4, 9.4, 1, ⁻6.2, 6.2, 1]
$0° \le \theta \le 360°$

c.

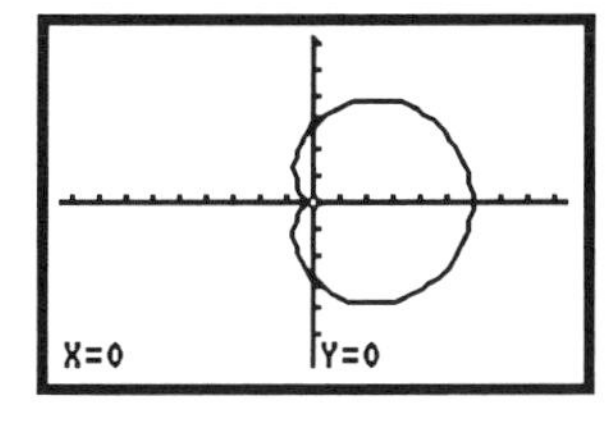

[0, 360, 10, ⁻9.4, 9.4, 1, ⁻6.2, 6.2, 1]
$0° \le \theta \le 360°$

d.

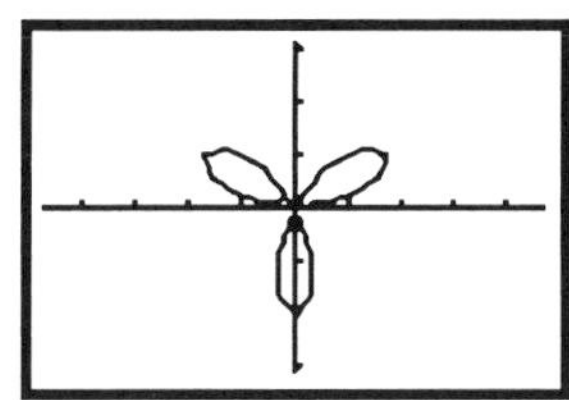

[0, 180, 10, ⁻4.7, 4.7, 1, ⁻3.1, 3.1, 1]
$0° \le \theta \le 180°$

- Graph each complex number below. Then, rewrite each complex number in polar coordinates.

a. $8 + 3i$ b. $5i$ c. $4 - 4i$
d. $-6 - 3i$ e. $-7 + i$ f. $-12 - 9i$

a. (8.5, 20.6°) b. (5, 90°) c. ($4\sqrt{3}$, 315°)

d. (6.7, 206.6°) e. (7.1, 171.9°) f. (15, 216.9°)

- Perform the indicated complex arithmetic. (You may want to change some of the numbers to polar form before doing the arithmetic.) Write your answers in rectangular form.

a. $(8 + 3i) - (4 - 9i)$ b. $(3 - 6i)(4 + 7i)$ c. $\frac{1}{6 + 6\sqrt{3}\,i}$

d. $(5 - 4i)^3$ e. $\frac{12 + 5i}{5 - 12i}$ f. $(-3(\cos 34° + i \sin 34°))^{-1}$

a. $4 + 12i$ b. $54 - 3i$ c. $\dfrac{1 - \sqrt{3}\,i}{24}$

d. $-115 - 236i$ e. i f. $-0.28 + 0.19i$

- In each sequence below, describe what would happen if the points were plotted in order. Justify your answer.
  a. $(3 + 3i), (3 + 3i)^2, (3 + 3i)^3, (3 + 3i)^4, (3 + 3i)^5, (3 + 3i)^6, (3 + 3i)^7$
  b. $(0.2 + 0.2i), (0.2 + 0.2i)^2, (0.2 + 0.2i)^3, (0.2 + 0.2i)^4, (0.2 + 0.2i)^5, (0.2 + 0.2i)^6$

  a. Points will spiral out.

  b. Points will spiral in.

Group Problems

- You have been studying functions for several months now. You know that functions have inputs (the domain), and for each input there is one and only one output (the set of which makes up the range). In this problem, two segments, of lengths 8 and 12 centimeters, are joined at one endpoint. Consider a function defined as follows: the input is the degree measurement of the angle formed by these two segments; the output is the length of the third side. Tell me everything you can about this function.

  $r = \sqrt{208 - 192 \cos A}$; domain: all values of A; range: $4 \le r \le 20$; period = 360°

- The diagonals of a parallelogram are respectively 6 inches and 10 inches, and they intersect at an angle of 50°. Find the lengths of the sides of the parallelogram to the nearest tenth of an inch.

  3.8 and 7.3 in.

Introduction to the Additional Take Another Look Activities

Throughout the student text you will find Take Another Look activities following some of the problem sets. These activities ask students to look at a concept presented in the section or the problem set in another way. The additional Take Another Look activities in the *Teacher's Resource Book* are numbered to indicate to which section they belong. Answers for these activities are also provided in this book. The activities can be used to supplement regular assignments or as extra credit assignments. You may want to use some of the Take Another Look activities as group problems or portfolio assignments.

Take Another Look 1.4

Take another look at the model you found in Problem 3 of Problem Set 1.4. How well does your model fit the actual data points representing population growth by decade in the United States? Write a paragraph summarizing your conclusions.

Year	Population given by the model	Actual population	Difference
1790	3,929,000	3,929,214	
1800		5,308,483	
1810		7,239,881	
1820		9,638,453	
1830		12,866,020	
1840		17,069,453	
1850		23,191,876	
1860		31,443,321	
1870		39,818,449	
1880		50,155,783	
1890		62,947,714	
1900		75,994,575	
1910		91,972,266	
1920		105,713,620	
1930		122,775,046	
1940		131,669,275	
1950		150,697,361	
1960		179,323,175	
1970		203,302,031	
1980		226,545,805	
1990		248,709,873	

Solution

Year	Population given by the model	Actual population	Difference
1790	3,929,000	3,929,214	⁻214
1800	4,871,960	5,308,483	⁻436,523
1810	6,041,230	7,239,881	⁻1,198,651
1820	7,491,126	9,638,453	⁻2,147,327
1830	9,288,996	12,866,020	⁻3,577,024
1840	11,518,355	17,069,453	⁻5,551,098
1850	14,282,760	23,191,876	⁻8,909,116
1860	17,710,622	31,443,321	⁻13,732,699
1870	21,961,172	39,818,449	⁻17,857,277

(table continued on next page)

Year	Population given by the model	Actual population	Difference
1880	27,231,852	50,155,783	⁻22,923,931
1890	33,767,498	62,947,714	⁻29,180,216
1900	41,871,697	75,994,575	⁻34,122,878
1910	51,920,905	91,972,266	⁻40,051,361
1920	64,381,922	105,713,620	⁻41,331,698
1930	79,833,583	122,775,046	⁻42,941,463
1940	98,993,643	131,669,275	⁻32,675,632
1950	122,752,117	150,697,361	⁻27,945,244
1960	152,212,625	179,323,175	⁻27,110,550
1970	188,743,655	203,302,031	⁻14,558,376
1980	234,042,133	226,545,805	7,496,328
1990	290,212,245	248,709,873	41,502,372

To find the population given by the model, use $u_0 = 3{,}929{,}000$ and $u_n = 1.24 \cdot u_{n-1}$ for $n > 0$, where n represents decades since 1790. The model does not fit the data very well.

Take Another Look 4.2

Now that you have completed the Investigation 4.2.1, it is a good time to make an important connection with one of your earlier discoveries. Look again at the 11%, 60-month, $12,000 car loan—but this time follow a strategy you first considered in Take Another Look 2.1.

a. Find the amount of money needed to just cover the first month's interest on the loan (that is, the entire payment would be used to pay the month's interest).

b. Create a table similar to the one pictured. Enter the payment you discovered in part a and four more monthly payment amounts in the first column. (The five payments in the first column should form an increasing arithmetic sequence with a common difference of $1.) Compute and record the final loan balance (after 60 months) for each of the five payments.

Monthly payment	Final balance after 60 months	Common difference

c. Describe in detail and write out the procedure you used to answer part b of this activity.

d. Complete the third column of the table, describe the pattern, and then write a few sentences describing how this common difference fits into your solution of the Car Loan Investigation.

Solution

a. $12{,}000\left(\frac{0.11}{12}\right) = \$110$

b.

Monthly payment	Final balance after 60 months	Common difference
110	12,000.00	
111	11,920.48	−79.52
112	11,840.96	−79.52
113	11,761.45	−79.51
114	11,681.93	−79.52

c. One option is to use *sequence* mode with $u_0 = 12{,}000$ and $u_n = u_{n-1}(1 + \frac{0.11}{12}) - payment$. After plugging in a payment amount, find $u(60)$, which will give the final balance.

d. Each one dollar increase in payment decreases the balance after 5 years by about $79.52. The correct payment is $260.91.

Take Another Look 4.3

You can check or verify your work by using combinations of graphs, table values, and equations. Suppose, for example, that you are asked to find the line through the points (4, 45623) and (9, 45831).

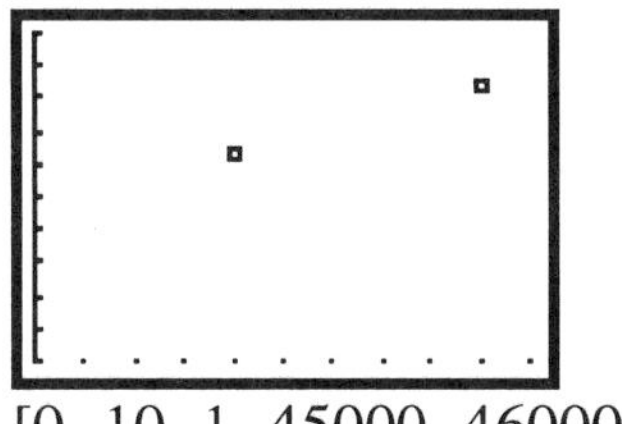

[0, 10, 1, 45000, 46000, 100]

You might begin by plotting the two points on your calculator screen. Then you could write an equation and check to see if the calculator's graph contains the two points. The graph should look correct and calculator table values should confirm your work. If something doesn't check then make some changes or corrections and try again. Keep trying this combination of trial, check, and retrial with your graphs, table values, and equations until you are successful.

a. Use this strategy on Problem 3 of Problem Set 4.2.

Suppose you are asked to graph $4.7x + 3.2y = 22.56$ and to name the slope, y-intercept, and x-intercept of your graph. You might start by writing the equation in $y =$ form and then entering the equation into your calculator. How will you know if you have rewritten the equation correctly?

One technique is to look at the table values for your new equation in $y =$ form. Find the x- and y-coordinates of a point in the table and substitute them in the original equation, $4.7x + 3.2y = 22.56$. When substituted, the table values should make a true statement. Do you need to do this for a second or third point? Explain. How can you locate the y-intercept and x-intercept in your table?

b. Graph $4.7x + 3.2y = 22.56$ and name the slope, y-intercept, and x-intercept of your graph.

c. Use this strategy on Problem 2, part e of Problem Set 4.2.

Solution

a. You will know that you have written an equation correctly if you check the x- and y-intercepts. $y = \frac{3}{2}x - 6$; $y = {}^{-}1.124x + 2.643$.

b. slope $= {}^{-}1.469$; y-intercept at (0, 7.05); x-intercept at (4.8, 0)

c. $y = {}^{-}1.46875x + 4.03125$

Take Another Look 4.4

Tickets sold	Profit
400	$^-840$
600	$^-680$
800	$^-520$
...	...
2200	600

Assume the pattern in the table relating (*tickets sold, profit*) for a concert series continues for a 4000-seat auditorium. By taking another look, you will investigate and discover a connection involving recursive equations and explicit equations.

a. On your calculator and on your graph paper, plot the (*tickets sold, profit*) data pairs listed in the table. What is a reasonable domain for these data? What is a reasonable range for these data?

b. What is the change in profit for each additional ticket sold? Use this information to write a recursive routine providing the overall profit when each additional ticket is sold. (If you need help, refer to your earlier work in Chapter 1.)

c. Use the results of part b to complete this recursive model of the concert situation.

$$u_n = \begin{cases} \_\_\_\_\_\_\_\_ & \text{if } n = 0 \\ \_\_\_\_\_\_\_\_ & \text{if } n > 0 \end{cases}$$

d. Find the slope and y-intercept for your graph in part a. Use this information to write an equation which models (*tickets sold, profit*).

e. Carefully describe the connection between the slope of the line and one of the components of your recursive model.

f. Carefully describe the connection between the y-intercept of the line and one of the components of your recursive model.

g. Now take another look at Problem 6 of Problem Set 4.3 and complete a recursive model $u_n = \begin{cases} \_\_\_\_\_\_\_\_ & \text{if } n = 0 \\ \_\_\_\_\_\_\_\_ & \text{if } n > 0 \end{cases}$ for the problem.

Solution

a. $0 \le x \le 4000$; $^-1000 \le y \le 2100$

b. \$160 per 200 tickets or \$0.80 per ticket

c. $u_0 = {}^-1160$; $u_n = u_{n-1} + 0.8$

d. slope = 0.8; y-intercept = $^-1160$; $y = 0.8x - 1160$

e. \$0.80 profit is made for each ticket sold.

f. If no tickets are sold, there would be a \$1,160 loss.

g. $u_0 = 17{,}109$, $u_n = u_{n-1} + 847$

Take Another Look 4.6

Part 1

Take another look at the least-squares line—what it does and what it means. You will use the "Predicted length using least-squares model" data you collected in the investigation in Section 4.4. If those data are not available, use the data in this table.

	Mass in grams	Length in centimeters	Predicted length	Residual	Residual^2
1	50	5.0			
2	60	5.5			
3	70	6.0			
4	80	6.3			
5	90	6.8			
6	100	7.1			
7	110	7.5			
8	120	7.7			
9	130	8.1			
10	140	8.5			
11	150	8.8			
12	160	9.2			
13	170	9.5			
14	180	9.9			
15	190	10.3			
16	200	10.7			
17	210	11.3			
18	220	11.4			
19	230	11.9			
20	240	12.4			
					Total Sum =

a. Find the mean *mass* and mean *spring length* for the spring data.

b. Use your calculator to find the least-squares model for the (*mass, spring length*) data values. (For additional help, see **Calculator Note 4E**.)

c. Verify that the point $(\bar{x}, \bar{y})$ is on the least-squares line. The point $(\bar{x}, \bar{y})$ is called the centroid of the scatter plot.

If you have been using the data provided in this table, the mean *mass* = 145 g and the mean *spring length* = 8.695 cm. The calculator's least-squares equation for these data choices is $y = 0.0373308271x + 3.282030075$.

Any line through the point (145, 8.895) can be expressed with the point-slope equation $y = A(x - 145) + 8.695$. Different choices for the slope A will produce different lines through the point (145, 8.895).

d. Verify that by substituting $A = 0.0373308271$ in the equation $y = A(x - 145) + 8.695$, you will get the least-squares equation provided by the calculator.

e. Find the sum of the squares of the residuals for the line $y = 0.0373308271(x - 145) + 8.695$.

Part 2

This part of this investigation will help explain why the calculator gives 0.0373308271 as the slope. Ideally the work will be shared so that each person can get the results by substituting several of the slopes from this table into the equation $y = A(x - 145) + 8.695$.

a. Enter the equation as y_1 using one of the slope values given in the table. List the residuals between actual spring lengths and lengths predicted by the equation. Find the sum of the squares of the residuals.

b. Collect the results and enter all of the sums into the table.

c. Make a scatter plot of (*slope, sum of squared residuals*). At what x-value does the minimum y-value occur? What is significant about this graph?

	Slope	Sum of squared residuals
1	0.025	
2	0.026	
3	0.027	
4	0.028	
5	0.029	
6	0.030	
7	0.031	
8	0.032	
9	0.033	
10	0.034	
11	0.035	
12	0.036	
13	0.037	
14	0.038	
15	0.039	
16	0.040	
17	0.041	
18	0.042	
19	0.043	
20	0.044	
21	0.0373308271	

Solution

Part 1

	Mass in grams	Length (cm)	Predicted length	Residual	Sum of squared residuals
1	50	5.0	5.1486	⁻0.1486	0.02207
2	60	5.5	5.5219	⁻0.0219	0.00048
3	70	6.0	5.8952	0.1048	0.01099
4	80	6.3	6.2685	0.0315	0.00099
5	90	6.8	6.6418	0.1582	0.02503
6	100	7.1	7.0151	0.0849	0.00721
7	110	7.5	7.3884	0.1116	0.01245
8	120	7.7	7.7617	⁻0.0617	0.00381
9	130	8.1	8.135	⁻0.035	0.00123
10	140	8.5	8.5083	⁻0.0083	0.00007
11	150	8.8	8.8817	⁻0.0817	0.00667
12	160	9.2	9.255	⁻0.055	0.00302

(table continued on next page)

	Mass in grams	Length (cm)	Predicted length	Residual	Sum of squared residuals
13	170	9.5	9.6283	⁻0.1283	0.01645
14	180	9.9	10.002	⁻0.102	0.01032
15	190	10.3	10.375	⁻0.075	0.00561
16	200	10.7	10.748	⁻0.048	0.00232
17	210	11.3	11.122	0.178	0.03186
18	220	11.4	11.495	⁻0.095	0.00899
19	230	11.9	11.868	0.032	0.00102
20	240	12.4	12.241	0.159	0.02514
					Total Sum =

a. mean *mass* = 145; mean *spring length* = 8.695

b. $y = 0.0373308271x + 3.282030075$

c. Y(145) = 8.695

d. $y = 0.0373308271(x - 145) + 8.695 = 0.0373308271x + 3.282030075$

e. 0.195722

Part 2

a. See table.

b. See table.

c. The minimum y-value occurs when x equals 0.0373308271. The sum of the residuals squared is minimized when $x = 0.0373308271$.

	Slope	Sum of squared residuals
1	0.025	10.307
2	0.026	8.7335
3	0.027	7.293
4	0.028	5.9855
5	0.029	4.811
6	0.030	3.7695
7	0.031	2.861
8	0.032	2.0855
9	0.033	1.443
10	0.034	0.9335
11	0.035	0.557
12	0.036	0.3135
13	0.037	0.203
14	0.038	0.2255
15	0.039	0.381
16	0.040	0.6695
17	0.041	1.091
18	0.042	1.6455
19	0.043	2.333
20	0.044	3.1535
21	0.0373308271	0.195722

Take Another Look 4.8

According to the U.S. Bureau of the Census, *World Population Profile (1989),* and the *1994 Universal Almanac* (p. 331), 9 babies are born and 3 people die every 2 seconds. Wow! This is a net increase of 3 people per second. Ratios are useful for comparing a wide variety of relationships. In this Take Another Look, you will explore some of these relationships.

a. The population density of a city or country provides a valuable comparison among populations. The U.S. population density in 1990 is estimated at 69 people per square mile. By comparison, China has a population of 311 people per square mile, India has 667 people per square mile, and Japan has 847 people per square mile. Find the 1990 population density for each of the cities listed. Explain how you did this.

City	Population (thousands)	Land area (square miles)
Baltimore	736	80.8
Chicago	2,784	227.2
Denver	468	153.3
Detroit	1,028	138.7
Houston	1,631	539.9
San Francisco	724	46.7
Your city (town)?	?	?

Source: *The American Almanac, 1994–95 Statistical Abstract of the United States.*

b. Given the following data, what ratio might you use to determine the best customer option for a pizza? Ciceros sells a three-item, 10-inch pizza for $8.50. They also sell the three-item 12-inch pizza for $10.25. What is the best customer option? Explain.

c. Find the student-teacher ratios for colleges in your area or for colleges you may be interested in attending. Describe how you found this information and compare these results with the model found in Problems 8 and 9 of Problem Set 4.7.

Solution

City	Population (thousands)	Land area (square miles)	Population per square mile
Baltimore	736	80.8	9,109
Chicago	2,784	227.2	12,254
Denver	468	153.3	3,053
Detroit	1,028	138.7	7,412
Houston	1,631	539.9	3,021
San Francisco	724	46.7	15,503
Your city (town)?	?	?	?

a. See table.

b. $\text{Area}_{10\text{ inch}} = 25\pi$; $\text{Cost}_{10\text{ inch}} = \frac{\$8.50}{25\pi} \approx \$0.11$; $\text{Area}_{12\text{ inch}} = 36\pi$;

$\text{Cost}_{12\text{ inch}} = \frac{\$10.25}{36\pi} \approx \$0.09$. Therefore, the 12-inch pizza is the better buy.

c. Answers will vary.

Take Another Look 5.2

The growth of money-related accounts is an application that you will revisit throughout the text. For an account that offers 6% annual interest compounded monthly, the equation $y = 1 \cdot \left(1 + \frac{0.06}{12}\right)^x$ can be used to model the growth of \$1 over several months. When $x = 12$, the equation provides the value of \$1 after 1 year.

a. What equation and substitution would you use to find the 1-year balance of a 6% account that is compounded daily? Compare this 1-year balance with the 1-year balance based on monthly compounding.

b. Provide a real-world meaning involving the growth of money for the expression $1 \cdot \left(1 + \frac{0.06}{365}\right)^x$ when $x = 365$.

c. Find the value of $y = 1 \cdot \left(1 + \frac{0.06}{x}\right)^x$ when x = the number of hours in 365 days. Provide a real-world meaning involving the growth of money for this answer.

d. Explore and describe the values of $y = 1 \cdot \left(1 + \frac{0.06}{x}\right)^x$ as x gets very large.

e. Provide a real-world meaning for $y = 1 \cdot \left(1 + \frac{1.00}{x}\right)^x$ that involves the growth of money. Find and describe the value of y as x gets very large. Is there a limit on the size of y? If so, what is it? What does this mean?

Solution

a. Daily: $y = 1 \cdot \left(1 + \frac{0.06}{365}\right)^{365} = \$1.0618$; Monthly: $y = 1 \cdot \left(1 + \frac{0.06}{12}\right)^{12} = \$1.0617$

b. The equation will give the total balance at the end of 1 year for \$1 invested at 6% interest compounded daily. The amount invested grows at a rate of 0.016% daily.

c. The final balance after 1 year for \$1.00 invested at 6% interest compounded hourly will be \$1.06.

d. It remains at \$1.06.

e. This equation will give the final balance of \$1.00 invested at 100% for one year. As x gets very large, the amount will reach \$2.72.

Take Another Look 5.4

The goal of this Take Another Look is to provide further work with graphs and equations of perpendicular lines. Work with a partner using only one calculator. Start with a friendly graphing window, centered at (0, 0), in which the distance between pixels is 0.2 on both the x- and y-axes. Turn the background grid on.

a. First person: Create a graph with the Lines Program (Problem 6 in Problem Set 5.3 and **Calculator Note 5B**), and then locate a point on the calculator screen. The point can be on or off the given line. Turn the calculator over to your partner and record his or her trials and results (see part b).

b. Second person: Write (and verify) an equation that produces a line through the identified point and perpendicular to the original line. You can use the calculator's *trace* feature or *table* feature to help identify the required line, but don't force the calculator to identify the original equation.

c. Switch roles and repeat parts a and b several times.

Start with a friendly graphing window, centered at (0, 0), in which the distance between pixels is 0.1 on both the x- and y-axes.

d. First person: Name and plot a point in the graphing window. Turn the calculator over to your partner and record his or her trials and results (see part e).

e. Second person: Write (and verify) two equations that intersect perpendicularly at the given point.

f. Switch roles and repeat parts d and e several times.

g. Write the equation of a line that contains point (x_1, y_1) and is perpendicular to the line $y = (\frac{A}{C})x + E$.

Solution

This activity gives students the opportunity to work with graphs and equations of perpendicular lines.

a.–f. Answers will vary.

g. $y - y_1 = (\frac{-C}{A})(x - x_1)$

Take Another Look 5.9

Your calculator can be extremely valuable as you gain an understanding of composition of functions, the important topic introduced in Section 5.9. Take another look at **Calculator Note 5E** to see if your calculator will allow you to use the following method for investigating and graphing the function $g(f(x))$ in Example 2 of this section.

If $f(x) = \frac{3x}{4} - 3$ and $g(x) = |x|$, then $g(f(x))$ will be the absolute value of the inner linear function $f(x)$; that is, $g(f(x)) = \left|\frac{3x}{4} - 3\right|$. You can think of $y_1(x)$ as $f(x)$ and $y_2(x)$ as $g(x)$. Then, $g(f(x))$ could be listed as a new function, $y_3 = y_2(y_1(x))$.

a. If your calculator allows this strategy, then confirm the graph presented in Example 2.

b. Use this strategy to work parts a–d of Example 3 in this section.

Solution

a. Students should confirm the graph.

b. Let $Y1 = 3x - 7$, $Y2 = \frac{1}{x}$

a. $Y2(Y1(4)) = \frac{1}{5}$

b. $Y2(Y1(x)) = \frac{1}{3x - 7}$

c. $x \neq \frac{7}{3}$

d. $Y1(Y2(4)) = {}^{-}6.25$

Take Another Look 6.5

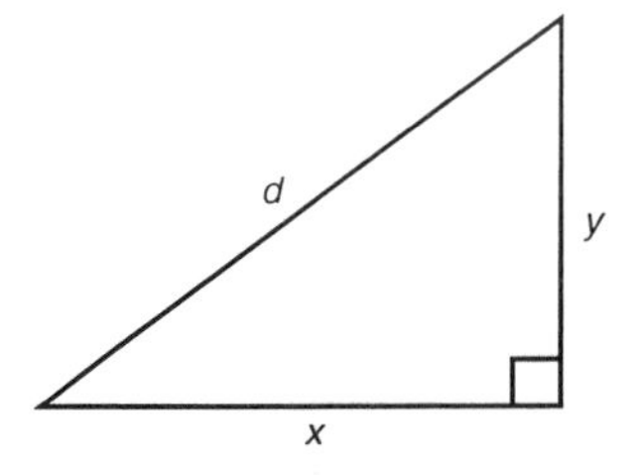

In Example 1 of Section 6.5 you used the parametric equations $x = 4t$ and $y = 3t$ to model the motion of Pat's boat. You found the angle of the actual path of the boat by tracing to any point (x, y) on the path and then finding $\tan^{-1}\left(\frac{y}{x}\right)$. The angle between the boat's path and the horizontal line across the river is about 36.9°. In this investigation you will explore some alternative methods for obtaining the measure of this same angle.

Method 1: The distance traveled at any given time is $d = \sqrt{x^2 + y^2}$. Enter the parametric equations above, trace to any point on the path, and then find the values of

$$\sin^{-1}\left(\frac{y}{\sqrt{x^2+y^2}}\right) \quad \text{and} \quad \cos^{-1}\left(\frac{x}{\sqrt{x^2+y^2}}\right)$$

Explain what these expressions represent and why they work.

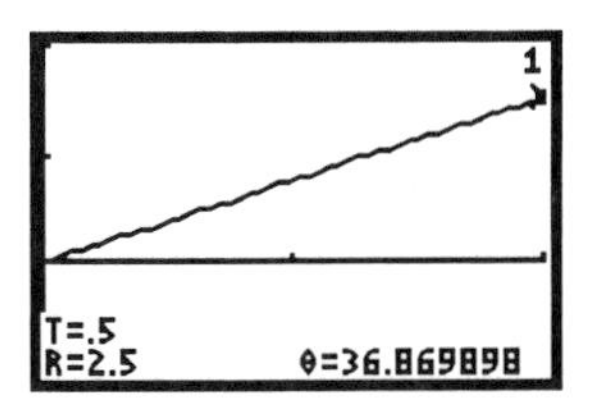

Method 2: This method involves an alternative to the (x, y) representation on the rectangular coordinate plane. Set your calculator so that it provides polar trace coordinates rather than x and y coordinates. Explore the sense of these new values displayed by the calculator as you trace the boat's path. (Be sure your calculator is in degree mode.)

Now rework Example 2, but this time find the actual angle of motion using each method. Be sure to interpret the answers your calculator provides. Write a paragraph explaining what you have learned in this investigation.

Solution

Method 1: The inverse sine and cosine functions will give the angle.
Method 2: In polar coordinates, T = time, R = distance, and θ = angle (θ is given in degrees). Your calculator should be in parametric mode with equations $x = 4t$ and $y = 3t$. In the format menu change from rectangular to polar coordinates.

Take Another Look 7.3

This Take Another Look is based on an activity written by Sal Quezada and Bob Drake, Los Angeles Unified School District.

Field Biologist Mayra Verduzco, introduced ten red foxes into a wild animal refuge in 1994. She needs to (a) predict how many foxes there will be in 40 years and (b) know what year (if ever) when the fox population first reaches a total of 400. As a group, your task is to use simulation as a solution strategy for this situation.

Start with 10 dice. Each die represents a fox and each throw represents one year. A die showing a 1, 2, 3, or 4 represents the birth of a baby fox, so each time one of these numbers occurs, you should add a die to the population. If a 5 or a 6 comes up, a death has occurred, so remove one die from the population. Hence, you are modeling a situation in which the birth rate is twice the death rate. (Can you explain that?) Continue the above simulation until the population reaches or exceeds 300 foxes. Record the data in a table similar to the following.

Year	Births	Deaths	Population
0			10
1			
2			
3			
...			

a. Enter the data into your graphing calculator and make a (*year, fox population*) scatter plot. Find an equation that best fits or models the data.

b. Use your mathematical model to predict the fox population after 40 years. Justify the reasonableness of your response. In what year will the population reach 400 foxes?

c. Summarize your results and prepare a report for the class.

Solution

Sample data:

Year	Births	Deaths	Population
0			10
1	7	3	14
2	9	5	18
3	12	6	24
4	16	8	32

Solutions based on sample data:

a. $y = 10.197(1.332)^x$

b. After 40 years, the fox population will be 968,297. This result does not seem reasonable. Other factors will most likely limit the population growth.

The population will reach 400 in 12.8 years, or in the thirteenth year.

c. Answers will vary.

Take Another Look 7.5

Use the graph to estimate the doubling time for this exponentially increasing bank account. Explain how you arrived at this answer. Verify and explain why this answer doesn't depend on where you start on the graph. What factor(s) determine(s) the doubling time for an exponentially increasing function?

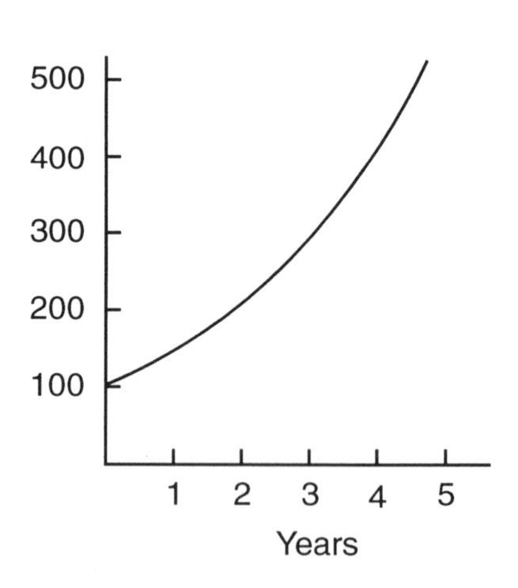

People who work with financial accounts generally use the rule of 72 to estimate doubling times. An investment compounded at $r\%$ will double in approximately $\frac{72}{r}$ years. This means a 9% investment will double in about 8 years. Certainly, the compounding frequency makes a difference, but the rule is very good for making quick approximations. Use the rule and your doubling time answer for the investment pictured by the graph to estimate the approximate growth rate involved. Write a function that you can use to confirm your estimate.

Solution

$\frac{200}{100} = \frac{72}{r}$; $r = 36\%$; $y = 100\,(1 + 0.36)^x$

Take Another Look 7.8

Part 1

You have been concentrating on a particular logarithm base for the function $y = \log_b x$. It should come as no surprise that the base 10 has been used, since most of your arithmetic computation experiences have been in the decimal (base 10) number system.

Your logarithmic ruler is based on decimal logarithms. Before calculators were so readily available, people used more sophisticated slide rules and log tables for tedious arithmetic calculations like $\sqrt[5]{68.2} \cdot (4.027)^{2.5}$. Essentially the slide rules and log tables allowed them to apply the logarithm properties to calculate products like $a^b \cdot c^d$ by finding $\log(a^b \cdot c^d) = b \log a + d \log c$. The final product is the value of 10^{ans} (that is, 10 raised to the preceding logarithmic sum), or the anti-log of the answer.

As an extra project, you could either locate a slide rule (and directions for use) or a set of log tables and find the answer to $\sqrt[5]{68.2} \cdot (4.027)^{2.5}$. Remember, $\sqrt[5]{68.2}$ is equivalent to $68.2^{0.2}$. Do you see why?

However, in this solution use your calculator to confirm $\log\left(\sqrt[5]{68.2} \cdot (4.027)^{2.5}\right) = \log \sqrt[5]{68.2} + \log (4.027)^{2.5} = 0.2 \log 68.2 + 2.5 \log 4.027 = 1.879210949$. Then, the final answer is $10^{1.879210949} = 75.72005992$.

Part 2

The logarithm properties apply to bases other than base 10. You will find another standard base used in mathematics on your calculator. Take a minute to investigate the graph of $y = \ln x$. Use a friendly window with the y-axis as its left boundary, which results in the view screen on the right, wherein you can see when $\ln x = 1$.

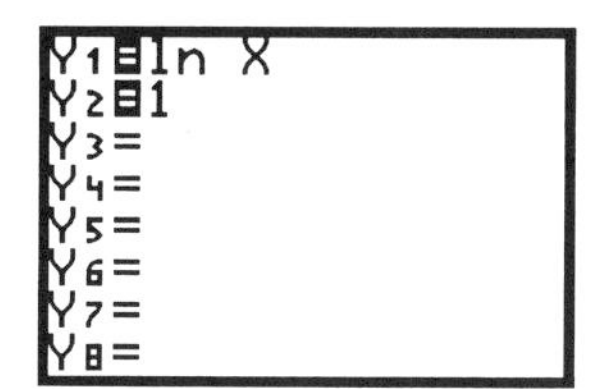

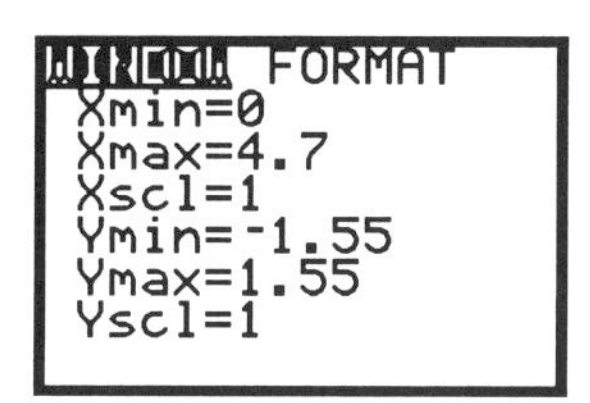

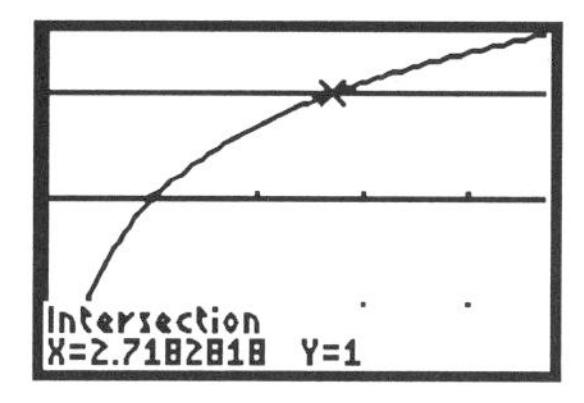

This means $\ln x = 1$ when x is approximately 2.7182818. Since it is true that $\log_b b = 1$, the exploration shows that the base for the ln function has the approximate value 2.7182818, or $\ln x \approx \log_{2.718} x$. Think about this and discuss it with someone until it makes sense to you.

The functions $y = \log x$ and $y = 10^x$ are inverses of each other, and you can see this relationship is maintained on your calculator's keypad. Similarly, $y = \ln x$ and $y = e^x$ are inverses of each other. Graph both $y = \ln x$ and $y = e^x$ and verify this. Write a convincing argument explaining why they are inverse functions.

Now, use the natural logarithm, $\ln x$, to evaluate $\sqrt[5]{68.2} \cdot (4.027)^{2.5}$.

Solution

Answers will vary. Students should come to the conclusion that $y = \ln x$ and $y = e^x$ are inverses of each other.

Take Another Look 8.2

The Dow-Jones annual averages of daily figures for industrial stocks are listed in the table below. These New York Stock Exchange averages have increased quite steadily over this time period. Find a best-fit model for the data, and use it to predict the average stock value during the current year. How does this compare with the Dow-Jones average for today? for yesterday? for last week? You can find these values in the newspaper, and they are reported daily on radio and TV newscasts.

Year	1980	1981	1982	1983	1984	1985	1986
Average	891	933	884	1190	1179	1328	1793

Year	1987	1988	1989	1990	1991	1992	1993
Average	2276	2061	2509	2679	2929	3284	3754

Source: *The American Almanac,* 1994–1995.

The exponential model that you found for this data is a smooth increasing curve. Actually, the daily averages fluctuate widely, almost randomly. Many people make their living by predicting and advising others about the next upturn or trend in this important financial figure.

Assume the daily averages can fall randomly, but within \$25, about your exponential model. This means that the daily average can be any random amount as much as \$25 less than or as much as \$25 more than the model's value. Explain how you can adjust your exponential model to accommodate this randomness of values.

Solution

Best-fit exponential model: $y = 0.05756(1.1268)^x$
Average stock value for current year: $f(97) = \$6{,}176.34$
(Note: In February 1997, the DOW went over 7000.)
To include \$25 randomness: $y = 0.05765(1.1268)^x + 25\text{ rand} - 25\text{ rand}$

Take Another Look 8.3

Whenever you repeat the simulation in Investigation 8.2.1, the target area ratio will be slightly different. This is because there are infinitely many points that can be plotted. Results are better when larger numbers of random points are generated. As you know, however, more points means more time to complete the simulation. These random simulation processes are generally known as Monte Carlo simulations. Though individual results are generally unpredictable, the long-run results with large numbers of points are predictable.

You have considered the ellipse in Chapters 5 and 6, and you will study this mathematical curve again in Chapter 12. Find the area bounded by the curve by using a Monte Carlo simulation on the quadrant 1 region.

Do some research to find an area formula for an ellipse. Compare your simulation results with a calculation using this formula.

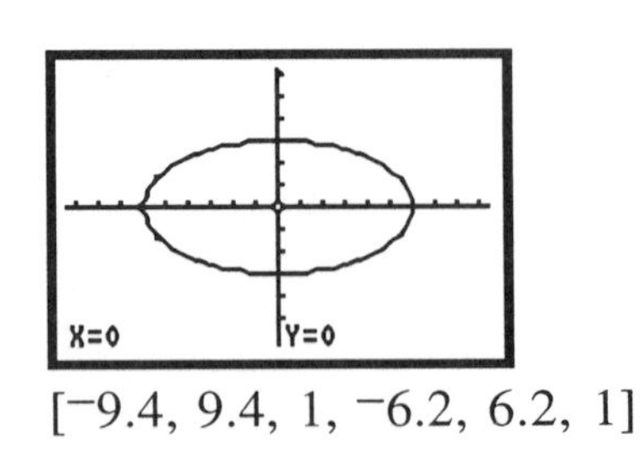

[⁻9.4, 9.4, 1, ⁻6.2, 6.2, 1]

Solution

Equation for the ellipse: $\frac{x^2}{36} + \frac{y^2}{9} = 1$

Solve for y: $y = 3\sqrt{1 - \frac{x^2}{36}}$

Change the following lines in the Ratio program found in **Calculator Note 8D**.

Existing line	New line
`"√(1-x²)" Y1`	`"3√(1-(x²/36))" Y1`
`rand X`	`6rand X`
`rand B`	`3rand B`

Use window dimensions of [0, 6, 1, 0, 3, 1]. The area of the rectangle enclosing the ellipse = 12 • 6 = 72. Using sample results from a simulation, the area of the ellipse = 0.79 (72) = 56.88. In general, the area of an ellipse = $ab\pi$, which here is $3(6)\pi = 56.5487$.

Take Another Look 10.8A

Besides using synthetic division to find a factor, there is also a connection between the synthetic division and writing the equation as nested linear factors, such as

$$6x^2 - x - 15 = (6x - 1)x - 15 \text{ or}$$

$$6x^3 + 11x^2 - 17x - 30 = [(6x + 11)x - 17]x - 30.$$

See if you can figure out this connection.

$P(x) = (6x - 1)x - 15$

$P(-1.5) = (6(-1.5) - 1) \cdot -1.5 - 15$

$P(-1.5) = 0$

−1.5	6	−1	−15
		−9	15
	6	−10	0

Solution

Answers will vary. This process is known as synthetic division or Horner's algorithm. (William Horner, 1786–1837, was an English mathematician.)

Take Another Look 10.8B

When is the last time you divided a five-digit number by a three-digit number without using a calculator? Here is one paper-and-pencil algorithm that you may have used to divide 18,084 by 347.

	52
Divide 3 into 18 to get 5 (actually 50).	347) 18084
Multiply the divisor by 50.	1735
Subtract, and divide 3 into 7 to get 2.	734
Multiply the divisor by 2.	694
The remainder is 40.	40

Invent a real-life situation that could be represented by this division problem, and explain what the meaning of the number 40 is in your situation. Describe how to check the results of this division problem by using multiplication and addition. Explain what it would mean if the remainder were 0 instead of 40.

Division, remainders, and factors are also meaningful when you are working with polynomials. When polynomials do factor, finding solutions to $P(x) = 0$ is easy.

Compare the long division algorithm with the polynomial division developed in this section. List a few methods for convincing your teacher that $(x - 2)$ will divide into $x^5 - 6x^4 + 20x^3 - 60x^2 + 99x - 54$. What does this mean about the graph of $P(x) = x^5 - 6x^4 + 20x^3 - 60x^2 + 99x - 54$? How does this result relate to factoring $P(x)$? What does this mean about zeros of $P(x)$?

Solution

Answers will vary. The process of polynomial division is nearly identical to long division. Divide x into x^5 to get x^4 (just as 3 into 18). Multiply the divisor by x^4, subtract, and continue the process.

When $P(x)$ is divided by $x - 2$, the remainder is 0, which additionally means:

1. 2 is a solution of $P(x) = 0$
2. 2 is a zero of $P(x)$.
3. 2 is a root of $P(x)$.
4. $(x - 2)$ is a factor of $P(x)$.
5. 2 is an x-intercept of the graph of $y = P(x)$.

Take Another Look 11.1

If you ignore February 29, how many students would have to be gathered together before you could be absolutely 100% certain that at least two of them have the same birthday? Explain your reasoning. Now guess the number of students that would be needed to be 25% or 50% certain that at least two of them have the same birthday. How certain are you that at least two people in your classroom have the same birthday? Is there a match in your classroom?

One way to think about this problem is to break it down to two people and then consider how the probability changes as another person enters the room, then another, and so on.

a. Suppose you and one other student are the first to arrive. What is the probability that the other student's birthday does not match yours? What is the probability that there is a match?

b. When the third student enters the room, what is the probability that there still is no matching birthday? How is this answer related to the probability that there is a match?

c. Relate this situation to the following product and provide an interpretation: $\frac{364}{365} \cdot \frac{363}{365} \cdot \frac{362}{365} \cdot \frac{361}{365} \cdot \ldots \cdot \frac{356}{365}$. How many students are in the room now? What is the probability that there is still no matching birthday? What is the probability that there is a match?

d. Write a similar expression that represents everyone in your classroom. What is the probability that there is still no matching birthday? What is the probability that there is a match?

e. Write expressions which generalize this problem for n people in a room. If you haven't already, rewrite these expressions using permutation notation.

Solution

a. If there are only two people in the room, the probability of different birthdays is $\frac{365}{365} \cdot \frac{364}{365} \approx 99.73\%$. The probability of matching birthdays is $1 - 99.7\% = 0.27\%$.

b. If there are three people in the room, the probability of different birthdays is $\frac{365}{365} \cdot \frac{364}{365} \cdot \frac{363}{365} \approx 99\%$. The probability of matching birthdays is about 1%.

c. Continuing in like fashion, if there are ten people in the room, there is an 88% probability of no matches or a 12% probability of matching birthdays.

d. For a class of 30, there would be a 71% probability of having at least one pair of matching birthdays.

e. For n students, compute $\frac{365P_n}{365^n}$

Take Another Look 13.4

Two propositions, one for acute triangles and one for obtuse triangles, which together are equivalent to the Law of Cosines appear in Euclid's *Elements*. The proposition for obtuse triangles is:

> In obtuse-angled triangles the square on the side subtending the obtuse angle is greater than the squares on the sides containing the obtuse angle by twice the rectangle contained by one of the sides about the obtuse angle, namely that on which the perpendicular falls, and the straight line cut off outside by the perpendicular toward the obtuse angle.

Explain why this proposition gives the Law of Cosines for obtuse triangles.

Solution

Answers will vary.

Take Another Look 13.5

In the days before calculating machines of any sort, multiplying and dividing numbers with many digits was a lot of work. This was of particular concern to astronomers. Around the sixteenth century they started using trigonometric identities, such as $(\cos A)(\cos B) = [\cos (A + B) + \cos (A - B)]/2$, to help them multiply and divide. (This identity was discovered by the astronomer Ibn Yunus who lived in Egypt in the first half of the tenth century.) Here is an example of how to use this identity to multiply numbers.

Suppose you wanted to multiply 74.314 by 95,106. Neither of these numbers would be in a table of trigonometric values because they are both larger than 1. If you change the problem to $0.74314 \cdot 0.95106$ and remember to switch the decimal places later, then you can use 0.74314 as the cosine of some angle A. Angle A can be found in the table—it's 42 degrees. Another way to say this is $\cos^{-1}(0.74314) = 42°$. Looking up 0.95106 in the table gives $B = 18$ degrees and $\cos^{-1}(0.95106) = 18°$. Now the problem is $0.74314 \cdot 0.95106 = (\cos 42°)(\cos 18°)$. Using the trigonometric identity given above, this expression is equal to $[\cos (42° + 18°) + \cos (42° - 18°)]/2 = (\cos 60° + \cos 24°)/2$. Again use the table of trigonometric values: $\cos 60° = 0.5$ and $\cos 24° = 0.91355$. So $(\cos 60° + \cos 24°)/2 = (0.5 + 0.91355)/2 = 1.41355/2 = 0.706775$. Remembering that the original problem was $74.314 \cdot 95{,}106$, you get 7,067,750. Because most of the calculation involved in this method is addition and subtraction, it's called *prosthaphaeresis*, a Greek word meaning addition and subtraction. It was used at major observatories, including that of Tycho Brahe in Denmark.

Show how you would use this method to multiply 45.512 by 76,235. If you have a table of trigonometric values, use it. Otherwise, you can use your calculator instead of a table of trigonometric values. Be sure to check your result on your calculator.

Solution

Answers will vary.

Introduction to the Calculator Programs and Data Disk

You will find two disks in pockets on the inside back cover of this book. One disk is for computers running Microsoft® Windows® (version 3.1 or later) and the other is for Macintosh® computers (System 7.0 or later).

Each disk contains programs and data to accompany the student text for the most popular graphing calculator models with computer linking capabilities. To use these disks you will need the appropriate computer software and linking cables. The tables on the next several pages list the programs and data lists included on the disks for various calculators as well as the student text and *Calculator Notes* references. The program listings are found in the *Calculator Notes*.

Special Instructions for Downloading Data Files

All Texas Instruments Calculators

There are three data programs on the disk called C3DATA, C4DATA, and C513DATA. These programs include data for Chapter 3, Chapter 4, and Chapters 5–13, respectively. Each program is menu driven and will load one or more data sets into lists. The data is organized in the same order as it appears in the book. In some cases, you can load all the data for a section or for a particular problem set. The programs are large, but you only need one program in your calculator at a time depending on where you are in the book. When you execute the program, you will overwrite existing data in the targeted lists without a warning message. If you use the data programs, then your students will only have to link once to get all the data for a chapter. In fact, the C513DATA program will provide your students with all the data lists for Chapters 5–13.

Texas Instruments TI-92

The data programs for the TI-92 will store data in lists. To see the data list, you can enter l1, l2, and so on in the home screen, press ENTER, and then highlight the list and use the arrow keys to scroll through the list. If you want to graph the data or calculate any statistics, you must go to a data list in the Data/MatrixEditor and rename list c1 as list l1, c2 as l2, and so on for as many lists as there are in the set. To unlock a list, highlight the name of the list (c1, c2, and so on) and press CLEAR.

Casio CFX-9800G

There are several separate data programs. These programs are in the program folder and are called S31DATA, S41DATA, C5DATA and so on, meaning they include data for Section 3.1, Section 4.1, and Chapters 5, respectively. Each program is menu driven and will load one or more data matrices into Mat A through Mat F, with the lengths of each data set stored in Mat G. In some cases you can load all the data for a section or for a particular problem set. The programs may be a more convenient way to transfer data sets because you can send several sets at once without having to select individual ones. When you execute the program, you will overwrite existing data in the targeted matrices without a warning message. When you run a data program, it will direct you to create a list of a certain length. Create the list and then set it. After running the data program, you will also need to run the program FILLLIST, because the data is imported as a matrix. If the data program has more than one list, then after you run FILLLIST follow the on-screen directions for what to do next. When you transfer the data matrices directly from the computer or transfer them from another calculator, you will also need to run FILLLIST and follow the on-screen directions.

Casio CFX-9850G

There are several separate data programs. These programs are in the program folder and have names like called C3DATA, C4DATA, C91011DA and so on, which mean they include data for Chapter 3, Chapter 4, and Chapters 9–11, respectively. Each program is menu driven and will load one or more data sets into lists. In some cases, you can load all the data for a section or for a particular problem set. The programs are large, but you only need one program in your calculator at a time depending on where you are in the book. When you execute the program, you will overwrite existing data in the targeted lists without a warning message. If you use the data programs, then your students will only have to link once to get all the data for a chapter. In fact, the C91011DA program will provide your students with all the data lists for Chapters 9–11. Or you can load the master files into one calculator and download separate lists as the students need them.

Hewlett-Packard HP-38G

There are three main data programs on the disk called C3DATA, C4DATA, and C513DATA. In addition, there are many subprograms. Memory limitations will likely not allow you to have more than a couple of these programs loaded in your calculator at one time. You will have to select the programs for sections you are working with and delete these programs when you are done. These programs include data for some sections and chapters such as Section 3.1, Sections 4.1–4.4, Chapter 5, and so on. Each program is menu driven and will load one or more data sets into lists. In some cases you can load all the data for a particular problem set or for a section. The programs are large, but you only need one program in your calculator at a time depending on where you are in the book. When you execute the program, you will overwrite existing data in the targeted lists without a warning message. Or you can load the master files into one calculator and download separate applets as the students need them.

Data Lists on Disk

Data List	Text Reference
Home Prices	3.1
Homeless	3.1
Per Capita Tax	3.1
Toothpaste	3.1
Hot Chocolate	3.2
Student Heights	3.2
Student Teacher Ratio	3.2
Earthquakes	3.2
AK/NY Temps	3.2
Ball Parks	3.3
City Growth	3.3
Fast Food	3.3
Pulse Rates	3.3
Space Flights	3.3
TV Homework	3.3
Car Production	3.4
Non-English All	3.4
Non-English Regional	3.4
Acres of Corn	4.1
Dress Sizes	4.1, 4.2
Income Tax	4.1–4.3
Planet Orbits	4.1–4.3
Trash	4.3
Life Expectancy	4.4
Median Median	4.4
Mile Run	4.4
Polygons	4.5
Smoking CHD	4.5
Temperature	4.5
Children Heights	4.5, 4.7
Latitude Temp	4.6
Volts Amps	4.6
Women Labor	4.6
Bulls	4.7
Cereal	4.7
HS Drop-outs	4.7
Libraries	4.7

Data List	Text Reference
Planes	4.7
Student Faculty	4.7
Votes	4.7
Single Males	4.7, 4.8
DDT Trout	4.8
Transmitter	4.8
Wave	4.8
World Health	4.9
Drop Velocity	5.5
Homing Transmitter	5.6
Judge Scores	5.6, 5.7
Stopping Distance	5.8
Melting Ice	5.10
Baseball Salaries	7.1
Altitude Temp	7.4
US Population	7.5
Moon Orbits	7.5, 7.9
Cooling	7.9
Gender Income	7.9
Pendulum	7.9
Planet Orbits	7.9
Salmon	7.9
Sound Dist	7.9
Viewing Distance	7.9
Minimum Wage	7.10
Speed Skating	9.1
San Juan Det	9.3
Sunburn	10.4
Resistors	11.4
Pres and V-Pres	11.4
Women Heights	11.5
Normal Heights	11.7
Grasshoppers	12.3
Comet	12.5
Homing Transmitter	12.7
Daylight N.O.	13.2
Daylight Maine	13.8

Calculator Programs on Disk (Listed Alphabetically)

Program Name	Text Reference	Note	TI-82	TI-83	TI-85	TI-86	TI-92	CFX-9800	CFX-9850	HP-38G
ALTER	7.9	7I						√		
AREA	11.5	11H	√	√	√			√	√	√
AREA2	11.6	11J	√	√	√	√	√	√	√	√
AVEVAL	5.7	5D	√	√	√	√	√	√	√	√
BINODATA	11.4	11G						√		
BOX	3.1	3C			√			√		
CHAOS	1.5	1F	√	√	√	√	√	√	√	√
CUBEROOT	13.7	13F	√	√	√	√	√	√	√	√
ESERIES	2.1	2A	√	√	√	√		√	√	√
FILLLIST								√		
FREETHRO	11.3	11B	√	√	√	√	√	√	√	√
GENERATE	8.1	8B						√		
GMAN	1.4	1E	√	√	√	√	√	√	√	√
GUMBALLS	8.4	8F	√	√	√	√	√	√	√	√
JULIA	13.7	13E	√	√	√	√	√	√	√	√
LINES	5.3	5B	√	√	√	√	√	√	√	√
MAD	3.2	3D						√		
MANDELBR	10.8	10F	√	√	√	√	√	√	√	√
MATPWR	8.7	8I						√		
MEDMED	4.4	4C			√	√		√		√
PARABOLA	5.4	5C	√	√	√	√	√	√	√	√
PLOTDATA	4.1	4A						√		
POLREC	13.7	13D								√
POLYFIT	10.7	10C						√		
PROGRAMS								√		
PROTECT	8.4	8H	√	√	√	√	√	√	√	√
QUAD	10.7	10B	√	√						
RATIO	8.2	8D	√	√	√	√	√	√	√	√
RECPOL	13.7	13D								√
RECUR	1.5	1C	√	√	√	√		√	√	√
RESID	4.5	4D	√					√	√	√
RHO	10.6	10A	√	√	√	√		√	√	√
S1	4.5	4D			√			√		
SERIES	1.6	1D	√	√	√	√		√	√	√
STDEV	11.4	11E					√			
SUMBI	11.3	11C	√		√	√		√	√	√
SYNDIV	10.8	10D	√	√	√	√		√	√	√
TWODIE	11.6	11F						√		
WEB	5.9	5G			√	√		√		
WINDOW	5.3	5A						√		

Calculator Programs on Disk (Listed by Section Number)

Text Reference	Program Name	Note	TI-82	TI-83	TI-85	TI-86	TI-92	CFX-9800	CFX-9850	HP-38G
1.4	GMAN	1E	√	√	√	√	√	√	√	√
1.5	RECUR	1C	√	√	√	√		√	√	√
1.5	CHAOS	1F	√	√	√	√	√	√	√	√
1.6	SERIES	1D	√	√	√	√		√	√	√
2.1	ESERIES	2A	√	√	√	√		√	√	√
3.1	BOX	3C			√			√		
3.2	MAD	3D						√		
4.1	PLOTDATA	4A						√		
4.4	MEDMED	4C			√	√		√		√
4.5	RESID	4D	√					√	√	√
4.5	S1	4G			√					
5.3	WINDOW	5A						√		
5.3	LINES	5B	√	√	√	√	√	√	√	√
5.4	PARABOLA	5C	√	√	√	√	√	√	√	√
5.7	AVEVAL	5D	√	√	√	√	√	√	√	√
5.9	WEB	5G			√	√		√		
7.9	ALTER	7I						√		
8.1	GENERATE	8B						√		
8.2	RATIO	8D	√	√	√	√	√	√	√	√
8.4	GUMBALLS	8F	√	√	√	√	√	√	√	√
8.4	PROTECT	8H	√	√	√	√	√	√	√	√
8.7	MATPWR	8I						√		
10.6	RHO	10A	√	√	√	√		√	√	√
10.7	POLYFIT	10C						√		
10.7	QUAD	10B	√	√						
10.8	MANDELBR	10F	√	√	√	√	√	√	√	√
10.8	SYNDIV	10D	√	√	√	√		√	√	√
11.3	SUMBI	11C	√		√	√		√	√	√
11.3	FREETHRO	11B	√	√	√	√	√	√	√	√
11.4	BINODATA	11G						√		
11.4	STDEV	11E					√			
11.5	AREA	11H	√	√	√			√	√	√
11.6	AREA2	11J	√	√	√	√	√	√	√	√
11.6	TWODIE	11F						√		
13.7	CUBEROOT	13F	√	√	√	√	√	√	√	√
13.7	POLREC	13D								√
13.7	RECPOL	13D								√
13.7	JULIA	13E	√	√	√	√	√	√	√	√
	FILLLIST							√		
	PROGRAMS							√		

Advanced Algebra Through Data Exploration

Comment Form

Please help us correct and improve *Advanced Algebra*. If you find mistakes in the text or the teacher support materials, use this form to let us know. If you have general comments or suggestions about the materials, we'd like to hear those as well. Once you've filled out this form, all you have to do is fold it and drop it in the mail. We'll pay the postage. Thank you!

Your name ______________________________
School ______________________________
School address ______________________________
City/State/Zip ______________________________
Phone ______________________________

Advanced Algebra student text

Page ____ Comment ______________________________
Page ____ Comment ______________________________
Page ____ Comment ______________________________

Teacher's Guide and Answer Key

Section ____________ Page ____ Comment ______________________________
Section ____________ Page ____ Comment ______________________________
Section ____________ Page ____ Comment ______________________________

Teacher's Resource Book

Section ____________ Page ____ Comment ______________________________
Section ____________ Page ____ Comment ______________________________
Section ____________ Page ____ Comment ______________________________

Quizzes, Tests, and Exams

Section ____________ Page ____ Comment ______________________________
Section ____________ Page ____ Comment ______________________________
Section ____________ Page ____ Comment ______________________________

Solutions Manual

Section ____________ Page ____ Comment ______________________________
Section ____________ Page ____ Comment ______________________________

Calculator Notes (calculator model __________)

Section ____________ Page ____ Comment ______________________________
Section ____________ Page ____ Comment ______________________________

Do you have any other comments about *Advanced Algebra* or any suggestions for improving the student text or the teacher's material? ______________________________

____

____

____

Fold carefully along this line.

NO POSTAGE NECESSARY IF MAILED IN THE UNITED STATES

BUSINESS REPLY MAIL

FIRST CLASS PERMIT NO. 151 BERKELEY, CA

POSTAGE WILL BE PAID BY ADDRESSEE

KEY CURRICULUM PRESS
P.O. Box 2304
Berkeley, CA 94702-9983

Attention: Editorial—*Advanced Algebra*

Fold carefully along this line.

Advanced Algebra Through Data Exploration

Comment Form

Please help us correct and improve *Advanced Algebra.* If you find mistakes in the text or the teacher support materials, use this form to let us know. If you have general comments or suggestions about the materials, we'd like to hear those as well. Once you've filled out this form, all you have to do is fold it and drop it in the mail. We'll pay the postage. Thank you!

Your name ______________________________
School ______________________________
School address ______________________________
City/State/Zip ______________________________
Phone ______________________________

Advanced Algebra student text

Page ____ Comment ______________________________
Page ____ Comment ______________________________
Page ____ Comment ______________________________

Teacher's Guide and Answer Key

Section ____________ Page ____ Comment ______________________________
Section ____________ Page ____ Comment ______________________________
Section ____________ Page ____ Comment ______________________________

Teacher's Resource Book

Section ____________ Page ____ Comment ______________________________
Section ____________ Page ____ Comment ______________________________
Section ____________ Page ____ Comment ______________________________

Quizzes, Tests, and Exams

Section ____________ Page ____ Comment ______________________________
Section ____________ Page ____ Comment ______________________________
Section ____________ Page ____ Comment ______________________________

Solutions Manual

Section ____________ Page ____ Comment ______________________________
Section ____________ Page ____ Comment ______________________________

Calculator Notes (calculator model __________)

Section ____________ Page ____ Comment ______________________________
Section ____________ Page ____ Comment ______________________________

Do you have any other comments about *Advanced Algebra* or any suggestions for improving the student text or the teacher's material? ______________________________

____

____

____

Fold carefully along this line.

NO POSTAGE
NECESSARY
IF MAILED
IN THE
UNITED STATES

BUSINESS REPLY MAIL

FIRST CLASS PERMIT NO. 151 BERKELEY, CA

POSTAGE WILL BE PAID BY ADDRESSEE

KEY CURRICULUM PRESS
P.O. Box 2304
Berkeley, CA 94702-9983

Attention: Editorial—*Advanced Algebra*

Fold carefully along this line.